HOSPITAL
HEALTH
PROMOTION

Neil Sol, PhD
The Houstonian
Houston, Texas

Philip K. Wilson, EdD
University of Wisconsin-La Crosse

Editors

Human Kinetics Books
Champaign, Illinois

Library of Congress Cataloging-in-Publication Data

Hospital health promotion.

    Includes bibliographies.
    1. Hospitals--Health promotion services. I. Sol,
Neil, 1952-   . II. Wilson, Philip K.
RA975.5.H4H67 1989   362.1'1   88-34782
ISBN 0-87322-929-0

Materials on pages 35 and 36 were reprinted with permission of the American Hospital Association, copyright 1979.

ISBN: 0-87322-929-0

Developmental Editor: Lisa Busjahn
Managing Editor: Valerie Rose Hall
Copyeditor: Barbara Walsh
Proofreader: Dianna Matlosz
Production Director: Ernie Noa
Typesetters: Angela Snyder and Cindy Pritchard
Text Design: Keith Blomberg
Text Layout: Denise Lowry
Cover Design: Jack Davis
Illustrations: Gretchen Walters
Printer: Braun-Brumfield

Printed in the United States of America

10 9 8 7 6 5 4 3 2 1

Human Kinetics Books
A Division of Human Kinetics Publishers, Inc.
Box 5076, Champaign, IL 61825-5076
1-800-DIAL-HKP
1-800-334-3665 (in Illinois)

Contents

Preface   v

Part I   **Defining Health Promotion**   **1**

Chapter 1   **Health Promotion: A Conceptual Perspective**   3
                Stephen M. Schmitz

Chapter 2   **The Historic Role of Hospitals in Health Promotion**   33
                Barbara K. Burke

Chapter 3   **Current Involvement of Hospitals
                in Health Promotion**   43
                Daniel J. Bonk
                Jeffrey M. Bensky

Part II   **Why Hospitals Should Participate
                in Health Promotion**   **59**

Chapter 4   **Overall Benefits of Health Promotion to Hospitals**   61
                Christine A. Aguiar

Chapter 5   **Revenue Benefits of Health Promotion**   69
                Neil Sol

Chapter 6   **Providing Corporate Health Promotion Services**   83
                Kevin M. Clair

Part III   **How Hospitals Engage in Promotion**   **95**

Chapter 7   **Designing Hospital Health Promotion Programs**   97
                Laurie A. Kelley

Chapter 8   **Marketing and Selling Hospital-Based Health Promotion**   129
Jeffrey M. Bensky

Part IV   **The Multidisciplinary Approach to Hospital Health Promotion**   147

Chapter 9   **The Physician's Role in Health Promotion**   149
Stephen M. Schmitz

Chapter 10   **The Nurse's Role in Health Promotion**   171
Carolyn I. Speros

Chapter 11   **The Administrator's Role in Health Promotion: Preparing A Broader Perspective for the Future**   181
Jeffrey M. Bensky
Daniel J. Bonk

Chapter 12   **The Roles of Other Professionals in Hospital Health Promotion**   193
Philip K. Wilson

Part V   **Case Studies of Hospital Health Promotion Programs**   201

Chapter 13   **Health Promotion in Hospitals of 200 or Fewer Beds**   203
Barbara K. Burke

Chapter 14   **Health Promotion in a 686-Bed Hospital**   209
Christine A. Aguiar

Chapter 15   **Health Promotion in a 1,400-Bed Hospital**   219
Carolyn I. Speros

Part VI   **The Future of Hospital Health Promotion**   227

Chapter 16   **Hospital Innovation and Entrepreneurship**   229
Jean Storlie
Debra Daly-Gawenda

Chapter 17   **The Future of Hospital-Sponsored Health Promotion**   263
Neil Sol

Contributing Authors   277

Preface

The provision of health promotion programs and services by health care institutions has grown exponentially in the last decade. Health care institutions have developed these programs to achieve a variety of goals ranging from fulfilling community needs and enhancing goodwill to maintaining profitability and expanding patient referral networks. The commitment to maintaining profitability can be perceived in at least two ways. For those nations where hospitals are operated on the principles of profit making, the focus on health promotion is increasingly on revenue generation. In nations where principles of socialized medicine influence health care delivery, the focus of health promotion is cost containment. Both delivery systems benefit from methods of health education and disease prevention created by health promotion programs. Because these formal comprehensive health promotion programs are still in the early stages of their evolution, little literature exists as a guide or reference for successful development and management.

A number of significant events have called attention to health care and health promotion. These include the development of the American Hospital Association Center for Health Promotion and its associated publications, the origination of *Optimal Health* and its annual conferences, and the inclusion of hospital health promotion interest tracts at national conferences such as the Association of Fitness and Business (AFB), the Club Industry, the International Racquet Sports Association (IRSA), and the National Wellness Conference.

This book represents a strategic approach to hospital health promotion and is designed to enlighten and convince health care administrators of the current and future importance of this avenue of care. Part I defines and describes health promotion programs in historical and current terms. Part 2 examines the need to establish programs in the health care setting, and explains why hospital administrators should be aware of the contributions of health promotion programs to the goals of their institutions. Part 3 offers a "how to" strategy for program development, management, marketing, selling, and delivery. Part 4 explores the multidisciplinary nature of comprehensive health promotion and presents evidence that the health care institution is the best provider of these services. Part 5 reviews exemplary programs in institutions that vary in size from small, rural community hospitals to large, urban tertiary-care medical centers. Part 6 looks into the future, verifying the importance of well-managed health promotion ventures to the continued viability of health care institutions and the maintenance of institutional, community health service goals.

The editors and the authors believe that this book will aid in the continued establishment of health promotion programs as integral components of health care institutions.

Neil Sol
Philip Wilson

PART I

Defining Health Promotion

No single definition is universally accepted for *health promotion*; the term conjures many different meanings to professionals in the field. For this reason, Part I is concerned with identifying, defining, and describing health promotion in the health care setting. Understanding health promotion from the perspective of this text is important to make all chapters meaningful. Part I establishes a common ground upon which all future actions of this text are built.

Chapter 1 delineates the conceptual perspective of health care and health promotion and defines health promotion with reference to other commonly used terms such as wellness, health, fitness, and health enhancement. Chapter 2 describes a historical perspective of health promotion in health care institutions and explains how and why health promotion should be part of this setting. This chapter also explores the development of health promotion's structure and philosophy. Chapter 3 examines the extent to which hospitals are now involved in health promotion.

CHAPTER 1

Health Promotion: A Conceptual Perspective

Stephen M. Schmitz

The study of health promotion has grown tremendously within the past 15 years. This growth has resulted in the birth of a discipline that is now producing articles, books, and research at an impressive rate. A number of factors have made this decade ideal for the early development and growth of the discipline of health promotion. Health promotion will play an increasingly important role in the health care delivery system of the next decade and may revolutionize the way in which individuals and organizations view health and health care.

Health, the subject that health promotion addresses, is much more than merely the absence of disease. It is a "state of complete physical, mental and social well-being" (World Health Organization, 1960, p. 1). Health is seen as "a resource for everyday life, not the objective of living. Health is a positive concept emphasizing social and personal resources, as well as physical capabilities" (World Health Organization, 1986, p. 73).

The promotion of health is complicated by our current health care system, which is more accurately termed a *disease* care system. This system, which is based on a mechanistic, disease-oriented medical model, is directed predominantly at disease treatment, and only minimally at health promotion. This model has dominated the health care system to the extent that it is difficult for most people to conceptualize health without reference to disease. It is essential, however, to the understanding of health promotion that health be viewed in terms not necessarily related to disease.

DEFINING HEALTH PROMOTION

Health promotion is an eclectic field, drawing from a large number of disciplines, including the following:

Exercise physiology	Nursing
Physical therapy	Cardiology
Finance	Biostatistics
Communication	Economics
Biomechanics	Health care administration
Family practice	Insurance
Osteopathy	Nutrition
Sports medicine	Program management
Psychiatry	Entrepreneurship
Occupational medicine	Ergonomics
Epidemiology	Political action
Training	Podiatry
Occupational therapy	Internal medicine
Health education	Organizational development
Psychology	Dentistry
Computer technology	Architecture
Marketing	Recreation therapy
Social work	Patient education
Chiropractic	Government policy[1]
Biochemistry	

This diversity of contributors has been both a blessing and a curse; it has produced a richness and dynamism of ideas that few other disciplines can claim, yet it has also generated a field so broad that it may defy systematic and scholarly study. This overly broad scope makes health promotion vulnerable to accusations that it is merely a repackaging of old concepts rather than a new concept.

Defining health promotion in a succinct, all-encompassing fashion is difficult yet important. A number of authors have contributed definitions that have en-

---

[1]From "Definition of Health Promotion" by M.P. O'Donnell, 1986, *American Journal of Health Promotion*, 1(1), p. 5. Copyright 1986 by *American Journal of Health Promotion*. Reprinted with permission.

riched the panoply of health promotion. The following contributions, made by some important personalities and organizations, demonstrate the richness and diversity of thought in the health promotion field.

Health promotion is the science and art of helping people change their lifestyle to move toward a state of optimal health. (O'Donnell, 1986b, p. 4)

Health promotion is any combination of health education and related organizational, political, and economic interventions designed to facilitate behavioral and environmental adaptions that will improve or protect health. (Nelson & Simmons, 1983, p. 57)

Wellness is a lifestyle approach to the pursuit of optimal physical, emotional and mental/spiritual health, and it is accomplished through five basic means: personal responsibility, nutritional awareness, physical fitness, stress management, and environmental sensitivity. (Dunn, Ardell, & Travis, cited by N. Sol, personal communication, May, 1985)

Health promotion (including health information and health education) is "the process of fostering awareness, influencing attitudes, and identifying alternatives so that individuals can make informed choices and change their behavior in order to achieve an optimum level of physical and mental health and improve their physical and social environment. (Breckon, 1982, p. 252)

Wellness is:

. . . a choice—a decision you make to move toward optimal health.

. . . a way of life—a lifestyle you design to achieve your highest potential for well-being.

. . . a process—a developing awareness that there is no end point, but that health and happiness are possible in each moment, here and now.

. . . a balanced channelling of energy—energy received from the environment, transformed within you, and returned to affect the world around you.

. . . the integration of body, mind and spirit—the appreciation that everything you do, and think, and feel, and believe has an impact on your state of health.

. . . the loving and acceptance of yourself. (J. Travis, personal communication, July, 1986)

The most complete definition is, "Health promotion is the maintenance and enhancement of existing levels of health through the implementation of effective programs, services and policies'' (Goodstadt, Simpson, & Loranger, 1987, p. 61). This definition underscores several key points about health promotion:

- Though applicable to persons in all degrees of sickness and health, health promotion focuses mainly on populations in the context of everyday life rather than on people with disease or at risk for specific diseases.
- The maintenance and enhancement of current health levels is an active, not passive, process requiring time, effort, and resources. This is true on both an individual and a collective level. It is a lifelong process best accomplished through consistent rather than episodic action directed at the determinants of health.
- The policies that an organization or country adopt greatly influence the individuals within it. Policies that promote health send out clear messages to those affected and have the potential to reach vast numbers of people. For health promotion to succeed, policies must reflect a sincere commitment to health.

This definition underscores the importance of a multidimensional, integrated approach to the promotion of health, one that involves individuals and groups working together toward a common goal—the maintenance and enhancement of health. In the next 5 years, as the discipline of health promotion develops more fully, it will be increasingly important to arrive at a consensus definition. Such a definition would clearly articulate the discipline's purpose and help focus its efforts. The definition by Goodstadt is an excellent one that deserves serious consideration.

HEALTH PROMOTION TERMINOLOGY

Certain terms frequently appear in the context of health promotion, and though they are often used in a fashion that implies interchangeability, they are distinct. These terms are *preventive medicine, disease prevention, health education,* and *wellness.* Defining these terms will help increase the clarity and specificity of health promotion.

Preventive Medicine and Disease Prevention

Jonas (1981) defines preventive medicine as "the application of biomedical and epidemiological science to the promotion of health and to the elimination or early detection of disease in populations and individuals" (p. 9). Preventive medicine came about in the early 19th century and since then has made numerous invaluable contributions to society, including the discovery of vaccines and antibiotics, and the institution of public health measures to improve nutrition, sanitary practices, and food and water supplies. This approach of preventive medicine is disease-dominated; that is, it accomplishes its aims through disease prevention by detecting risk factors for disease and limiting the detrimental effects of disease through early intervention. There are three classifications of intervention (Last, 1986).

- Primary prevention is preventing the occurrence of disease or injury (e.g., immunization against infectious diseases and use of safety equipment to protect workers in hazardous occupations).
- Secondary prevention is early detection and intervention, preferably before the condition is clinically apparent, with the aim of reversing, halting, or at least retarding the progress of a condition (e.g., screening newborns for phenylketonuria, and if found, recommending a lifelong phenylalanine-restricted diet).
- Tertiary prevention is minimizing the effects of disease and disability by surveillance and maintenance aimed at preventing complications and premature deterioration (e.g., splints and remedial exercises to prevent contractures and deformities associated with rheumatoid arthritis).

Preventive medicine has grown from a disease-oriented medical model. Whereas health promotion encourages certain health behaviors as a means of enhancing health, preventive medicine encourages many of the same behaviors as a means of preventing disease. Although distinct entities, disease prevention and health promotion actually have more similarities than distinctions. For health promotion to succeed optimally in the current disease-dominant health care system, it must thoughtfully integrate disease prevention into its tenets. By building on and enhancing the gains in disease prevention already made by preventive medicine, the discipline of health promotion can more quickly influence the populace. (See chapter 9, "The Physician's Role in Health Promotion" for a more detailed discussion of the distinctions between health promotion and disease prevention).

Health Education

One definition of health education is "any combination of learning opportunities designed to facilitate voluntary adoptions of behavior (individuals, groups, or communities) conducive to health" (Nelson & Simmons, 1983, p. 57). Health education is not synonymous with health promotion. Health education is essential to health promotion, for increased awareness must occur before behavior changes. Health education is one of the most powerful tools health promotion uses to accomplish its goals, but health promotion goes beyond that.

Wellness

Some authors have distinguished wellness from health promotion by positioning wellness as more of an innovative, experiential, grass-roots approach that has as its ultimate goal the creation of healthy cultures, viewing health promotion as an approach oriented to individuals and aimed primarily at risk reduction (Opatz, 1985). This distinction is confusing. The term wellness is an important one, however, for it is more commonly used by lay persons. Although the term health promotion is used far more frequently by health care professionals, government policymakers, and corporations, the term wellness has a higher overall recognition among the public. For purposes of this chapter, the terms are viewed synonymously.

The most problematic aspect of health promotion is defining its scope. What subject areas does it include? Better yet, what subject areas does it exclude? Because health is such a comprehensive and pervasive subject, and its boundaries so difficult to define, health promotion is burdened with a similar limit-setting dilemma. Health promotion approaches and programs occur in a wide variety of settings, are delivered by professionals and nonprofessionals of disparate backgrounds, and cover a range of subjects from alcohol counseling to fitness and weight control. As the discipline of health promotion matures, its scope will narrow and its identity will become clearer.

FACTORS LEADING TO THE GROWTH OF HEALTH PROMOTION

A number of factors occurring in a timely fashion have facilitated the growth of health promotion. To a large degree, each of these factors has its own unique historical perspective, which developed independently of the other factors. The simultaneous occurrence of these factors has made the current environment an excellent one for the growth of health promotion. If the discipline is to thrive, and if its ideals are to spread to the populace, it must capitalize on this excellent growth opportunity. Growth will occur only if steps are taken to integrate health promotion into the current health care system—to coordinate and expand the delivery of services, to train and certify professionals in the field, and to do scientific research and evaluation in a systematic fashion. If optimal growth is to occur, we must capitalize on the following factors:

- The shift in disease burden from acute to chronic
- The health care cost crisis
- Increased corporate receptivity
- A realistic assessment of the current health care system
- Increased governmental intervention
- The wellness movement
- Major cultural changes

The following sections explore these factors and their impact on health promotion.

The Shift From Acute to Chronic Disease

A radical shift in the causes of death in the United States has occurred within the past century (see Table 1.1). In 1900, the 3 leading causes of death were infectious diseases, and 6 out of 10 were infectious- or infancy-related. The implementation of a broad array of public health measures improving nutrition, sanitation, and food and water supplies as well as the development of effective antibiotics and vaccines has nearly eliminated infectious disease as a cause of death and has drastically altered the spectrum of disease in this country.

Table 1.1 Death Rates (per 100,000) From 10 Leading Causes of Death, 1900 and 1985

1900	1985
1. Influenza and pneumonia (202.2)	Heart disease (325.0)
2. Tuberculosis, all forms (194.4)	Cancer (191.7)
3. Gastroenteritis (142.7)	Cerebrovascular disease (64.0)
4. Heart disease (137.4)	Accidents (38.6)
5. Cerebrovascular disease (106.9)	Chronic obstructive pulmonary diseases and allied conditions (31.2)
6. Nephritis (81.0)	Influenza and pneumonia (27.9)
7. Accidents (72.3)	Diabetes mellitus (16.2)
8. Cancer (64.0)	Suicide (12.0)
9. Certain diseases of infancy (62.6)	Chronic liver disease and cirrhosis (11.2)
10. Diphtheria (40.3)	Atherosclerosis (9.9)

Note. Data in column 1 are from *Health Promotion: Principles and Clinical Applications* (p. 5) by R.B. Taylor, J. R. Ureda, and J.W. Denham (Eds.), 1982, Norwalk, CT: Appleton-Century-Crofts. (Original source: Statistical Abstract of the U.S., 79th ed., 1958, Washington, DC: U.S. Government Printing Office.) Data in column 2 are from *National Center for Health Statistics*, Vol. 34, No. 13, September 19, 1986, Washington, DC: U.S. Department of Health and Human Services, Public Health Service.

Today, chronic disease accounts for 7 of the 10 leading causes of death. The emergence of chronic disease as the major cause of death has stimulated vigorous analysis of the contributing factors to these diseases. In 1974, The Lalonde Report, *A New Perspective on the Health of Canadians: A Working Document*, was released and the health field concept was introduced. The concept identified four determinants of health:

- Human biology
- Environment
- Lifestyle
- Health care organization

Prior to this time, health care organization, the system of facilities and providers of disease treatment (i.e., hospitals, outpatient clinics, physicians' offices, etc.), had dominated the view of health care. The Lalonde Report dramatically raised awareness about the importance of lifestyle, biology, and environment and questioned the overallocation of funds to health care organization.

Lifestyle factors consistently account for 50% of the causes of death, regardless of etiology. Thus, improving lifestyle practices has the greatest potential for influencing mortality and morbidity. Interestingly, the National Planning Association estimated that in 1976, less than 1% of federal health expenditures was devoted to lifestyle issues, while 92% went into health care organization. This discrepancy has improved only slightly in the past decade.

Scientific evidence is accumulating for both the beneficial effects of a healthy lifestyle and the detrimental effects of an unhealthy lifestyle. The landmark Alameda County study by Belloc and Breslow (1972) identified seven health practices associated with enhanced physical health status and longevity:

- Sleeping 7 to 8 hours per night
- Eating breakfast daily
- Not eating between meals
- Maintaining weight (minus 5% to plus 19.9% for men; minus 5% to plus 9.9% for women)
- Exercising regularly
- Using alcohol moderately or not at all
- Never smoking cigarettes

Belloc and Breslow extrapolated these findings in specific terms (see Table 1.2.). This seminal study marked the formal beginning of the scientific basis of health promotion.

Health Care Cost Crisis

In the past 10 years, national health expenditures have tripled (see Table 1.3). If this continues at the current rate, we will spend $1 trillion in the year 2010. This country cannot and will not support such expense.

Another factor in the health care cost crisis is the source of funding (see Table 1.3). In 1935 more than 80% of funding for health care came from private funds

Table 1.2   Health Practices and Expected Longevity: 45-Year-Old Man

Number of health practices	Expected longevity
3 or fewer	22 years
4–5	28 years
6–7	33 years

Note. From "Relationship of Physical Health Status and Health Practices" by N.B. Belloc and L. Breslow, 1972, *Preventive Medicine, 1*, pp. 409-421. Copyright 1972 by *Academic Press, Inc.* Reprinted by permission.

Table 1.3   National Health Expenditures According to Source of Funds and Gross National Product (GNP)

Year	Total (in millions)	% GNP	% Private funds	% Public funds
1935	2.9	4.0	80.8	19.2
1950	12.7	4.4	72.8	27.2
1960	26.9	5.3	75.3	24.7
1965	41.9	6.1	73.8	26.2
1970	75.0	7.6	63.0	37.0
1975	132.7	8.6	57.5	42.5
1980	247.5	9.4	57.4	42.6
1984	387.4	10.6	58.6	41.4

Note. From "Health Care Financing Review" by the Office of the Actuary, 1985, HCFA Publication No. 03200, Washington, DC: U.S. Government Printing Office.

and less than 20% from public funds. That has changed significantly in the past 50 years, and in 1984, public funds paid for more than 40% of health care expenditures. If health care expenditures continue to increase, this country runs the risk of bankrupting its public fund source. Innovative programs that aggressively address economic issues of health are needed to meet this crisis.

An assumption underlying health promotion is that promoting health and preventing illness will decrease health care costs. A growing number of studies support this hypothesis, yet some authors question it, presenting data that show promoting health actually increases health care costs for certain populations. Future research will help clarify many of these issues. The success and longevity of health promotion depends on more than its ability to cut health care costs; however, the more financially sound it is, the more assured it will be of a solid place in the health care system.

Increased Corporate Receptivity

For at least the past 10 years, corporations, particularly certain larger ones, have sponsored health promotion programs. Such programs are a means of containing costs for the corporation and providing a benefit for employees. Benefits to a corporation are sometimes categorized and contrasted as direct versus indirect, hard versus soft, and economic versus noneconomic. Direct benefits include decreased health care and life insurance costs, reduced absenteeism and employee turnover, and decreased workers' compensation claims. Indirect benefits include improved employee morale, enhanced corporate image, and happier, healthier employees. Though the direct economic benefits are more easily quantifiable and tangible, they must not be the sole focus of corporate programs. Ultimately, both direct and indirect benefits interact to create an environment in which the organization benefits in multiple ways (see Fig. 1.1).

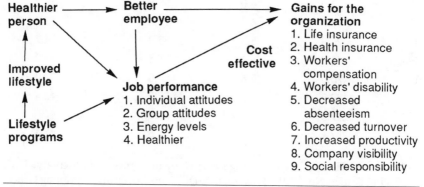

Figure 1.1.   Benefits of health promotion. *Note.* From "Health Promotion: Is It Good Business?" by D.W. Edington, 1986, *Optimal Health,* **2**(3), p. 33. Copyright 1986. Reprinted by permission.

In the early years of corporate health promotion, providing an employee benefit was far more important than cost containment. That has changed, and we are now in a transition period in which cost containment assumes far greater importance. A recent study by Warner (1987) that examined the reasons corporations provide health promotion programs revealed a balance of direct and indirect benefits. The number following each benefit indicates the percentage of corporations that listed that benefit as one the reasons they provide health promotion programs.

- Improved employee health (82%)
- Improved employee morale (59%)
- Reduced health care cost (57%)
- Decreased absenteeism and employee turnover (51%)
- Increased productivity (50%)
- Response to employee demand (33%)
- Desire to be part of an innovative trend (32%)
- Improved business image (20%)

This healthy balance of interests and expectations is the best approach to health promotion in the corporate sector.

Corporations are becoming increasingly interested in the cost-saving aspects of health promotion, and many providers are making unsubstantiated claims of financial savings from health promotion programs. Although recent studies show consistent economic benefits resulting from health promotion programs, it is too early to make grandiose claims. Warner cautions against abuse of the economic argument, noting that assumptions are made by providers and employers, and if the evidence for cost-savings does not hold up, the stability of this relationship may not last. The balanced approach, which emphasizes economic as well as noneconomic benefits, is the most prudent.

Realistic Assessment of the Current Health Care System

The current health care system has come under attack for contributing to, if not causing, most of the health problems that exist today. Illich (1976) states that "the medical establishment has become a major threat to health" (p. 3). Such a sweeping statement is cheaply and easily made in this "blame-the-medical-establishment" era, but it does little to seriously address shortcomings in the system.

The major problem is not the medical establishment itself, but rather our assessment and expectations of it. The current health care system is undeniably disease- rather than health-oriented. Hospitals, physicians, various health care professionals, and the reimbursement system are disease-oriented. The majority of patients are oriented to disease and disease treatment, not to health and health promotion. As René Dubos (1961) has written, "To ward off disease or recover health, men as a rule find it easier to depend on healers than to attempt the more difficult task of living wisely" (p. 114).

The disease orientation of the health care system is not surprising given that most health care professionals are trained in the hospital setting. This setting is skewed toward disease because the patients who are admitted to the hospital represent a small subset of the population that is significantly ill. It is often overlooked that for every hospitalized patient in a given community, there are hundreds who are well or who are not significantly ill enough to warrant a hospital admission. This latter group represents the majority of the total population and is a group for which health promotion programs may be particularly beneficial.

Until recently the hospital setting provided health care professionals incentives and nearly unlimited rewards for discovering and treating illness, but few opportunities for health promotion or preventive medicine. In fact, only 2% of total health care expenditures in this country are devoted to prevention (Nelson & Simmons, 1983). The treatment versus prevention mismatch will continue as long as the reimbursement system preferentially rewards disease treatment and as long as the medical education system ignores health promotion.

The role of medicine and the efficacy of clinical treatment in determining health status has been questioned by McKeown (1979). He hypothesizes that the predominant influences that have led to health improvements over the past 300 years are nutritional, environmental, and behavioral and are not directly related to the health care delivery system. Though he finds nothing seriously wrong with traditional services and research, he does find fault with the glaring imbalance between cause and care.

The current health care system is quite competent at doing what it is trained to do, treating disease, but is ultimately limited if it ignores health promotion. Just as a health care system that tried only to promote health and prevent illness would be sorely inadequate, so is a system that regards disease detection and treatment as its sole reason for existence. An equitably balanced health care system, one that supports both disease treatment and health promotion through policies, education, research, funding, and reimbursement, is necessary to optimally care for the populace.

Government Intervention

The governments of Canada, the United Kingdom, Australia, and the United States have published official policy statements advocating personal health promotion (Mason & Tolsma, 1984).

- *A New Perspective on the Health of Canadians*, Canada, 1974
- *Prevention and Health: Everybody's Business*, United Kingdom, 1976
- *Disease Prevention and Health Promotion: Federal Programs and Prospects*, United States, 1978
- *Model Standards for Community Preventive Health Services*, United States, 1979
- *Healthy People: A Report of the Surgeon General on Health Promotion and Disease*, United States, 1979
- *Promoting Health: Prospects for Better Health Throughout Australia*, Australia, 1979
- *Promoting Health, Preventing Disease: Objectives for the Nation*, United States, 1980

These statements represent major collaborative efforts, calling together experts in a variety of disciplines. In the past, governments, particularly through their public health service components, have championed and implemented preventive health policies leading to significant improvements in health. This emphasis on health promotion by governments is a positive new direction and marks the beginning of what some have called "the second public health revolution" (Nelson & Simmons, 1983).

Healthy People: The Surgeon General's Report on Health Promotion and Disease (1979) listed 15 priorities for prevention (See Table 1.4). One year later, *Promoting Health, Preventing Disease: Objectives for the Nation* was published, listing over 200 specific national objectives. A recent interim report reveals that although our nation has improved in nearly all areas, we still fall short of meeting

Table 1.4   Priorities for Prevention from Healthy People

Preventive health services

High blood pressure control

Family planning

Pregnancy and infant health

Immunization

Control of sexually transmitted diseases

Health protection

Toxic agent and radiation control

Occupational safety and health

Accident prevention and injury control

Fluoridation and dental health

Surveillance and control of infectious diseases

Health promotion

Smoking and health

Reducing misuse of alcohol and drugs

Improved nutrition

Physical fitness and exercise

Control of stress and violent behavior

Note. Adapted from *Healthy People: The Surgeon General's Report on Health Promotion and Disease Prevention* (p. xii), by U.S. Department of Health, Education, and Welfare, Public Health Service, 1979, Publication No. 79-55071, Washington, DC: U.S. Government Printing Office.

the objectives. Overall, this report is encouraging and reveals that articulating a national policy of health promotion and prevention is a potent agent of behavior change.

The Lalonde Report, hailed as one of the great achievements of the modern public health movement (Terris, 1984) and profoundly influential in other parts of the world, has not led to major changes in Canada. The report was criticized on a number of grounds, most notably for paying too much attention to lifestyle and not enough to environment. Additionally, no mechanism existed to implement the recommendations of the report. Despite these shortcomings, the report served to stimulate the development of a clearer and more sophisticated model of health promotion in Canada. Hancock (1986) urges us to accept the Lalonde Report for what it is, "a signpost pointing the way at the start of a journey" (p. 100).

The Wellness Movement

The term *wellness movement* is used here to characterize a grass-roots organization that has grown remarkably over the past 15 years and has made and will continue to make valuable contributions to the health promotion field. A book published in 1961 called *High Level Wellness* is credited with initiating the wellness movement. Its author, Halbert Dunn, a retired public health physician, stressed the importance of mind/body/spirit connections and articulated the view of health as much more than the absence of disease. John Travis, inspired by Dunn's work, created the Wellness Resource Center and became the first physician to offer wellness services and educational opportunities for health care professionals and the public.

In 1977 Donald Ardell wrote a book entitled *High Level Wellness: An Alternative to Doctors, Drugs and Disease*, which was instrumental in bringing the wellness concept to the public. It formulated the most commonly quoted definition of wellness as a five-dimensional approach (personal responsibility, nutritional awareness, stress control, physical fitness, and environmental sensitivity) and challenged individuals to take control of their own health.

The need to analyze and understand cultural norms when addressing health promotion was proposed by Robert Allen, who developed the Lifegain Model (1981). This is a systematic approach to culture change, which is vital when attempting to successfully modify behavior and support the desired behavior change. Allen's ideas will be especially important in the next decade, when health promotion will have the greatest opportunity to influence this country on both an individual and a cultural level.

Another major contributor in the wellness movement is the University of Wisconsin–Stevens Point, which developed the first university-based wellness environment. William Hettler, medical director of Student Health Services, and others at the university have developed a wellness model used by numerous colleges and universities. The university also sponsors an annual week-long National Wellness Conference, which brings together nearly 1,000 wellness professionals. In July 1987, the National Wellness Institute signed an agreement with the Japanese Wellness Association to share information, resources, and people in the future. This new affiliation is exciting for the university and for the movement.

Until recently, the major contributors to the wellness movement have been loosely affiliated at best. The main focus of the work to date has been on individuals and individual behavior. This focus, together with the fact that the majority of people in our culture are not wellness-oriented, leaves significant numbers of people untouched by the movement. Contributors to the wellness movement, particularly the National Wellness Institute, are now assuming leadership roles in trying to integrate the manifold providers of wellness and health promotion. Only through this integration of thought and expertise can wellness become the cultural norm in this country.

Major Cultural Changes

In the past 25 years, significant cultural changes have occurred related to health and health practices. Prior to the 1960s, most people passively placed their health into the hands of the medical profession. Few patients asked questions of their physicians, and most believed they had little influence on their own health. The 1960s era was characterized by the public's increasing skepticism and questioning of many types of authority, including political, educational, and medical. This resulted in greater personal responsibility and increased individual self-determination. In the health area, this translated into significant lifestyle changes, including greatly increased interest in exercise, smoking control, nutrition, and health foods. These lifestyle changes contributed to the 22% decrease in mortality from cardiovascular disease between 1968 and 1977 and paved the way for the "new individualism" (Harris, 1987, p. 141), in which good health becomes a positive means of more fully experiencing oneself.

Medical self-care, defined by Vickery (1986) as all those actions taken by an individual with respect to a medical problem, has flourished in the 1980s. Individuals are becoming more involved in the medical decision-making process, asking such questions as, "Do I need to see a doctor? What can I do for myself?" People are learning cardiopulmonary resuscitation (CPR) and the Heimlich maneuver and learning more about self-care for chronic diseases. Some authors assert that medical self-care is the dominant form of medical care, accounting for 85% to 95% of all medical care. Because of this heightened interest in self-care and success so far, it is likely that further efforts in fostering self-care will lead to improved health and decreased health care costs.

Other cultural changes are occurring that will influence the success of health promotion. Futurist John Naisbitt noted in *Megatrends* (1984) that people in our society are becoming more interested in self-help opportunities and are focusing more on long-term planning and goal setting. Naisbitt's evidence indicates that people are assuming a more active role in their own lives and are no longer content with short-term, patchwork solutions. These changes bode well for society's receptivity to health promotion.

RATIONALE FOR HEALTH PROMOTION

The rationale for health promotion is threefold: to decrease mortality and morbidity (increase longevity), to improve overall health status (increase the quality of life), and to contain costs. Each of these aspects is discussed in detail here.

Decrease Mortality and Morbidity

A number of studies since the Alameda County study (Belloc & Breslow, 1972) have shown a positive correlation between healthy lifestyle practices, decreased morbidity, and increased longevity. These studies are important; yet they raise the nagging question, "Is living longer beneficial?" Some authors have argued that adding extra years will produce an excessive societal burden from chronic disease at a later age. Others foresee a compression of mortality for a healthy aged population (Fries, 1980). Research during this generation will help clarify the issue.

It is also unclear whether longevity data influence individual behavior. The main reason people stop smoking is not to increase their longevity, but rather their desire to rid themselves of a chronic cough and a habit that society frowns upon. So despite the recent study by Paffenbarger, Hyde, Wing, and Asieh (1986) that showed an extra 2 years of life for those who exercised, it is unreasonable to assume that people will start exercising in great numbers just because of the data. Motivation for healthy lifestyle change is complicated and requires a multifaceted approach.

Improve Overall Health Status

It is assumed that in addition to having longer lives, a healthier population is happier, is more productive, and enjoys a higher quality of life. The World Health Organization views health as "a resource for everyday life, not the objective of living. [Health] is a positive concept emphasizing social and personal resources, as well as physical capabilities" ("A Discussion Document," 1986, p. 73). Without good health, quality of life is diminished. Regrettably, this rationale is not given the importance it deserves, partly because mortality and costs are easier to quantify, but also because quality is so difficult to define (Pirsig, 1976). What is an enhanced quality of life? Though difficult to articulate clearly, it is undeniably important, certainly far more than commonly accepted.

Contain Costs

Cost containment is a major reason for increased interest in health promotion, particularly in the corporate sector. Our economy can no longer fully subsidize the unhealthy lifestyles of employees or other members of society. Health promotion programs that effectively contain costs will be received enthusiastically by corporations, government, and the reimbursement system. But there are dangers inherent in focusing too narrowly on cost containment. Many of the actual benefits of health promotion are realized years after a particular lifestyle intervention has occurred. How does one easily quantitate that gain?

Additionally, a particular program may not contain costs but may substantially improve the quality of life. Should that program be discarded? Efforts must be made to maximize the benefits of health promotion, cost containment and otherwise, but to rely obsessively on cost issues is a mistake.

COMPONENTS OF A COMPREHENSIVE HEALTH PROMOTION PROGRAM

When we discuss health promotion programs, semantics occasionally get in the way. A *program* implies some type of organized assemblage of health promotion services. A *service* might be a stress management seminar, a cholesterol screening, or a fitness evaluation. A program includes a number of services, preferably linked in cohesive, integrated fashion. Most services are highly portable and can be delivered wherever the participants, staff, and necessary equipment can locate. Programs originate from a limited number of sources, sources with access to manifold resources.

As O'Donnell (1986b) has pointed out, health promotion programs are defined at three levels: awareness, behavior change, and supportive environments. Each of these levels has its own goals and specific services that help it accomplish these goals. Though the levels are distinct, they are intimately connected and interact at many points. If any one of the levels is deficient, the other two levels will suffer accordingly.

Raising awareness, the vital first step, is accomplished through a variety of educational opportunities. This heightened awareness prepares an individual to change behavior; without it, behavior change rarely occurs. Behavior change itself involves additional educational opportunities, motivational assistance, and skill-building programs. If the behavior change occurs in an environment that facilitates, supports, and rewards the behavior, that change is most likely to occur and be maintained.

Examples of awareness-raising programs include payroll inserts, posters, lectures, seminars, workshops, health risk appraisals, wellness inventories, and health fairs. Such programs are largely educational in nature, intended to arm the participants with information that may influence their decision to try to make a behavior change. Information alone does not change behavior but is almost always necessary before such change occurs.

Behavior change programs include weight control, stress management, time management, nutrition, cardiac rehabilitation, fitness, and cancer prevention. These programs contain awareness-raising information as well as specific skill-building and motivational assistance that will actually result in an observable change in behavior. Programs that do not result in behavior change may still be useful; for example, a smoking cessation program that is unsuccessful with an individual may still bring that individual closer to becoming a nonsmoker.

Supportive environments are any settings in which groups of individuals regularly meet. Such environments include families, schools, corporations, health clubs, and others. In these environments, healthy lifestyle practices are taught, encouraged, and supported. Specific examples of environmental support include providing healthy foods in cafeteria vending machines, instituting corporate and public no-smoking policies, providing additional insurance benefits for employees participating in health promotion programs, and involving key family members in programs. Supportive environments are critical to maintaining behavior change.

A health promotion program must address all three levels to be optimally successful. Studies have shown that information alone, written or verbal, is not extremely effective at behavior change. Effective behavior modification requires information, motivation, healthy role models, skill building, and practice. Supportive environments enable individuals to change and maintain behaviors on a long-term basis.

PROVIDERS AND DELIVERY SITES FOR HEALTH PROMOTION PROGRAMS

Most health promotion services are highly portable, so delivery can occur in a variety of sites. The type of provider and the delivery setting does, however, strongly influence the nature of a particular program and its potential for success. The major providers of programs are hospitals, health care organizations, corporations, insurance companies, schools, and individual consultants. The major delivery sites are similar, and include communities in addition to hospitals, health care organizations, and schools.

Hospitals

Within the past 5 years, hospitals have become increasingly active in health promotion. Hospitals have responded positively to the charge that they "have a responsibility to take a leadership role in helping ensure the good health of their communities" (Breckon, 1982, p. 251). This has resulted in the development of many hospital-based health promotion programs. Hospital sponsorship of such programs is an aggressive response to the new demands of the rapidly changing health care environment. This environment requires that hospitals find innovative ways to increase market share, to find new revenue sources, to expand outpatient services, and to more efficiently utilize current staff. Successful health promotion programs can provide that innovation. Hospital-based programs can deliver services to inpatients, outpatients, the community, and area corporations. Hospital strengths include existing medical expertise, high community and corporate visibility, and readily available physical facilities. Hospital weaknesses include a strong disease-care orientation, slow-moving administrations, and inexperience in the entrepreneurial field of health promotion. Hospitals have the most to lose and the most to gain in the health care industry. Those that provide well-planned, adequately funded, dynamically marketed health promotion programs will stand a much greater chance of survival in the unpredictable and unforgiving hospital environment of the next decade.

Health Care Organizations

Health care organizations such as health maintenance organizations (HMOs) have begun to provide on-site programs for their subscribers. HMOs have tremendous potential as providers because they can reach large numbers of people in a relatively inexpensive fashion. Subscriber cost is low because it is covered in the cost of membership. Although the potential for health promotion delivery is great at HMOs, the results have been extremely disappointing so far. The major reason is financial; it is more profitable to have more numerous new patient visits than it is to have established patients come in for health promotion-related visits. A few of the larger HMOs actively incorporate health promotion into their organizations, and it is likely that more will follow suit in the near future.

Corporations

The corporate community introduced large-scale health promotion programs to the world, and it may also determine the future success of such programs. Corporations, most notably Johnson & Johnson, Campbell Soup, and Control Data have created cultures that embrace health promotion and believe heartily in its long-term benefits. These corporations have initiated vital studies of their own employees to determine as precisely as possible the costs and benefits of prospective health promotion programs. Corporate strengths include the corporate culture, which can provide the all-important supportive environment needed for sustained behavior change. Corporations can provide financial incentives, on-site programming and facilities, and programs delivered during work hours. Some weaknesses include predictable programming, failure to involve family members (noncorporate culture), and unrealistic expectations for the return on investment.

Communities

Programs and services sponsored by the community are an excellent opportunity to reach large numbers of individuals. Numerous community sites can be utilized, including churches, YMCAs, YWCAs, public libraries, health clubs, shopping centers, and others. Most often, these programs are delivered by a hospital-based program or as a public health offering of the local health department. These programs afford hospitals the chance to gather market-share information and attract new patients and give health departments the information they need to deliver more community-specific health care. Strengths of community programs include a large client population base, high media visibility, and low cost. Weaknesses include logistical difficulty with follow-up and the occasional impersonality of large groups.

School Systems

Although our educational system has the greatest potential for influencing large numbers of people, it has received little attention. The excellent university-based program at Stevens Point, Wisconsin, mentioned earlier is one of a growing number of programs. Additionally, curricula in many high schools now include a variety of health promotion topics. Queen (1986) has published an excellent wellness programming guide for kindergarten to junior high school age children. Strengths of this site include a large captive audience, reasonably motivated participants, and the facile incorporation of health promotion into the existing health curriculum. Weaknesses include the inability to consistently affect the home environment, time limitations, competition with other subjects, and the lack of time-tested teaching methods. It is imperative that we devote time, energy, and research funds to maximizing the impact of health promotion in our school systems.

Individual Consultants

The rapidly developing field of health promotion has produced a number of consultants with a wide range of expertise. These consultants can provide services in many different types of settings. Consultants can often provide excellent and timely advice to developing programs, advice based on firsthand experience. They are also frequently recognized in their respective fields and provide innovative, dynamic service. The major disadvantage of consultants is that they are sometimes quite expensive, are present only for the duration of the service, and may be relied upon at the expense of existing in-house expertise.

A SYSTEMS APPROACH
TO HEALTH PROMOTION

The ultimate success of health promotion will depend on the meaningful integration of providers and participants. This means developing a system of delivery and a systems approach to health promotion that connects individuals, patients, health care providers, corporations, governments, cultures, and the reimbursement system. One model of that system is shown in Figure 1.2. This model calls for better coordination and integration of treatment and health promotion modalities in the current health care system, and more stringent control of health care costs through enhanced quality of care monitoring and utilization controls.

Health promotion must play a prominent role in this integration. Health promotion is in a unique and powerful position. In today's extremely competitive health care environment, health promotion is relatively nonthreatening, approaching a new market with new services. Its activities can benefit other health care providers—screening programs can identify "undoctored" clients and refer them

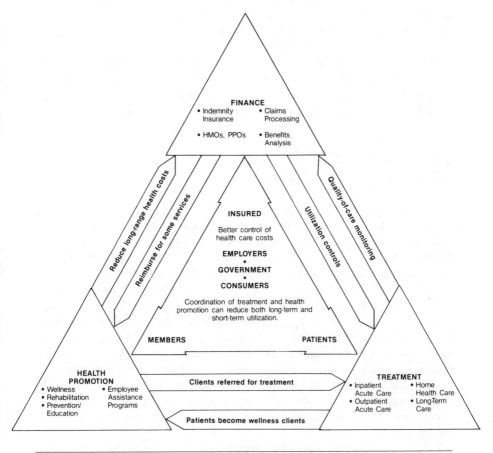

Figure 1.2. One model of an integrated health care system. *Note.* From "Refining the Integrated Health Care System" by R. Berg, 1986 (January/February), *Optimal Health*, p. 9. Copyright 1986 by Optimal Health. Reprinted by permission.

to physicians, testing and screening programs can identify patients with symptomatic and asymptomatic diseases and refer them to hospitals and their staffs, and educational programs can utilize health education specialists in the community.

Health promotion programs also allow individuals to acquire knowledge and develop skills often not appreciated by the traditional health care system. This increased sense of autonomy and personal responsibility will make a valuable contribution to the health of this country.

Of the providers already mentioned, hospitals are the best qualified to offer comprehensive health promotion. Hospitals have the medical expertise to treat disease on an inpatient basis and are developing health promotion programs that apply to inpatients as well as outpatients. Hospitals are acutely aware of cost containment issues and are motivated to implement programs that cut health care costs and benefit patients. Hospitals can provide an array of services ranging from prenatal nutrition classes and physical therapy to cardiac surgery. Hospitals must take innovative steps to work with patients, physicians and other health care professionals, insurance companies, and government to sculpt a system that values health promotion, disease prevention, and disease treatment.

The model seen in Figure 1.2 can become reality, though it will require tremendous effort. Recognizing that each of the supposedly disparate components shown actually belong in the same model is a significant step. Having a vision of the integrated health care system is an important prerequisite to attaining it.

CULTURAL ACCEPTANCE OF HEALTH PROMOTION

The culture in which an individual lives—be it the culture of the home, worksite, or community—is vitally important to behavior and behavior change. Cultures that support health behaviors make it easier for an individual to change to and maintain a healthy lifestyle. Individuals who receive little support from their cultural environments stand a greatly diminished chance for success.

How supportive is our culture of health promotion? Although significant changes have occurred and greater numbers of people exercise, eat more healthfully, and avoid risky behaviors, the majority of Americans are not health promotion-oriented. The average American adult takes frequent doses of fast food, uses elevators instead of stairs, utilizes alcohol and medication as primary stress reduction techniques, and watches an inordinate amount of television. Madison Avenue advertising, music videos, and inertia are phenomenally powerful influences. As long as the average American adult engages in unhealthy behaviors, the average American child will do the same, thwarting the health promotion efforts of the school system.

In the corporate arena, overall participation and commitment to health promotion is low. Although a number of companies sponsor programs, many do not, especially the small- and medium-sized companies that employ the great majority of workers in this country. And although interest level is often quite high, companies often balk when it comes time to pay for services.

In the health care provider network, disease treatment, not health promotion, is the norm. Disease treatment is taught, fostered, and reimbursed. This environment is not optimally receptive to the ideas and programs health promotion offers.

The potential for cultural change in our country is great. For this to occur, however, we must recognize the interrelationships of individuals and their cultures. Western society has staunchly supported the primacy of the individual, without considering cultural variables. Only by a systematic approach to culture change, such as that proposed by Allen (1981), will significant and lasting changes occur.

IMPEDIMENTS TO HEALTH PROMOTION

Although the environment has never been better for the spread of health promotion, significant impediments to its growth still exist. These impediments include the following:

Cultural Resistance

Despite positive trends, the majority of our culture is still not health promotion-oriented. Special interest groups like the tobacco industry continue to exert powerful negative cultural influence. Health promotion must be viewed in a societal and cultural context. Unless society is willing to take responsibility for its lifestyle actions, transformation to a health promotion-dominated culture will be slow.

Treatment-Dominated Reimbursement System

Few health promotion activities are currently reimbursed. The reasoning behind such practices is specious. Failure to reimburse a service sends out a powerful message to all involved and diminishes the likelihood that the service will be requested again. Better balance between disease treatment and health promotion reimbursement practices is absolutely essential.

Obsession With Personal Freedom

Our national obsession with personal freedom stems from the profound influence of liberalism in American social thought and frequently interferes with proactive attempts to modify individual behavior. This obsession may buckle under the economic pressure of the escalating costs of unhealthy behavior and our country's unwillingness and inability to pay. It is important to strike a balance between personal and societal freedom.

Physician's Disease-Care Orientation

The practicing physician, the key gatekeeper in the health care system, has received scanty education and training in health promotion and receives few incentives, economic or otherwise, to practice health promotion. Until the medical education system changes and incentives to practice health promotion are added, this orientation will continue.

Questionable Identity as a Discipline

Health promotion is in its infancy and, as Nicholas, Gobble, and Schmottlach (1987) have written, has yet to satisfy three criteria for a discipline: an identifiable domain, a substantial history with time-tested works, and a systematic means of acquiring knowledge. They assert that health promotion is a technology rather than a discipline, based mainly on empirical findings gathered without the benefit of a scientific theoretical basis. These are valid and important points that deserve serious consideration and debate. However, given that significant strides are being made in each of these three areas, this author prefers to consider health promotion as a nascent discipline on its way to becoming "a full-fledged discipline, comparable in impact, sophistication, and opportunity to medical practice" (O'Donnell, 1986c, p. 1).

Health Promotion Providers' Disdain for the Medical Profession

Many health promotion providers behave as though the medical profession were the enemy, which tends to obstruct any efforts to spread health promotion. Some manifestations of this attitude include failure to involve physicians in the planning of programs that affect their patients, poor communication with physicians on multiple levels, and unwillingness to even try to work with physicians on programs. Providers and physicians must work collaboratively if health promotion is to have the significant impact it is capable of having. Physicians in the preventive medicine field have made contributions that have greatly influenced the health of this nation. Health promotion providers have utilized these contributions and yet have rarely given recognition to their source. As long as disease dominates our culture, physicians will play a prominent role in our health care system. The new health promotion provider must strive to establish cooperative and productive relationships with physicians.

Uncoordinated Approach of Health Promotion Providers

A large number of providers from diverse disciplines now deliver health promotion programs. Unfortunately, these providers rarely collaborate and are often competing to deliver the same services. It is self-destructive for providers to compete for a small segment of the market when they could collaborate and reach the larger, currently untapped market. Failure of providers to work more cooperatively will surely slow the progress and growth of the discipline of health promotion.

Each of these impediments is surmountable. To overcome them a cooperative, multidisciplinary approach is necessary. Representatives from all of the disciplines contributing to health promotion, particularly those in the areas of business medicine, economics, education, government, insurance, and media, must sit down together and establish formal communication. This communication must be action-oriented, aimed at exploring theoretical and pragmatic models of health promotion. These models will recognize that health promotion, because of its integrative nature, relies heavily upon other disciplines for its knowledge base.

Even so, the discipline of health promotion is beginning to develop its own original scientific base, that will supplement and be incorporated into the existing one. This new discipline, unlike any other, will have as its reason for existence the discovery and implementation of the optimal methods of maintaining and enhancing health. Realizing the potential of this discipline will require a common vision of health and a commitment to action. It will require significant effort to accomplish this, but it is an effort well worth making.

CONCLUSION

The discipline of health promotion has reached a critical point on its growth curve. From small, grass-roots beginnings, it has grown rapidly so that now a tremendous number of disciplines contribute to it. Its scope is becoming more clearly defined, and it is on the verge of becoming a more powerful force in the health care system.

Because health promotion is a new discipline, it must establish its identity and clarify its scope. Neither of these is easy to do. Given the large number and diversity of disciplines that health promotion draws from, it is difficult, even counterproductive, to make claims of health promotion being a totally new discipline. Indeed, its unique contribution to health care will come from its thoughtful, innovative, and integrative efforts.

For such integrative efforts to occur, health promotion providers must have a comprehensive vision of an integrated health care system. In this system, the participants and providers work together in a cooperative and coordinated fashion. The development of this integrated system will require a multifaceted approach, one that simultaneously considers financial, political, social, and medical issues.

Developing this system is made more difficult by our country's lukewarm cultural acceptance of health promotion. Approaches geared for individuals have been relatively successful so far, but it is unlikely that major gains will occur without efforts at cultural change. Models for such change do exist, and we must explore them to determine the best approaches.

The next decade will be one of opportunity for the discipline of health promotion. A number of factors have contributed to its growth so far, but in this fast-changing health care environment, these factors could rapidly fluctuate. For health promotion to establish itself, it must do many things: It must accurately assess the current health care system and its own strengths and weaknesses; it must develop a sound theoretical framework and contribute to ongoing research; it must develop an integrative systems approach that utilizes and recognizes existing expertise; it must be flexible enough to withstand fluctuations in the health care setting; it must articulate its tenets in a language that can be clearly understood; and, it must accomplish all this within the next 15 years. Health promotion will never again have such an excellent opportunity.

BIBLIOGRAPHY

Allen, R. (1981). *Lifegain*. New York: Appleton-Century-Crofts.

American Hospital Association. (1979). *The hospital's responsibility for health promotion* [Policy and statement of the American Hospital Association]. Chicago: Author.

Ardell, D.B. (1977). *High level wellness: An alternative to doctors, drugs, and disease*. Berkeley: Ten Speed Press.

Ardell, D.B. (1983). *The history and future of the wellness movement* (In the National Wellness Institute campus wellness workbook). Stevens Point, WI: Stevens Point Foundation.

Bayer, R., & Moreno, J. (1986). Health promotion: Ethical and social dilemmas of government policy. *Health Affairs*, 5(2), 72-85.

Belloc, N.B., & Breslow, L. (1972). Relationship of physical health status and health practices. *Preventive Medicine*, 1, 409-421.

Blum, A. (1982). Medical activism. In R.B. Taylor, J.R. Ureda, & J.W. Denham (Eds.), *Health promotion: Principles and clinical applications* (pp. 373-391). Norwalk, CT: Appleton-Century-Crofts.

Breckon, D. (1982). *Hospital health education: A guide to program development*. Rockville, MD: Aspen Systems.

Brody, D.S. (1980). The patient's role in clinical decision-making. *Annals of Internal Medicine*, 93, 718-722.

Collins, C.A. (1986). *Health promotion profile of beliefs, attitudes and activities of Tennessee primary care physicians*. Unpublished doctoral dissertation, The University of Tennessee-Knoxville.

Currie, B.F., & Beasley, J.W. (1982). Health promotion in the medical encounter. In R.B. Taylor, J.R. Ureda, & J.W. Denham (Eds.), *Health promotion: Principles and clinical applications* (pp. 143-160). Norwalk, CT: Appleton-Century-Crofts.

A discussion document on the concept and principles of health promotion. (1986). *Health Promotion*, 1(1), 73-76.

Dubos, R. (1961). *The mirage of health: Utopias, progress and biological change*. New York: Anchor Books.

Dunn, H.L. (1961). *High level wellness*. Arlington, VA: R.W. Beatty.

Fries, J.F. (1980). Aging, natural death, and the compression of morbidity. *New England Journal of Medicine, 303,* 130-135.

Goodstadt, M.S., Simpson, R.I., & Loranger, P.O. (1987). Health promotion: A conceptual integration. *American Journal of Health Promotion,* 1(3), 58-63.

Gray, J.A.M. (1977). The failure of preventive medicine. *Lancet,* pp. 1338-1339.

Hancock, T. (1986). Lalonde and beyond: Looking back at "a new perspective on the health of Canadians." *Health Promotion: An International Journal,* 1, 93-100.

Harris, T.G. (1987, February). The new individualism. *Fitness in Business,* pp. 141-145.

Illich, I. (1976). In *Medical nemesis—the expropriation of health* (pp. 3-10). New York: Pantheon Books.

Jonas, S.J. (1981). Prevention: Helping patients "up front." *Colloquy,* pp. 9-12.

Kannel, W.B., & Thom, T.T. (1979). Implications of the recent decline in cardiovascular mortality. *Cardiovascular Medicine,* 4, 983-997.

Lalonde, M. (1974). *A new perspective on the health of Canadians: A working document.* Ottawa: Government of Canada.

Last, J.M. (1986). Scope and methods of prevention. In J.M. Last (Ed.), *Public health and preventive medicine* (p. 3). Norwalk, CT: Appleton-Century-Crofts.

Mason, J.O., & Tolsma, D.D. (1984). Personal health promotion. *Western Journal of Medicine,* 141(6), 772-776.

McGinnis, J.M. (1983). Recent health gains for adults. *New England Journal of Medicine,* 306, 671-673.

McKeown, T. (1979). *The role of medicine: Dream, mirage or nemesis?* Princeton, NJ: Princeton University Press.

McPhee, S.J., & Schroeder, S.A. (1987). Promoting preventive care: Changing reimbursement is not enough. *American Journal of Public Health,* 77, 780-781.

Murphy, R.J., Gasparotto, G., & Opatz, J.P. (1987). Current issues in the evaluation of worksite health promotion programs. In J.P. Opatz (Ed.), *Health promotion evaluation: Measuring the organizational impact* (pp. 1-14). Stevens Point, WI: National Wellness Institute.

Naisbitt, J. (1984). *Megatrends.* New York: Warner Books.

Nelson, E.C., & Simmons, J.J. (1983). Health promotion—the second public health revolution: Promise or threat? *Family and Community Health,* 5(4), 57-60.

Nicholas, D.R., Gobble, D.C., & Schmottlach, R.N. (1987). Health promotion: A discipline or a technology? *American Journal of Health Promotion,* 1(3), 75-77.

1985 Findings on health promotion and disease prevention. (1986). *Public Health Reports,* 101, 566-599.

Oberman, A. (1987). Components of health promotion. *Family and Community Health,* 7(1), 1-11.

O'Donnell, M.P. (1986a). Definition of health promotion. *American Journal of Health Promotion*, **1**(1), 4-5.

O'Donnell, M.P. (1986b). Definition of health promotion, Part II: Levels of programs. *American Journal of Health Promotion*, **1**(2), 6-9.

O'Donnell, M.P. (1986c). Publishers welcome. *American Journal of Health Promotion*, **1**(1), 1.

O'Donnell, M.P., & Ainsworth, T. (1984). *Health promotion in the workplace.* New York: Wiley.

Opatz, J.P. (1985). *A primer of health promotion: Creating healthy organizational cultures.* Washington, DC: Oryn Publications.

Paffenbarger, R.S., Hyde, R.T., Wing, A.L., & Hsieh, C.C. (1986). Physical activity, all-cause mortality, and longevity of college alumni. *New England Journal of Medicine*, **314**, 605-613.

Pirsig, R. (1976). *Zen and the art of motorcycle maintenance.* New York: Bantam.

Profile: Ottawa charter for health promotion. (1987). *American Journal of Health Promotion*, **1**(4), 61-63.

Queen, S. (1986). *Wellness for children: Programming guide kindergarten-junior high.* Columbia, MD: Lifeworks.

Somers, A.R. (1978). [Editorial: Response to "Perils of Prevention" article]. *New England Journal of Medicine*, **298**, 746-747.

Somers, A.R. (1984). Why not try preventing illness as a way of controlling Medicare costs? *New England Journal of Medicine*, **311**, 853-856.

Stamler, J. (1978). Lifestyles, major risks factors, proof and public policy. *Circulation*, **58**, 3-19.

Stamler, J. (1985). Coronary heart disease: Doing the "right things." *New England Journal of Medicine*, **312**, 1053-1055.

Terris, M. (1984). Newer perspective on the health of Canadians: Beyond the Lalonde Report (Rosenthal lecture). *Journal of Public Health Policy*, **5**, 327-337.

U.S. Department of Health, Education, and Welfare, Public Health Service. (1979). *Healthy people: The Surgeon General's report on health promotion and disease prevention* (DHEW Publication No. 79-55071). Washington, DC: U.S. Government Printing Office.

U.S. Department of Health and Human Services, Public Health Service. (1980). *Promoting health, preventing disease: Objectives for the nation.* Washington, DC: U.S. Government Printing Office.

U.S. Department of Health and Human Services, Public Health Service. (1983). Public health service implementation plans for attaining the objectives for the nation. *Public Health Reports* (Suppl. to September/October, 1983 issue). Washington, DC: U.S. Government Printing Office.

Vickery, D.M. (1986). Medical self-care: A review of the concept and program models. *American Journal of Health Promotion*, **1**(1), 23-28.

Warner, K.E. (1987). Selling health promotion to corporate America: Uses and abuses of the economic argument. *Health Education Quarterly*, **14**, 43.

Wilner, S. (1986). Health promotion and disease prevention in HMOs. *Health Affairs,* **5**(1), 122-134.

Windom, R.E., McGinnis, J.M., & Fielding, J.E. (1987). Examining worksite health promotion. *Business and Health,* pp. 36-37.

World Health Organization. 1960. *Constitution.* Geneva: Palais des Nations.

World Health Organization. (1986). World Health Organization charter. In *International yearbook and statesmen's who's who* (p. 43). West Sussex, England: Thomas Skinner Directories.

SUGGESTED READINGS

American Journal of Health Promotion, published quarterly by AJHP, P.O. Box 1287, Royal Oak, MI 48068-1287.

American Journal of Preventive Medicine, published bimonthly by Oxford University Press, 200 Madison Ave., New York, NY 10016.

American Journal of Public Health, published monthly by the American Public Health Association, Inc., AJPH, 1015 15th St. NW, Washington, DC 20005.

Health Promotion: An International Journal, published quarterly by Oxford University Press, Walton St., Oxford OX26DP, UK.

Journal of Occupational Medicine, published monthly by Williams and Wilkins, 428 E. Preston St., Baltimore, MD 21202.

Optimal Health, published bimonthly by Athletic Business Publications, 1842 Hoffman St., Suite 201, Madison, WI 53704.

Perspectives on Prevention, published quarterly by the Association of Teachers of Preventive Medicine, 1030 15th St. NW, Suite 1020, Washington, DC 20005.

Public Health Reports: Journal of the United States Public Health Service, published bimonthly by the office of the Assistant Secretary for Health, Room 721-H, Hubert Humphrey Building, 200 Independence Ave. SW, Washington, DC 20201.

CHAPTER 2

The Historic Role of Hospitals in Health Promotion

Barbara K. Burke

The roots of hospital involvement in health promotion go back to community education programs. As knowledge of early detection of disease and trauma treatment grew, hospitals translated this knowledge into health screenings and education programs. High blood pressure screenings and first aid and cardiopulmonary resuscitation (CPR) classes were all offered to the community by hospitals in the 1960s. From these beginnings a wide range of educational programs and services have developed to meet the changing needs and expanding potential of health education.

THE EARLY YEARS OF HOSPITAL HEALTH PROMOTION

In the 1960s another type of community education program gained prominence—prenatal classes. A generation ago most mothers were anesthetized during delivery; fathers assumed their role as "pacers" outside the delivery room in the fathers' lounge. Yet today, one generation later, most couples would be embarrassed to admit that they have not attended prenatal classes or that the father doesn't intend to be an active participant in the delivery of the baby. Both mother and father now want the knowledge and skills that allow them to make delivery as stress-free, medication-free, and personally memorable as possible. A whole industry has developed around the education and training of expectant and new parents. Many hospitals began, and continue, to cater extensively to these needs.

During the 1970s hospitals initiated efforts toward extensive patient education with an emphasis on patient choice and personal responsibility. Because of break-throughs in the treatment of diabetes and heart disease, diabetic education and cardiac rehabilitation were two specific services extended not only to inpatients, but to outpatients and their families as well. The more that patients knew and understood about their diseases, their ongoing treatment, and the impact of their lifestyle habits on the diseases, the better these patients could live with their ill-nesses.

These initial efforts in health education brought the hospitals unexpected success. The popularity of all of these programs was due in part to an underlying axiom of adult education: People learn things that have immediate application to their lives. Work with people at teachable moments when they feel the need for certain knowledge or skills, and the program will be successful. People participating in these early community and patient education programs were certainly being touched at the right moments.

In addition to their good timing, these programs succeeded because hospital sponsorship gave them credibility. The programs generally were of a high quality, taught by trained professionals with good support equipment and materials. Hospi-tals soon found that large numbers of people who typically never before used their services were now coming through their doors to participate in the programs.

These programs consequently gave hospitals access to new people ("new mar-kets" was not yet a term in use in health care). Outpatients, patients' family mem-bers, and people who just thought it would be good to know how to do CPR, for instance, began coming to hospital facilities and getting to know hospital per-sonnel. Their experiences were generally positive. These programs then generated free publicity in the community, and the publicity was positive. The hospitals liked this.

POLICY DEVELOPMENT

As these events were occurring in hospitals around the country, the policy under-pinning for these efforts was being developed at a national level. In 1975 the American Hospital Association issued a statement approved by its board, entitled "Health Education: Role and Responsibility of Health Care Institutions." This document stated that a complete system of health care should offer services in a variety of areas, including health education and prevention. Health education, including health promotion, is described as being involved in illness prevention but also as helping people clarify their responsibilities for their health, maintain their health, and receive the most appropriate level of care.

This statement also alluded to the need to address health education to specific target populations. Already, the groundwork for health promotion was being laid in terms of its scope and intent.

This statement continues with more prophetic suggestions. It mantains that there are three target groups for health education efforts:

- Patients and their families
- Personnel, including employees, medical staff, volunteers, and trustees
- The community at large

The statement also suggested that health education efforts be joint-ventured through collaboration with other professional groups, consumer groups, the educational community, and health associations concerned with specific diseases.

The final insight of this document discussed here is its position on the funding for health education. The concept of providing health education and health promotion as free community services, or "loss leaders," is laid.

In 1979 the AHA issued a policy and follow-up statement entitled "The Hospital's Responsibility for Health Promotion," which is truly a landmark for hospital-based health promotion programs. This statement is much more comprehensive than its predecessor on health education. Its theme is helping consumers to take responsibility for their health and to be able to make informed choices about their health.

The highlights of the policy include statements that the hospital has a responsibility

- to work with others in the community to assess the health status of the community,
- to identify target areas and population groups for hospital-based and cooperative health promotion programs,
- to develop programs to help upgrade the health in those target areas,
- to ensure that persons who are apparently healthy have access to information about how to stay well and prevent disease,
- to provide appropriate health education programs to aid those persons who choose to alter their personal health behaviors or develop more healthy lifestyles, and
- to establish the hospital as an institution in the community that is concerned about good health in addition to being concerned about treating illness.

The follow-up statement elucidates many aspects of this policy. It notes that hospitals are now involved in the areas of lifestyle and personal behavior. It defines lifestyle in terms of such personal choice factors as the use or abuse of alcohol, drugs, tobacco, and the automobile, as well as exercise, nutrition, and sleep habits.

These documents contain the first suggestion that businesses that are concerned about rising health care costs should get involved with health information and education programs that relate to lifestyle and personal health behaviors. One final direction offered in this statement is the need for enlarging the financial base for these activities so that they do not contribute to rising health care costs. Financial mechanisms suggested are third-party reimbursement, fee-for-service, contributions, grants, and contracts.

The American Hospital Association continued its leadership in health promotion by starting the Center for Health Promotion in 1979 and beginning publication of the magazine *Promoting Health* in 1980.

In a 5-year period from 1974 to 1979, the AHA, the primary voice for national hospital policy, legitimized hospitals' expanded role as purveyors of health care rather than just illness care. It legitimized the role of education to attune people to their responsibility for their own health and the important role that lifestyle plays in the quality of consumers' health. It acknowledged that, with this responsibility for an expanded view of health care, hospitals would not be working just with patients and their families, but with individuals from the community and with corporations as well.

While these activities were occurring at the hospital policy level, the federal government was taking historic action related to health promotion. In 1976 the Health Information and Health Promotion Act (Public Law 94-317) created the Office of Health Information and Health Promotion (now the Office of Disease Prevention and Health Promotion) to coordinate federal health promotion programs.

In 1979 "Healthy People: The Surgeon General's Report on Health Promotion and Disease Prevention" was issued by the then-Department of Health, Education and Welfare, establishing health goals for the country.

In 1980 the prevention focus and goals of "Healthy People" were translated into "Promoting Health, Preventing Disease: Objectives for the Nation," published by the Department of Health and Human Services. This document set quantifiable objectives in 15 areas of prevention to reach the goals outlined in "Healthy People," and set the public health agenda for the next decade.

PROGRAM DEVELOPMENT

Though the focus of these governmental actions was appropriately public health, hospital policy and programs focused on translating this same information to patients, patients' families, and employer/employee groups. Hospitals began talking about and offering fitness classes, smoking cessation programs, and other staples of health promotion programming. A review of the 1980 annual index of *Promoting Health* is useful in showing what topics were of interest at that time:

- "Fitness Center Builds Community Support at Base"
- "Long Standing Hospital Seeks New Look, New Life in Health and Fitness Center"

- "A Lot of Planning and a Little Luck Help Launch Employee Health Promotion Program"

By 1981 a review of that year's annual index of *Promoting Health* shows hospital implementation of health risk appraisals, the search for third-party reimbursements for health promotion, and the development of such marketing techniques as hospital-sponsored parties in neighborhood homes on health education and employer-sponsored weight loss contests. By 1982 the index reveals hospitals were getting involved in employee assistance programs (EAPs) for businesses, using health promotion as a key to generate nonpatient revenue, implementing occupational health services as a component of wellness, and targeting programs to such specific groups as the elderly.

A brief review of articles that appeared during a 3-year period from 1980 through 1982 shows that the program agenda was laid early on for hospital-based health promotion and has been followed throughout the 1980s in the use of health risk appraisals, the design of new approaches to community health education, the development of fitness centers, the integration of occupational health and EAP services as part of health promotion, and the expansion of services to specific target groups such as corporate clients and the elderly.

HEALTH PROMOTION TRENDS

In 1984 the Center for Health Promotion of the American Hospital Association, joined with The Center for Health Services and Policy Research of Northwestern University to do an extensive survey of community and federal hospitals (of 6,264 contacted, 3,565 responded). In 1987 *Optimal Health* magazine and Price Waterhouse of St. Louis, Missouri, did a joint survey of hospital-based health promotion programs ("Health Promotion Young, But Growing," 1987). Their survey response was 397 hospitals from a geographically representative distribution. Although it is not entirely useful to compare them given their different respondent groups, the results of these national surveys represent two of the few sources that suggest the direction and trends hospital health promotion has taken in the past 7 years.

Key issues raised by these surveys included what target groups were being addressed, what programs were being offered, where health promotion resided in the hospital, and what the funding sources, financial goals, and success measures were for health promotion programs.

Target Groups

When asked to what groups they offered health promotion, the hospitals in the AHA survey indicated that 76.8% had programs for outpatients, 74.3% had programs for the community, 78% had programs for their own employees, but only

42% had programs for corporations. When asked what health promotion programs hospitals offered to special target groups, the AHA respondents said 52% of them had programs for parents, 49% of them had programs for women, but only 33% had programs for adults 65 to 74 years of age or for children under 10 (Lee et al., 1984).

Programs by Target Groups

The four most commonly offered programs to outpatients were diabetes education, nutrition, prenatal education, and cardiac rehabilitation. The most commonly offered health promotion programs to community groups were cardiopulmonary resuscitation, prenatal education, smoking cessation, diabetes education, and nutrition. The most commonly offered health promotion programs for corporations were cardiopulmonary resuscitation, stress management, smoking cessation, weight control, and health risk appraisal.

Organizational Placement

No matter which target group was being served (the community, the outpatient, or the corporate client), in the AHA survey the department where health promotion most commonly resided was education. Nursing was the second most common department for inpatient, outpatient, and employee health promotion efforts. For both community and corporate health promotion, 13% of the hospitals reported having their own departments of health promotion; 3.8% reported that they had set up separate corporations to carry out health promotion, and 8.6% reported having their own fitness centers.

The roots of health promotion in education are also evident in the *Optimal Health*/Price Waterhouse survey, which asked a slightly different question. When asked the directors' areas of professional responsibility, 53% of the respondents reported education and training, 79% reported health education. The highest number (85%) reported health promotion and lifestyle modification (see Table 2.1). By 1987 44% of this sample noted that they operated fitness centers.

Funding

When respondents were asked about funding sources, the strong acceptance of health promotion as a service was apparent in the AHA survey. Regardless of target group, whether employee, corporate, or community, the major source of funding remained hospital underwriting and the next was fee for service.

In the *Optimal Health*/Price Waterhouse survey, again, a slightly different question was asked, one relating to financial goals rather than current financial sources for health promotion, but the popularity of using health promotion as a tool for public relations or public service was still reflected (see Table 2.2).

Table 2.1   Directors' Areas of Responsibility

Areas of responsibility	Percent of response
Health promotion—lifestyle modification	85
Health education	79
Education and training	53
Wellness fitness center	44
Cardiac rehabilitation	17
Occupational health	17
Employee assistance programs	13
Utilization review	5
Benefits redesign	2
Sports medicine	9
Other	21

Note. Data are from "Health Promotion Young, But Growing: The *Optimal Health*/Price Waterhouse Health Promotion Survey," 1987 (July/August), *Optimal Health*, p. 22. Copyright 1987 by *Optimal Health* and Price Waterhouse. Reprinted by permission.

Table 2.2   Financial Goals

Organizational goals	Percent of response
Public relations	62
Service	53
Break even	39
Profit	29
Loss leader	10

Note. Data are from "Health Promotion Young, But Growing: The *Optimal Health*/Price Waterhouse Health Promotion Survey," 1987 (July/August), *Optimal Health*, p. 23. Copyright 1987 by *Optimal Health* and Price Waterhouse. Reprinted by permission.

Few program directors or even hospital administrators talked about using health promotion to increase profits.

The *Optimal Health*/Price Waterhouse survey went on to ask one more question of significance here: How was the success of health promotion programs measured? The top four measures of success were all somewhat related to the hospital's

Table 2.3   Measurements of Hospital Health Promotion Success

Organizational areas measured	Percent of response
Public relations	69
Community service	66
Image enhancement	65
Customer satisfaction	62
Behavior change	48
Patient referral	41
Profitability	39
Other department support	25

Note. Data are from "Health Promotion Young, But Growing: The *Optimal Health*/Price Waterhouse Health Promotion Survey," 1987 (July/August), *Optimal Health*, p. 23. Copyright 1987 by *Optimal Health* and Price Waterhouse. Reprinted by permission.

image: public relations, community service, image enhancement, and customer satisfaction (see Table 2.3). The measure of success cited least often was profitability.

THE FUTURE

These responses reflect the history of health promotion. It was born from the roots of traditional patient and community education programming. It grew based on its strong qualities of providing good, topical health education, good public relations, and image enhancement for the hospital. Health promotion from its inception has been seen largely as a community service. Historically, health promotion has shown that it can fulfill these functions very well.

There is a strong sense developing, however, that health promotion is now entering a new stage, be it adolescent or pre-adult. Serious challenges and opportunities surely lie ahead. As inpatient revenues plateau or decline, health promotion programs will undoubtedly have to become more accountable in verifying their usefulness. Health promotion programs will need to expand their current fledgling successes in attracting new hospital customers and customers for physicians, in generating new nonpatient revenues for the hospital corporation, and in establishing new relationships for the hospital with outside corporations and third-party payers.

REFERENCES

American Hospital Association. (1975). *Health education: Role and responsibility of health care institutions* [Statement of the American Hospital Association]. Chicago: Author.

American Hospital Association. (1979). The hospital's responsibility for health promotion [Policy and statement of the American Hospital Association]. Chicago: Author.

Health promotion young, but growing: *Optimal Health*/Price Waterhouse health promotion survey. (1987, July/August). *Optimal Health*, pp. 22-24.

Lee, E. (1984, March/April). A capsule review of the health promotion literature of 1982. *Promoting Health*, pp. 7-9.

Lee, E., Ross, C., Giloth, B., Lange, M., Jones, J., Sherman, S., Radbill, L., & Barg, K.L. (1984). *Hospital-based health promotion program: Report and analyses of the 1984 survey*. Chicago: The American Hospital Association.

Promoting Health, 1980 annual index. Chicago: The American Hospital Association.

Promoting Health, 1981 annual index. Chicago: The American Hospital Association.

Promoting Health, 1982 annual index. Chicago: The American Hospital Association.

U.S. Department of Health and Human Services, Public Health Service. (1980). *Promoting health, preventing disease: Objectives for the nation*. Washington, DC: U.S. Government Printing Office.

U.S. Department of Health and Human Services, Public Health Service, The Office of Disease Prevention and Health Promotion. (1986, November). *The 1990 health objective for the nation: A mid-course review*. Washington, DC: U.S. Government Printing Office.

U.S. Department of Health and Human Services, Public Health Service, The Office of Disease Prevention and Health Promotion (1986, December). *A decade of progress*. Washington, DC: U.S. Government Printing Office.

U.S. Department of Health, Education and Welfare, Public Health Service. (1979). *Healthy people: The Surgeon General's report on health promotion and disease prevention* (DHEW Publication No. 79-55071). Washington, DC: U.S. Government Printing Office.

CHAPTER 3

Current Involvement of Hospitals in Health Promotion

Daniel J. Bonk

Jeffrey M. Bensky

The deregulation revolution of the health care industry has been led by the two largest buyers of health care, business and government. Factors from certificates of need to reshaped financial incentives for purchasing health care have not only changed the rules but have also begun to differentiate the winners from the losers.

We are all familiar with the costs that spurred this revolution. These have often been presented in comparisons. For example, 10% of the price of a Chrysler K-Car was directly due to the costs incurred for employee health care; in 1986 our nation's health care bill rose 7.7% to nearly $450 billion, or about 11% of our total GNP. Given this dramatic rise, along with pressure from government and business, health care has had to respond to the market and simultaneously lower its costs.

RESTRUCTURING THE HEALTH CARE SYSTEM

The necessity of responding to increased health care spending has dramatically changed the competitive dynamics of health care. Prior to the formal and informal deregulation of the health care industry, the existing health care environment did not require that hospital leadership think in strategic or marketing terms. In the past, competition between hospitals consisted primarily of getting the first, best, or biggest piece of technology. However, as we have learned, individual hospitals can no longer afford a "keeping up with the Joneses" mentality. For survival and profitability, each provider must strategically position itself within its market in a unique and distinctive way in order to attain a sustainable competitive advantage using its own array of services, products, and programming.

To attain this better position while shifting to survive, hospitals are also segmenting services in order to determine the current or potential profitability of their industry. Hospitals have begun to assess factors such as market share, demand growth trends, barriers to entry, ability to differentiate products, and competition.

In any industry, understanding industry economics and finding the right positioning is contingent upon comprehension of the many influencing forces, rules, and dynamics. These include rivalry among existing firms, bargaining power of buyers, bargaining power of suppliers, substitutes, and the threat of new entrants into the market.

Successfully balancing this matrix as it relates to hospitals is critical today. The forces within each market will vary in terms of importance, but satisfying the needs of buyers is essential. These buyers may include patients, consumers, businesses, and physicians.

As Michael Porter (1985) has pointed out, the necessity of thoroughly reviewing an organization's business strategies as they relate to all impacting factors is vital for its success. By reviewing Porter's model it is clear that today's health care providers are analyzing their markets from totally new perspectives. These new analytical perspectives, along with new competitive stances, are making a tremendous impact on health promotion providers.

As hospitals define and redefine their strategic plans and mission statements to cope with the changing environment, health promotion is viewed by some as fitting into these plans through the dual objectives of providing a prevention-oriented community service while also generating direct and indirect revenue streams for the hospital. Being a strategic business unit within this plan is essential for the survivability of health promotion within an organization. Health care restructuring has caused many administrators and boards of directors to reassess the long-term viability of health promotion when justified solely as a public relations or marketing tool. This reassessment has brought a business orientation to the field, which before had been primarily responding to perceived community needs without a focused business plan.

A BUSINESS ORIENTATION

As part of this change, today hospital-based health promotion departments and divisions are being asked to develop 5-year business plans and detailed market and competitor analyses, to track participants of programs for use of other hospital services, and to obtain a competitive advantage over other hospital-based and sometimes non-hospital-based competition.

Not all professionals in the field of health promotion have had the ability or the desire to make the transition to operation as a strategic business unit. Many of those who have survived restructuring have begun to see the need for the development of a product line mentality. Under this concept, traditional health promotion product lines (behavior modification programs, nutritional services, fitness programs and testing, and health education) are combined with related clinical services (sports medicine, cardiac rehabilitation, occupational medicine, and employee assistance). These packages are then taken to employers as units that have been designed with the goal of decreasing the company's overall health care cost expenditures.

As health promotion departments begin to create business units with specific products, markets, and channels, the validity or efficacy of for-profit ventures becomes easier to define. Their strategic roles, goals, and objectives are delineated in a fashion not uncommon in other, more traditional businesses. These range from joint ventures between two different hospitals' programs or between hospitals and physicians to development of for-profit fitness and wellness centers.

Many hospitals are in the process of developing for-profit fitness and wellness centers, ranging from the grandiose to the very modest. Hospitals have, in many cases, a competitive advantage over health clubs in the areas of capitation and complimentary services, and in achieving economies of scale through the use of existing staff expertise (physiology/prevention orientation). Even so, though health clubs in general still see many of the nonprofit YMCAs as unfair competition, they often view a hospital developing a for-profit fitness center as a viable market competitor and possibly a partner in a joint-venture arrangement.

Joint ventures and limited-partner arrangements are becoming more common between hospitals and health clubs. Hospitals are entering the club business for various reasons, including tapping markets within an existing club, expanding the fitness and health promotion niche, gaining an image as the hospital that "keeps you healthy," building spin-off services for other hospital departments, and in many cases, making a profit in this new product line. Still, hospitals are often poorly prepared due to lack of comprehensive market research, lack of solid business and marketing plans, lack of adequate or inappropriate space, and lack of experience in health club design.

Today funding for health promotion still comes primarily from funds generated by other hospital services. According to the 1987 *Optimal Health*/Price Waterhouse survey of hospitals regarding health promotion, the highest-ranking organizational goal for health promotion was still public relations (See Table 3.1).

If the financial goals of health promotion are to change, the trend of hospital health promotion toward standing on its own merits will also grow. Administrators see this bottom-line contribution as the major area of future concern for the field of health promotion. Continuing to form ties with other funding sources such as corporations, third-party payers, HMOs, PPOs, or wellness and fitness centers as part of a strategic plan will help hospital-based health promotion function with more stability in a more secure atmosphere while coping with a fluid environment.

Table 3.1   Financial Goals of Health Promotion

Organizational goals	Percent of response
Public relations	62
Service	53
Break even	39
Profit	29
Loss leader	10

Note. Data are from "Health Promotion Young, But Growing: The *Optimal Health*/Price Waterhouse Health Promotion Survey," 1987 (July/August), *Optimal Health*, pp. 22-24. Copyright 1987 by *Optimal Health* and Price Waterhouse. Reprinted by permission.

TRENDS IN HOSPITAL-BASED PROMOTION

Trends in recent developments in the hospital-based health promotion marketplace can be categorized into three areas for clarity: strategic, organizational, and operational.

Strategic Trends

Based on the *Optimal Health*/Price Waterhouse survey, over 50% of hospitals' mission statements reportedly referred in some manner to health promotion and disease prevention, and almost one in four mentioned wellness (Table 3.2). Many feel that the inclusion of health promotion as part of the hospital's mission statement is essential for the survivability of health promotion within the hospital.

Health promotion departments are organizing their own mission statements to include a more business-oriented philosophy. This approach does not preclude quality programming delivered by caring staff members. However, more and more health professionals are delineating goals and objectives that address the financial viability of their programs and services. Specific goals appear to be a function of how the organization measures the success of health promotion and how health promotion is expected to contribute to the strategic plan. In Table 3.3 we see how administrators perceived health promotion relating to their institution's strategic plan.

Target Markets

Hospital-based health promotion departments, targets, and programming are becoming more market-driven. Limited products are often provided that support or assist the hospital. Data from health promotion personnel collected via the

Table 3.2   Hospital Mission Statement References to Health Promotion

Health promotion references	Percentage of reported use
Health promotion/disease prevention	53
Health education	47
Health enhancement/improvement	43
Cost containment	37
Wellness	23
Lifestyle	18
Habits	3

Note. Data are from "Health Promotion Young, But Growing: The *Optimal Health*/Price Waterhouse Health Promotion Survey," 1987 (July/August), *Optimal Health*, pp. 22-24. Copyright 1987 by *Optimal Health* and Price Waterhouse. Reprinted by permission.

Table 3.3   Health Promotion's Contributions to Hospitals' Overall Strategic Plans

Very important contribution	Percent of response	Contributes very little	Percent of response
Image enhancement in the larger community	55	Contribution to referral network	55
Quality service	51	Revenue diversification	53
Enhancement of corporate relationships	48	Supplementation of alternative delivery service	51
		Patient utilization	48
		Provision of full services	48

Note. Data are from "Health Promotion Young, But Growing: The *Optimal Health*/Price Waterhouse Health Promotion Survey," 1987 (July/August), *Optimal Health*, pp. 22-24. Copyright 1987 by *Optimal Health* and Price Waterhouse. Reprinted by permission.

Table 3.4   The Four Major Health Promotion Categories

Target market	Related products
Corporations	Health education Health risk appraisal (HRA) Screening Smoking cessation Stress, occupational health (tie)
General public	Health education Fitness Nutrition/weight control Smoking cessation Stress management
Women	Health education Weight control OB/GYN Fitness Prenatal Osteoporosis
Hospital employees, senior citizens (tie)	Health education Fitness Screening Nutrition/weight control Smoking cessation

Note. Data are from "Health Promotion Young, But Growing: The *Optimal Health*/Price Waterhouse Health Promotion Survey," 1987 (July/August), *Optimal Health*, pp. 22-24. Copyright 1987 by *Optimal Health* and Price Waterhouse. Reprinted by permission.

Optimal Health/Price Waterhouse survey fell into four major categories. These categories and programs for each are listed in rank order in Table 3.4.

It appears that health education, long the cornerstone of health promotion, remains the most popular service for all groups. It also appears that corporations are receiving more attention than they have in the past, while women's programs and services are a vital market niche for some health promotion programs. Screening services appear most popular with corporations that may be interested in risk identification, and with senior citizens, who often make up the majority of community-based screening events.

Product Mix

Product mix, or types of programs and services offered by most health promotion programs, is getting more attention in relation to overall strategic positioning. As stated earlier, hospital health promotion departments are developing an integrated continuum of services containing both traditional services (health education, behavior modification, nutrition, and fitness), and related clinical services (occupational medicine, sports medicine, cardiac rehabilitation, and employee assistance programs).

Packaging of this product mix based on market need appears important, as does promotion or market planning based on perceived need. Both the pricing and packaging of this product mix is important when selling services to consumers and employers. It appears that some health promotion programs are able to differentiate their products on a "perceived value for price" basis, getting across to the buyer that the greater quality of their product makes it a better value even with its higher unit price. Often, with intangibles such as health promotion, it is possible to create this niche successfully.

Service Deliveries Strategies

Target markets are influenced by budgets but also by the channels that communicate the message. Hospital health promotion departments deliver programs and services to target markets using several vehicles.

- Marketing and promotion appear to be relative to the size of budget and to the emphasis placed on this medium within the hospital administrative structure.

- Pricing and packaging, as stated earlier, are becoming critical buying factors for consumers. Documenting need and competition will help drive both these closely related issues.

- Professional arrangements and joint ventures are becoming more commonplace. Other sources for ready-made clients and third-party payers such as HMOs and PPOs are being sought more often. Limited partnerships involving new ventures are creating new relationships between organizations. Those most frequently joint-venturing with hospital health promotion programs are physicians, other community organizations, and health clubs. These new professional arrangements help decrease the risk for each party and create new bonds that many hope will provide additional sources of revenue in the future.

- Over the last 5 years hospital health promotion departments have begun to utilize specially trained sales personnel. The American Hospital Association has offered basic sales training programs targeting sellers of health promotion services for several years, as have many other organizations. Most hospital health promotion programs have opted to train the health promotion professional in specific sales strategies relative to health promotion, while some programs have chosen to train sales personnel in the field of health promotion.

• The clients, consumers, and customers whom hospital health promotion primarily targets and those who generally participate in the programs report that they now place greater value on the discretionary time they have available. Today, as more and more families have two wage earners, their receptivity to health promotion is directly proportional to the program's convenience, length of time of the program or service, perceived immediacy of need, and participation options for other family members. To remain viable and reach these markets, health promotion must become conveniently accessible to its buyers.

Strategic issues are receiving greater attention today in the highly competitive area of health promotion. As business planning becomes the rule and not the exception for health promotion, strategic thinking will begin to play a major role in health promotion planning.

Organizational Trends

Results from professionals who responded to the *Optimal Health*/Price Waterhouse survey indicated that the average hospital health promotion department employed four full-time and five part-time individuals, with an average of eight persons reporting to the director. Eighty-three percent of these directors or health promotion managers had bachelors degrees, 58% held masters degrees, and 5% held PhDs. Forty-seven percent held the certification of registered nurse. The length of time in the field of health promotion ranged from 1 to 40 years, averaging 8. The number of years in current position ranged from 1 to 35 years, averaging out at 4. These individuals spent an average of 61% of their workday on health promotion.

This data appears to indicate that, in general, those involved with health promotion today have evolved into it from other hospital responsibilities. It also indicates that a significant amount of health promotion is delivered by persons who do not count health promotion as their sole responsibility. Organizationally, the directors reported the following responsibilities as shown in Table 3.5.

Organizationally, health promotion professionals are becoming more independently defined within the hospital, often in stand-alone departments or program areas. Reporting relationships for hospital health promotion professionals range from reporting directly to the CEO to being a function of another department that may add three to four levels of authority between the health promotion professional and the CEO. Additionally, as health promotion departments gain autonomy, the directors are assuming greater roles in supervision.

Performance and evaluation techniques specific to hospital health promotion personnel have been developed by some directors. Development of solid management skills by directors of health promotion appears critical for those joining the profession and also to the profession itself as it becomes better defined and is held more accountable.

Table 3.5 Health Promotion Directors' Responsibilities

Responsibilities	Percent of time spent
Health promotion (lifestyle modification)	85
Health education	79
Wellness fitness center	44
(commercial, 13%; employees, 21%; both, 62%)	
Cardiac rehabilitation	17
Occupational health	17
Utilization review	5
Benefits redesign	2
Employee assistance programs	13
Sports medicine	9
Education and training	53
Other	21

Note. Data are from "Health Promotion Young, But Growing: The *Optimal Health*/Price Waterhouse Health Promotion Survey," 1987 (July/August), *Optimal Health*, pp. 22-24. Copyright 1987 by *Optimal Health* and Price Waterhouse. Reprinted by permission.

As hospital health promotion begins to work more and more in a business environment, today's directors are concerned that this environment will limit creativity and growth. However, the reverse actually appears to be true. Those hospital health promotion programs that create detailed business plans and market research consider new product development a high priority. The truly market-driven program appears to be dependent on development of new programs, continuation of successful programs, and discontinuation of unsuccessful programs. Most newly initiated health promotion programs are given 2 years to achieve their performance criteria or goals.

Turf Issues

As hospital health promotion begins to play a greater role in the hospital strategic plan, it is gaining more credibility and integrating into new areas. Internal conflicts between hospital departments have resulted. Many professions, such as physical therapy, occupational therapy, psychology, nursing, health education, exercise physiology, recreation therapy, and many others are encouraging their people to jump on the health promotion bandwagon.

As hospital health promotion departments attempt to define and develop specific strategies for creating marketing and implementing and evaluating health promotion, other hospital departments often attempt to do it on their own. The issue of a specific mission directing top management's support for a health promotion strategy appears critical in this situation. Bringing the various players together under a united plan is essential. This involves utilizing other health professionals for health promotion programming who may not have been considered resources in the past. It may also involve a thorough explanation of market strategy and strategic plan of health promotion to those who desire entry into this arena.

Often a specific organizational structure can eliminate some of the turf issues relative to health promotion. The three most common structures of health promotion within the hospital structure are listed in Figure 3.1.

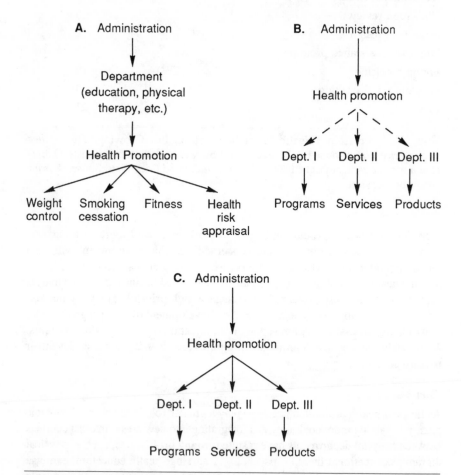

Figure 3.1. Health promotion within hospitals: (A) classic style; (B) reports directly to administration; (C) fully autonomous.

Structure A in Figure 3.1 is the classic style of health promotion within hospitals. Most health promotion has been initially developed within this format. It tends to be the easiest to start up, often with minimal political or financial risks. Often this type of health promotion effort is coordinated by a committee. Problems with this structure include the following:

- Often those responsible for health promotion have additional duties that take priority over health promotion.
- Persons who work with health promotion in this scenario are often very skilled clinically but lack specific training in health promotion business planning, implementation, and evaluation.
- Though a good resource, the committee structure often moves very slowly with decisions.

In structure B in Figure 3.1, health promotion is more distinct and is higher on the organizational ladder, reporting directly to administration. Though autonomy increases within this structure, control of health promotion may actually decrease. The dotted lines indicate a working, not a reporting, relationship. Often in this structure, each department attempts to incorporate health promotion activities in its own plan without looking at the bigger picture of the hospital. This can create a very delicate situation for the individual responsible for the coordination of health promotion services among many departments.

In structure C of Figure 3.1, health promotion is fully autonomous and in control of several departments. This structure allows a united effort in planning, budgeting, and staffing. Authority, responsibility, and accountability can also be delegated and measured under this scenario. This format also enhances the team effort of health promotion, which in turn creates an environment more conducive to integrated cross-referrals between departments such as sports medicine, cardiac rehabilitation, and health education, all under the health promotion umbrella.

Operational Trends

As health promotion has become more complex, business systems for health promotion have followed suit. Computers are being utilized for tracking health promotion participants back to other hospital programs as well as for in-depth program evaluation. Prepackaged and internally prepared budget analysis software is being used to document success while also planning for future requirements.

These specific business systems are generally accepted by successful hospitals as ways to better evaluate the various components of health promotion departments, to minimize the risk of new ventures, and to better allocate resources to those services or programs that command a high priority or are providing successful revenue streams. Often before this accounting assessment can take place, a detailed listing of budget and financial goals must be developed by those responsible for planning health promotion programming. These should be specific and measurable, aggressive but achievable.

Marketing and Sales

As a means of developing and sustaining an operational competitive advantage, health promotion is utilizing more and more marketing and sales techniques. A major function of such effort has been the development of an accurate competitive analysis, which defines what the competition is doing, what niches are currently filled, and what niches are available for future development in the marketplace. As sophistication increases, many health promotion departments are further separating marketing and sales into three distinct functions: marketing, sales, and advertising. Development of integrated strategies for each appears optimal. The *Optimal Health*/Price Waterhouse study indicated that health promotion marketing efforts were very diverse (Table 3.6).

Key to the assessment of this table is the recognition that this data is from hospitals of various sizes. This will influence the percentage of marketing budget column, and can make comparisons cloudy. Also, it is important to remember that "average dollars spent annually" is the average only of those hospitals that responded that they used a particular medium.

Also of interest operationally in the *Optimal Health*/Price Waterhouse survey were the ways in which health promotion directors reported measuring the success of their programs (Table 3.7). It appears that for most health promotion departments, nonfinancial, difficult-to-document measures are used to identify or quantify success. Of interest will be a repeat of this question in 1 or 2 years to assess any change.

Table 3.6 Marketing Budget and Approximate Percentage Breakdown

Marketing methods	Average dollars spent annually	Percent of marketing budget
Television ads	11,130	25
Radio ads	5,870	13
Magazine ads	10,024	12
Newspaper ads	8,987	43
Public relations/promotion	8,991	26
In-house	2,478	15
Planning	4,872	9
Agency fees	9,760	13

Note. Data are from "Health Promotion Young, But Growing: The *Optimal Health*/Price Waterhouse Health Promotion Survey," 1987 (July/August), *Optimal Health*, pp. 22-24. Copyright 1987 by *Optimal Health* and Price Waterhouse. Reprinted by permission.

Table 3.7 Measurements of Successful Health Promotion

Promotion categories	Percent success
Public relations	69
Community service	66
Image enhancement of hospital	65
Customer satisfaction	62
Behavior change	48
Patient referral	41
Profitability	39

Note. Data are from "Health Promotion Young, But Growing: The *Optimal Health*/Price Waterhouse Health Promotion Survey," 1987 (July/August), *Optimal Health,* pp. 22-24. Copyright 1987 by *Optimal Health* and Price Waterhouse. Reprinted by permission.

Prior to our development of plans for future programs, it is important to assess today's problems. Problems reported by health promotion directors in the *Optimal Health*/Price Waterhouse survey can be seen in Table 3.8. With "bottom-line contribution" ranking high on the list, it is apparent that with increased business autonomy comes increased responsibility for profitability.

Also important to future planning are the areas that health promotion personnel feel will be important in coming years. Results of the *Optimal Health*/Price

Table 3.8 Current Health Promotion Problem Assessment

Present problems	Percentage
Program coordination/selection	16
Bottom-line contribution	12
Cost containment	12
Meeting community needs/market sensitivity	7
Quality/participant satisfaction	6

Note. Data are from "Health Promotion Young, But Growing: The *Optimal Health*/Price Waterhouse Health Promotion Survey," 1987 (July/August), *Optimal Health,* pp. 22-24. Copyright 1987 by *Optimal Health* and Price Waterhouse. Reprinted by permission.

Table 3.9 Future Health Promotion Concerns Assessment

Future areas of concern	Percentage
Bottom-line contribution	12
Cost containment	11
Reimbursement	9
Program development/design	9
Competition	8

Note. Data are from "Health Promotion Young, But Growing: The *Optimal Health*/Price Waterhouse Health Promotion Survey," 1987 (July/August), *Optimal Health*, pp. 22-24. Copyright 1987 by *Optimal Health* and Price Waterhouse. Reprinted by permission.

Waterhouse survey in this area are found in Table 3.9. Again it is apparent that persons in health promotion are hearing the message from their administrators that they will need to justify their efforts financially in the future. Indeed, the top three responses, bottom-line contribution, cost containment, and reimbursement, all refer to financial aspects of health promotion.

Another critical view that will influence health promotion's future is that of hospital administrators. The *Optimal Health*/Price Waterhouse survey of administrators' wishes for the future of health promotion can be found in Table 3.10. This list can stand as a projection of potential future goals.

Table 3.10 Future Administrative Health Promotion Wishes

Administrators' wish list	Percentage
Expand/new center	27
Increase staffing	17
Increase capital/funds	15
Increase column/participation	9
Increase revenue/income	7
Increase physician support	7
Effective marketing effort	7

Note. Data are from "Health Promotion Young, But Growing: The *Optimal Health*/Price Waterhouse Health Promotion Survey," 1987 (July/August), *Optimal Health*, pp. 22-24. Copyright 1987 by *Optimal Health* and Price Waterhouse. Reprinted by permission.

SUMMARY

As administrators and health promotion personnel all look to the future, expansion, staffing, and increased capital funds top their priority lists. These expansions can come about only with a true commitment to health promotion, starting with the hospital mission or philosophy statement. Also, expansions and increases in staff must generate sufficient revenue to cover their costs or must help attain other goals in measurable ways, such as increasing the flow of patients to other departments. More staff will not necessarily solve today's problems nor prevent tomorrow's.

As we see health promotion take on a more business-oriented flavor, some persons in hospital health promotion seem to be put off by or fearful of this change. Actually, the reverse should be true. Most persons trained in hospitals and working in health promotion today have been trained to be calculating—to decrease risks. And risk aversion is a basic tenet of most business plans. But though trained in risk aversion, the successful health promotion specialist of the future must be willing to take more calculated risks, and to actually experience more limited failures than most programs do today. A key to expansion and growth in the field of hospital health promotion will be new product development and rewards for quality and creativity. Health promoters must learn from their successes and failures. They must also take pride in sometimes dropping programs that have been successful in the past to allow for the funds and time to develop new programs and services for the future.

The current involvement of hospitals in health promotion has come a long way in terms of quality, viability, and documented financial success. Critical to future success will be continued efforts at strategic planning and in-depth market analysis, and strict attention to strategic, organizational, and operational issues of the health promotion program as a business unit within the hospital.

BIBLIOGRAPHY

Health promotion young, but growing: *Optimal Health*/Price Waterhouse health promotion survey. (1987, July/August). *Optimal Health*, pp. 22-24.

Office of the Acutary. (1985). *Health care financing review* (HCFA Publication No. 03200). Washington, DC: U.S. Government Printing Office.

Porter, M. (1985). *Competitive advantage: Creating and sustaining superior performance*. New York: Macmillan.

PART II

Why Hospitals Should Participate in Health Promotion

The health care environment is in a state of change. No longer is it feasible for health care institutions to be focused solely on providing acute and chronic medical treatment. Health care is entering an era of diversification to meet the needs of a shrinking patient population. New methods of generating revenue and patient referrals are being implemented to ensure future institutional viability.

Health promotion programs have emerged as one nontraditional service that offers sponsoring institutions new revenue, the ability to generate new patient referrals, and access to the business community, all of which help counter the revenue lost because of declining patient admissions.

Chapter 4 outlines the general benefits of health promotion to sponsoring health care institutions. Chapter 5 examines the financial benefits that health promotion provides through direct and indirect revenue generation. Chapter 6 discusses health promotion's ability to reach corporate clients, as well as its importance in establishing relationships with other aggregate purchasers.

Overall Benefits of Health Promotion to Hospitals

Christine A. Aguiar

Health promotion . . . "the process of enabling people to increase control over and to improve their health" (World Health Organization, 1984).

Health promotion . . . "the science and art of helping people change their lifestyle to move toward a state of optimal health" (O'Donnell, 1986, p. 1).

Health promotion . . . "the process of fostering awareness, influencing attitudes, and identifying alternatives so that individuals can make informed choices and change their behavior in order to achieve an optimum level of physical and mental health and improve their physical and social environment" (American Hospital Association, 1979).

Health promotion has been defined in many ways and by various professionals and associations. For those of us in the health care setting, the most profound statement regarding our involvement came with the American Hospital Association's (AHA) publication in 1979 of a document that stated that hospitals had a leadership responsibility in ensuring the good health of their communities (AHA, 1979).

REASONS FOR HOSPITAL HEALTH PROMOTION

The AHA established the Center for Health Promotion, which in turn established the Innovators of Community Health Promotion program. Through this program, selected hospitals across the country participated in a process of sharing that made possible the development and advancement of hospital health promotion. The initiation of health promotion in the Innovator hospitals came about for a variety of reasons, including

• the improvement of the communities' health status,
• the improvement of the hospitals' image, and
• diversification of the hospitals' services (Longe & Wolfe, 1984).

Although these reasons still apply, dramatic changes in the health care environment are providing more incentives for hospitals to initiate and expand their health promotion efforts. Some of the factors influencing the provision of health promotion in the health care setting are

• decreased inpatient admissions, which followed Medicare's prospective pricing and peer review systems,
• increase in alternative delivery systems such as ambulatory care,
• decrease in length of hospital stay due to incentives for shorter stays,
• decrease in revenue growth due to a high level of cost-per-case,
• increase in the number of hospital closures (414 closed between 1980 and 1986, according to AHA data) (*Medical Benefits*, 1987),
• an aging population with increased health care needs,
• a change in disease patterns, with major diseases related to lifestyle, and
• increased competition for patients.

Due to these factors, profitability of programs has become a new benefit or measurement of success of hospital health promotion programs. Yet public relations, community service, and image enhancement are still the major success factors of health promotion programs as identified by a recent *Optimal Health*/Price Waterhouse survey ("Health Promotion," 1987).

The purpose of this chapter is a practical one—to highlight a few of the major benefits of health promotion and to cite examples of programs and services that can facilitate achieving those benefits.

To utilize this information effectively, health promotion managers should clearly understand their hospital's mission and strategic plan and the "charge" of the hospital for its health promotion program. For example, if the hospital expects enhanced public relations from the program, the services should promote goodwill in the community and present the hospital in a positive light. If a goal is profitability, a customer-driven product line that yields direct revenue should be developed and delivered to accomplish that goal.

Some products can reap multiple benefits—for example, improving corporate relationships while producing direct revenue. The product mix and focus of the services should be designed to meet the major goals of the program, and efforts should be focused to achieve the benefits desired.

EXTERNAL BENEFITS

By offering health programs in the community at large and to the corporate market-place, hospitals benefit in a variety of ways. Some of the key benefits are

- enhanced public relations or image enhancement,
- improved corporate relationships,
- profitability through the generation of direct revenue, and
- patient referrals to the hospital and to the medical staff.

Some of the types of programs and services that can contribute to these benefits are as follows.

Image Enhancement

A variety of methods can be used to enhance a hospital's image. A common factor is that all methods must be presented in a manner that is consistent with the image the hospital desires to project.

Fitness Events

Hospitals can co-sponsor 10-kilometer runs, marathons, or bicycle safety events with local companies and media. The presence of medical staff at the events ensures safety during the events and promotes direct visibility of the physicians and allied health professionals outside of their traditional medical and clinical roles. Health promotion can provide educational seminars prior to the event and can instruct participants in proper warm-up and cool-down activities.

Health Fairs

Multidimensional awareness events such as health fairs can provide the hospital with maximum visibility in the community. Offered in shopping malls or corporate cafeterias, these fairs can provide education in such areas as nutrition, physical fitness, diabetes, cancer prevention, AIDS, and back care. The popular screenings within these fairs may include health risk appraisals (HRAs), cholesterol and blood pressure screenings, and body fat analyses.

Newsletters

Health promotion newsletters can be distributed to multiple audiences, such as past participants of programs, patients of the hospital, community residents within identified geographical areas, and corporate leaders. These educational publications can provide a community service by providing up-to-date information on health topics and where to go for health care services. Promotion of wellness activities should be included in these quarterly or monthly publications to enhance registration and utilization of these services.

Sports Medicine

In cooperation with physical therapy and sports medicine programs, health promotion can provide a great community service through support of high school athletic programs. Orthopedic physicians and certified athletic trainers can be made available at the competitive events of a variety of sports within the area's high school system. These volunteer services are greatly appreciated, and referrals to rehabilitation programs can be made directly to the hospital and its clinics. Health promotion can facilitate these arrangements and can provide special educational programs to coaches and athletes regarding proper physical training and nutrition.

Improved Corporate Relationships

Hospitals strive to establish and maintain good working relationships with business and industry. The provision of health promotion programs at the worksite is one effective strategy. A variety of services can be delivered to a corporation based upon its particular needs.

Occupational Health Services

Successful health promotion programs are aligned with occupational health services provided at the worksite. From executive physicals to preemployment screenings, these services can facilitate a closer relationship between the company and the hospital. Safety and accident prevention, cardiopulmonary resuscitation training, and work-hardening programs all contribute to a health-conscious and safe work environment. Having a working relationship at the worksite can positively influence the corporation's continued involvement with the hospital in other arenas.

Health Screenings

Specialized screenings, such as blood pressure, glucose, vision, hearing, and cholesterol can be provided as loss-leader, break-even, or profit services at a company site. These programs accomplish many goals, including the referrals of employees to physicians, and the channeling of those found at risk to health promotion programs. By screening those individuals who need further medical assistance, a company detects early signs and symptoms of disease, thus potentially lowering their employees' utilization of expensive medical care.

Luncheon Seminars

Many wellness programs involve a wide array of health professionals, including registered dietitians, exercise physiologists, physicians, and psychologists, who can present interesting and relevant lectures. These seminars provided at the worksite can enhance the hospital's presence within the company and facilitate the utilization of more comprehensive services.

Profitability Through Direct Revenue

In hospital health promotion, as in other forms of health promotion, educational services are usually the revenue-generating products.

Aerobic Fitness Classes

While the marketplace is inundated with aerobics classes, a hospital can still be quite successful in providing these highly demanded services. In particular, joint-venturing with existing programs, such as with YMCAs, can produce direct revenue for both parties while eliminating the potential for unnecessary competition. In addition, by providing specialized aerobics programs for such select markets as older adults and high-risk populations, the hospital can capture a market that other providers can't reach with the same amount of expertise and credibility.

Weight Loss/Management Programs

Competing with all the different weight loss programs in the community can be a challenge. Yet the credibility of the hospital with its physicians and registered dietitians can ensure a quality program. In addition, specialized weight loss programs for the obese have become an appropriate offering to a market generally ignored. These clinical programs are medically supervised and complemented by the wide array of health promotion services, such as fitness classes. Partially reimbursed by third-party payers, these programs can be quite profitable for the hospital.

Smoking Cessation

With the increase in legislation for clean air, many cities are adopting strict no-smoking policies. This places corporations, in particular, in a position of providing support for their employees who want to quit smoking. High-quality, successful smoking cessation programs are in demand and can become a profitable product within the program's educational services.

Patient Referrals

A unique aspect of hospital health promotion is its ability to support other health care services through referrals.

Physician Seminars

Health promotion can coordinate educational forums for the community. These programs can cover multiple health topics and can be facilitated by physicians in many areas of specialization. For example, a special program for pregnant women can include information on proper nutrition and exercise during pregnancy and after childbirth. While the program can generate referrals to the health promotion's pregnancy exercise class, it can also generate referrals to the hospital's obstetricians and gynecologists.

Cholesterol Screenings

The new "finger-prick" technology has allowed screenings for blood cholesterol to become more accessible and convenient to the client. Screenings of this type provide referrals not only to health promotion programs, but to physicians and lipid clinics as well.

Blood Pressure Screenings

With hypertension known as the "silent killer," screenings are critical to detect those who have high blood pressure. These screenings reinforce the need for regular medical examinations and can refer individuals who are at risk to specialized hypertension clinics as well as to the medical staff.

INTERNAL BENEFITS

Offering a health promotion program to the hospital's own employees provides the hospital with an opportunity to present a model program to business and industry. Several internal benefits can be observed as well, such as

- improved health and morale of employees,
- retention of employees,
- enhanced cooperation among departments, and
- stronger relationship with the medical staff.

Specific programs and services can be established to accomplish each of these benefits.

Improved Health and Morale of Employees

Lifestyle change programs can be key factors in accomplishing the goal of improved employee health and morale. Health professionals are not immune to poor health habits. Stopping smoking, exercising regularly, and eating for optimal health are all positive lifestyle habits sought by hospital employees. By offering these programs to employees, particularly at subsidized rates and at times convenient to their work shifts, the hospital can reap the benefits of a healthier work force.

Recreational and lifestyle support activities can also be established to improve health and morale. Through the provision of hospital-sponsored recreational activities, the health promotion program can support leisure activities that reinforce healthy lifestyles and cooperation among employees. Special events, such as walk/runs in which participants estimate their finishing times, can encourage all employees to participate regardless of their level of physical fitness.

Retention of Employees

Health promotion discounts can be an attractive addition to any institution's attempts to retain employees. Where else but in their own health care facility should employees find quality health education programs at a great price? Hospitals can provide this "perk" to their personnel by allowing them to participate in programs free of charge or at a discounted rate. The employees appreciate the interest and support of the hospital's administration in their personal health, and this can influence their desire to remain a part of the hospital's health care team.

Access to fitness facilities is another benefit that many employees appreciate. Either through the provision of a fitness facility on the hospital's campus or through subsidization of memberships at reputable health clubs, the hospital can do much to support a corporate culture that promotes healthy lifestyles. Many hospitals are finding this perk to be valuable to all levels of employees, from housekeeping to administration and medical staff. Supportive environments for optimal health can have a positive influence on retaining a qualified work force.

Cooperation Among Departments

With the provision of health promotion programs to the community as well as to its own employees, a hospital can gain much from this unique multidisciplinary service.

Health promotion, in providing screenings and assessment services, can work cooperatively with other departments such as nursing services and pathology. Rather than competing with others for a particular product, departments can joint-venture with one another to provide quality, cost-effective services. The sharing of revenue and expenses can ensure profitability for the hospital without unnecessary duplication of services.

Health promotion can also be the leader in drawing the varied health professionals within the hospital into the task of providing educational services. Through food services, registered dietitians can be featured in special nutritional programs; through maternal and child care, specialized wellness programs for mothers and babies can be facilitated. Rather than arguing over whose "turf" health promotion falls into, the health promotion department can foster cooperation among the many professionals within the hospital, and the collaborative efforts can accomplish much for the hospital's overall success.

Strong Physician Relationships

By conducting health fairs and specialized screenings, as already mentioned, health promotion can enhance the hospital's relationship with physicians through the referrals made to them. Physicians can also provide educational seminars in cooperation with health promotion, which can enhance the physicians' visibility in the community.

Physicians appreciate the support that health promotion programs bring to their practices. Smoking cessation and weight loss programs provide the necessary information and support for their patients who need to make these lifestyle changes. By providing physicians with health promotion prescription pads and program discounts, the medical staff can work more closely with the wellness services in serving their patients. By generating referrals to each other, the medical staff and health promotion professionals truly serve as health care teammates in optimally serving the needs of the community.

SUMMARY

When you cease to make a contribution, you begin to die. Eleanor Roosevelt

The contributions of a health promotion program are many and varied. Yet the challenges within the health care setting will continue to have an impact on the goals, the direction, and the survival of hospital health promotion programs.

Health promotion programs should continually reexamine their missions and goals and not spin their wheels in directions that do not provide the benefits sought by their hospital. Providing programs across the three levels—awareness, lifestyle change, and supportive environment (O'Donnell, 1986)—can have a greater impact on an organization and maximize the hospital's potential for success.

The health promotion program should be interfaced with the hospital's mission and strategic plan. Efforts to update marketing and business plans annually are not misguided. As markets change and the demands of patient-clients are altered, health promotion should change to keep up and to ensure its place in the health care environment.

REFERENCES

American Hospital Association. (1979). *The hospital's responsibility for health promotion* [Policy and statement of the American Hospital Association]. Chicago: Author.

Health promotion young, but growing: *Optimal Health*/Price Waterhouse survey. (1987, July/August). *Optimal Health*, pp. 22-24.

Longe, M., & Wolfe, A. (1984). *Promoting community health through innovative hospital-based programs.* Chicago: American Hospital Publishing.

Medical benefits. (1987, June 15). Charlottesville, VA: Kelly Communications.

O'Donnell, M. (1986). *Design of workplace health promotion programs* (2nd ed.). Royal Oak, MI: American Journal of Health Promotion.

World Health Organization. (1984, September). *Health promotion: A discussion document on the concept and principles.* Copenhagen: Author.

CHAPTER 5

Revenue Benefits
of Health Promotion
Neil Sol

Historically, hospitals have provided health promotion services free of charge to the community. Health promotion was essentially considered a loss leader, serving as an attempt to maximize public relations, promote goodwill by establishing an image of the hospital as a good community citizen, and, it was hoped, generate patients. Unfortunately, actual results of these health-promoting/public relations efforts were seldom measured or analyzed. They were simply assumed to be positive for the hospital.

In recent years, however, changes in the health care environment have diminished hospitals' "warm and fuzzy" give-away attitude, with budgets too tight to offer complimentary services in the name of public relations. Hospitals have been forced to become more businesslike and have begun investing in programs and services that both meet strategic plans and provide a return on investment. Health promotion now offers hospitals the opportunity to diversify into providing full-service health care as opposed to merely sick care. In today's budget-conscious environment, however, the long-term success of a health promotion program is often dependent on its contribution of new revenue to the health care/hospital system.

A comprehensive health promotion program should be, and can be, a financial contributor to the hospital, meeting profitability goals and providing a reasonable return on the hospital's investment (the initial financial outlay to develop and deliver a comprehensive health promotion program). However, the financial return from a health promotion program is contingent upon appropriate management of the program.

To achieve a profit and return on investment, hospital administrators must assume an entrepreneurial perspective and must manage this new nontraditional product service line in a way unlike the management style for an acute-care hospital. A recent survey ("Should Health Promotion," 1986) revealed that 47% of 529 respondents indicated planned profitability goals for their health promotion programs. Also, 61.1% of hospitals with 300 to 499 beds confirmed incorporating profitability goals, as did 50% of the 500-plus-bed hospitals.

REVENUE SOURCES

Health promotion programs provide revenue to the hospital through both direct and indirect means. Direct revenue results from the sale of products and services in the marketplace, while indirect revenue results from savings accrued and from admissions and referrals as a result of health promotion services.

DIRECT REVENUE

For a successful health promotion program, the provider must develop and offer a full menu of services and products. This list represents a sample health promotion product line.

- Health fairs
- Health risk appraisals
- Health awareness programs
- On-site program management
- Health education classes
- Employee assistance programs
- Fitness evaluations
- Executive physicals
- Specialty exercise programs
- Preemployment physicals
- Industrial and occupational nurse services
- Sports medicine consultation
- Nutrition consultation

Products and services chosen for the product line should be based on market interest as assessed by a market survey. Specific target markets must be determined and their needs identified. A comprehensive, market-driven product line should include an abundance of nontraditional services and must also be flexible enough to customize specific products to meet various customers' needs. All product lines and promotional materials should include a note that products can be developed as desired or as needed, suggesting that, in addition to a fairly comprehensive menu, other products and services can be added per the client's request.

The market-driven orientation of health promotion products and services is different from the traditional production orientation of hospitals and their health care products. Hospitals, with their variety of allied health and medical staff, should be able to include any health promotion product to meet a client's needs, so no request is unreasonable. It is this type of market-driven attitude that leads to sales and, ultimately, to revenue-producing services.

The health promotion products and services that typically have been in greatest demand include the following:

- Health risk appraisals or health screenings
- Executive physicals
- Fitness assessments
- Exercise prescriptions
- Wellness center memberships
- Behavior modification and education programs (such as smoking cessation, stress management, and weight control)
- Clinical rehabilitation (such as occupational health and rehabilitation, cardiac rehabilitation, and sports medicine

A new product emerging within health promotion programs is clinical exercise therapy, applicable to programs for drug and alcohol abuse, eating disorders, and mental health disorders. As exercise has been accepted as an integral component of the rehabilitation process, it offers a health promotion product that is both lucrative to the hospital and beneficial to the client, because the patient's costs are usually reimbursable through insurance.

Pricing for Profit

For revenue-producing programs, pricing strategies are of critical concern. The basis of a profit-oriented product line requires that most or all products be priced at a predetermined profit to cover direct costs and include a reasonable margin of profit.

First, however, careful consideration must be given to the health promotion program's financial objectives, which are typically derived from the hospital's and program's strategic plan. There are three potential choices of financial objectives: (a) the program is to be a service program, which is essentially a loss leader; (b) it is planned to break even; or (c) it is to be profitable. Since the current hospital environment demands self-sufficient programs, the remainder of this chapter will be oriented to the profitability objective.

To generate a profit, direct costs of product delivery must first be examined, including staff, materials, equipment, and rentals. Then, a reasonable markup should be determined. For most products, a 30% to 40% margin above direct expenses will cover any additional indirect expenses. Finally, consideration must be given to market expectations. In other words, the determined price must be comparable to competitors' prices and must be reasonable with reference to the product quality.

Target Market Identification

Also critical to the direct sales of health promotion services is marketplace identification. Typically, target audiences for health promotion services are the general community (which can be further segmented into representative markets such as women, seniors, and youth) and corporations.

The corporate marketplace offers a prime audience for the direct sales of health promotion services because it represents a motivated consumer. Corporations are often willing to buy health promotion services in anticipation of the potential return in lower employee health care costs. From the hospital's perspective, sales to the corporate marketplace are relatively efficient efforts, as one corporate sale may potentially have impact on hundreds of employees.

Gross Profitability of Selected Health Promotion Products

In the past, health promotion products generally have not made money. In most cases, specific products were offered before the total program was established

Table 5.1 Corporate Health Screenings: Revenue, Expenses, and Gross Contribution Margin[a]

Sources of direct revenue	Revenue ($)
Health screenings (15 at $3,500 each)	52,500
Corporate screening reports (15 at $500 each)	7,500
Total	60,000

Sources of direct expenses	Expenses ($)
Staffing	19,000
Supplies, travel	15,000
Total	34,000

[a]The gross contribution margin is +42.5%, or $25,500.

and were supervised by inexperienced managers. With proper development and management, health promotion products and services need not be sold at a loss. On the contrary, each product in a total health promotion program should be able to stand alone as a profit generator.

From direct profitability considerations, products can be priced to exceed expenses and yield expected gross margins. Table 5.1 shows the revenue/expense ratio for corporate health screening services.

Table 5.2 shows the revenue/expense ratio for executive physical services.

Table 5.3 shows the revenue/expense ratio for health and fitness facility management contract services.

Each of these tables show a significant amount of direct profitability that can be gained if health promotional services and programs are correctly priced and managed.

Hospital-Owned Health and Fitness or Wellness Facilities

Another area of profitability lies in hospitals' owning or being affiliated with wellness centers or health and fitness facilities. A wellness center can offer a substantial

Table 5.2 Executive Physical Services:
Revenue, Expenses, and Gross Contribution Margin[a]

Source of direct revenue	Revenue ($)	
Executive physicals (200 per year, at $350 each)	70,000	
Total		70,000

Sources of direct expenses	Expenses ($)	
Physician fees	24,000	
Lab fees	8,000	
Staff	6,000	
Miscellaneous expenses	4,000	
Total		42,000
[a]The gross contribution margin is +40%, or		28,000

Table 5.3   Health and Fitness Facility Management Contract Services: Revenue, Expenses, and Gross Contribution Margin[a]

Sources of direct revenue	Revenue ($)	
Staff/benefits (pass through)	80,000	
Management fee	25,000	
Professional services	60,000	
• Fitness testing		
• Educational programs		
Total		165,000

Sources of direct expenses	Expenses ($)	
Staff/benefits	80,000	
Professional services	24,000	
Miscellaneous expenses	10,000	
Total		114,000
[a]Gross contribution margin is +31.0%, or		51,000

range of opportunities for direct sales as well as a variety of services for the hospital to generate new revenues. Sources of revenue can include enrollment fees, membership fees (usually monthly), court time fees for tennis or racquetball court reservations, class fees for aerobic or specialty exercise classes, food, beverage, and vending sales, pro shop or retail sales, testing or consultation revenues, and rehabilitation therapy fees.

Surprisingly, however, many hospitals' attempts at operating wellness centers have not resulted in expected revenue production. On the contrary, they have more often resulted in major financial losses. Facilities costing many thousands of dollars have been built without a strategic plan or sufficient programming. Additionally, administrators have not expected or required cost-effectiveness, much less profitability, from these facilities.

There are several advantages to a hospital-owned wellness center: a self-built or self-owned facility is a highly visible monument to the hospital's commitment to health promotion; the hospital has full control over program management; the facility can be an efficient referral source to direct patients into the hospital; it can generate new revenue streams; and it can generate valuable public relations for the hospital.

However, there are also significant disadvantages to hospital-owned facilities. Too often, hospital administrators do not know how to manage a health fitness facility, particularly in the critical area of membership renewal. Also, building or renovating a facility presents major capital expenses. Tax disadvantages offer little incentive for nonprofit hospitals to plan a revenue-producing facility. Negative press can result from a misdirected perception that the hospital is trying to put other community organizations, such as the local YMCA, out of business.

Joint-Venture Wellness Centers

When possible, it is often preferable for a hospital, especially a nonprofit hospital, to joint-venture with a preexisting, successful health and fitness facility. In a joint-venture relationship, all the advantages of a self-owned facility can be realized, and many of the disadvantages avoided. An example of the joint-venture organization model is show in Figure 5.1.

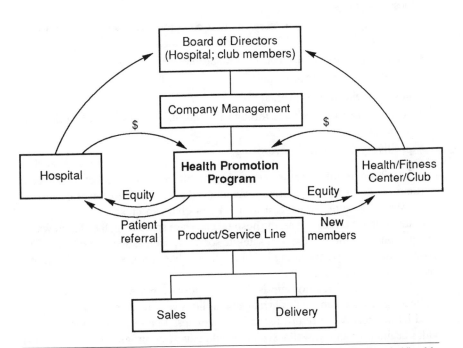

Figure 5.1.   This diagram represents the organizational structure of a hospital/health club joint venture.

In such a hospital/club affiliation, the benefits that accrue to the hospital are as follows:

- The relationship completes a comprehensive health promotion menu of services for the hospital.
- It gives the hospital access to a well-managed and attractive facility.
- It provides the hospital with a satellite site for the delivery of a variety of medical services ranging from physicals in a physician's office to cardiac rehabilitation and sports medicine.
- It offers access to a new potential patient market through the membership of the facility.
- It offers a new revenue source through either service fees or a percentage of return on the investment, depending on the nature of the joint-venture relationship.
- It generates positive publicity and advertising for the hospital.

The obvious benefits to the club are

- instant credibility through its affiliation with a medical institution,
- access to professionally developed and managed health promotion and wellness programs,
- the ability to broaden its services to a comprehensive wellness service as opposed to just strictly fitness or racquet sports,
- access to a variety of allied health and medical personnel,
- increased membership sales,
- development of new profits,
- access to corporate clients through the hospital's marketing and sales service, and
- positive publicity and advertising.

A hospital/club joint venture certainly presents a win-win situation for both partners, with direct and indirect revenue available. There are several types of joint-venture relationships that a hospital and club can create.

In the simplest arrangement, the hospital can lease space from the club in which to equip and staff on-site medical satellite services, such as sports medicine. The hospital then bills participating health club members for services rendered and retains all fees collected.

A second type of relationship is the cooperative venture, which is similar to the leasing relationship. In this arrangement, however, the club donates the space used by the hospital in return for in-kind services. In a sense, the hospital provides health promotion, wellness, and health education programs for the club at no cost.

The hospital management contract poses a different sort of relationship in which the hospital manages the center for a flat rate or a percentage of the gross or net profits. This type of joint venture is difficult to negotiate, inasmuch as the health and racquet club has to depend totally on the hospital to manage the wellness portion of its program. There is some merit for a club to consider a hospital management contract; however, with advantages primarily in professional liability insurance, the hospital can provide the club valuable benefits in such a management relationship.

A limited partnership joint venture is probably the most risky hospital/club arrangement, but also potentially the most lucrative to the hospital. In a limited partnership, the hospital and health club combine resources to establish a new corporation with equal or negotiated investments of seed capital. Profits are divided between the principal partners at the end of the year, according to investment percentages.

Clearly, there are definite benefits for hospitals owning or joint-venturing with health clubs and wellness centers. When profitability is a goal, this option should be given serious consideration.

There are several revenue-producing opportunities in direct sales of health promotion products. If priced appropriately and marketed in an entrepreneurial fashion, these nontraditional health care products and services can generate new dollars to augment lost revenues associated with a decrease in patient days. Indeed, the potential is limitless in terms of the products and services that can be developed and sold for profit under the umbrella of health promotion.

INDIRECT REVENUE

Indirect revenue is generated as a result of admissions or services that health promotion stimulates, or through savings of expenditures such as advertising or health care expenses. It is important to remember that, from now well into the future, the hospital's major source of revenue and its primary reason for existing will be hospital admissions and the treatment of sick and injured people. However, the percentage of contribution to the hospital's bottom line obtained from revenue sources associated with sick care is declining. It appears that, to maintain their current financial status, hospitals will be forced to augment patient care revenues with new sources, revenues most likely generated from health promotion.

Primary Care Referrals

In a sense, health promotion programs actually support the hospital's primary form of business, the treatment of sick and injured individuals, by contributing to hospital admissions and services through patient "case finding." Health promotion is a nonthreatening, nontraditional means of penetrating the community and enlightening people to health-related issues. While educating people, health promotion programs often help identify people with health problems, directing them to appropriate follow-up care. If a prospective patient does not have a personal physician, a referral can be made to a physician on the medical staff at the hospital. This is case finding at its best—identifying people with undetected illnesses and referring them to a hospital-affiliated physician. In this sense, health promotion becomes a major component of the primary care network.

The Center for Disease Control suggests that about 30% to 40% of randomly selected people have asymptomatic problems requiring physician follow-up (Berwick, 1985). Health promotion is a means of identifying these people. Masses of apparently "well" individuals participate in health promotion, from aerobics to health education classes and screenings. However, while helping these individuals stay healthy, health promotion can enlighten them to otherwise undetected problems.

Taking this thought process one step further, typically 10% to 20% of people within a hospital's service area do not have a physician relationship. This represents a remarkable number of potential incremental patients for the hospital. Table 5.4 illustrates the patient referral potential of a health screening program, assuming 35% of participants have asymptomatic problems and 15% of those do not have physician relationships.

Patient referral can potentially be accomplished through any service of the health promotion product line. Health screenings, as shown, are an excellent means of identifying people with health risks for referral to the hospital. Health promotion, then, is again a major contributor to the institution, directing incremental patients or even multiuser patients to the system and generating additional inpatient-care revenues.

Table 5.4   Theoretical Model for Patient Referral (Resulting from a Health Promotion Screening Program)

Health promotion screening program variables	Participant variables
Total number of participants	5,000
Percentage of participants with asymptomatic disease	35%
Number of participants with asymptomatic disease	1,750 (35% of 5,000)
Percentage of participants without physician affiliation (based on individual hospital demographic data)	15%
Number of participants with asymptomatic disease without physician affiliation	262.5 (15% of 1,750)
Potential incremental patients available for referral to hospital medical staff	**262.5**

Image Enhancement and Media Support

Another indirect revenue contribution to the institution is health promotion's role as an image enhancer, which is where health promotion efforts began. The image-enhancement qualities of health promotion programs are not sacrificed by fees charged for services once given away. In fact, today's consumers rarely expect (and are often suspicious of) free services and are more than willing to invest in health maintenance if assured of quality products delivered by reliable, respected professionals.

In addition to generating profit from direct sales, health promotion efforts can save advertising money through free media exposure. In response to public interest, the press has demonstrated an eagerness to devote media time to the newsworthy topic of health. In many cases during the last 5 to 10 years, hospitals' health promotion efforts have been covered by the media more than any other medical component. Obviously, free media exposure generated by health promotion efforts can offer some savings in paid advertising, savings that ultimately accrue to the hospital's bottom line.

Strengthened Corporate and Physician Relationships

Also, in an indirect fashion, health promotion contributes to the establishment of corporate relations. Gaining access to a corporation through the delivery of health promotion products and creating a satisfied client in the early stages of a corporate relationship can ultimately yield ongoing benefits through traditional utilization of hospital services.

The same holds true with hospital/physician relationships, where the benefits are mutual. By helping a physician establish a community image as a progressive professional allied with health promotion, the hospital can increase physician loyalty, ultimately encouraging the physician to become a key contributor to the hospital in terms of admissions, traditional acute-care services, and profits generated from those services.

On the other hand, affiliation with a hospital's health promotion program can help physicians market their practices and capture additional market share. Health promotion also gives the physician additional referrals (through health screenings, for example) and offers opportunities for the physician to joint-venture with the hospital on profit-oriented services and products, such as sports medicine and wellness centers.

Benefits Within the System

Health promotion can indirectly affect hospital revenues through its support of other institutional programs. For example, health promotion products offer value-added services that can help sell preferred provider organizations (PPOs) to corporations. Or, in health maintenance organization (HMO) relationships, health promotion helps HMO participants maintain their health, decreasing their utilization of hospital services and maximizing the HMO's profitability to the hospital.

Also, certain services within the health promotion product line can supplement services provided by clinical programs, such as cardiac rehabilitation, sports medicine, and occupational rehabilitation, making such combined programs unique in the marketplace. An example of such a synthesis could include an exercise therapy program in alcohol and drug rehabilitation or in eating disorders services. The addition of a wellness factor can make certain clinical programs unique in the marketplace among competitors, enabling them to capture a greater market share and, again, generate new dollars for the hospital.

A final consideration of the indirect benefits of health promotion concerns the provider's own health care costs. The hospital, which is most likely a fairly large employer in a given community, has the same problems in terms of health care payments as most other corporations. By providing a health promotion program to its own employees, the hospital can realize the same return in benefit savings that the program provides corporate clients (Wilbur, 1983; Baun, Bernacki, & Tsai, 1986). In this respect, health promotion saves the hospital employee health care dollars, whether in actual health care payments or life insurance.

SUMMARY

It is simply not necessary, as was previously assumed, for a hospital to give away health promotion services for its programs and products to be successful. Instead, health promotion can be a major contributor to the hospital's strategic and financial profitability goals through direct and indirect revenues.

With patient admissions and associated revenues trending downward, a look into the future suggests that the development of new nontraditional services, of which health promotion is one, is a necessity. The hospital that chooses to remain merely an inpatient facility, without implementing health promotion or preventive services as diversified product lines, stands to lose not only the revenue that could be generated from the sales of those services, but also revenues associated with potential admissions referred from those health promotion services. From a revenue perspective, it is critical for hospitals' survival to consider the comprehensive benefits that can be derived from a well-planned and properly managed health promotion program.

REFERENCES

Baun, W.B., Bernacki, E.J., & Tsai, S.P. (1986). A preliminary investigation: Effect of a corporate fitness program on absenteeism and health care cost. *Journal of Occupational Medicine, 28*(1), 18-22.

Berwick, D. (1985). Screening in health fairs. *Journal of the American Medical Association*, **254**, 1492-1498.

Should health promotion pay its own way? (1986, March/April). *Optimal Health*, pp. 48-49.

Wilbur, C.S. (1983). The Johnson & Johnson program. *Preventive Medicine*, **12**, 672-681.

CHAPTER 6

Providing Corporate Health Promotion Services

Kevin M. Clair

In the premier issue of *Optimal Health*, Joseph P. Smith (1984) asked the question, "Is Bad Health Good Business?" His answer: "Simply providing treatment for illness and emergencies—without a commitment to disease prevention, health promotion, and medical self-care—is not beneficial to either the physical health or financial health of the nation" (p. 14). Moreover, Smith pointed out that providing a broad menu of health promotion services is not only responsible behavior (American Hospital Association, 1979), it can also attract new revenue to the hospital.

One target market for these services is business. *Hospitals* reported in 1985 that among hospital health promotion markets that also include the general community, inpatients, outpatients, and hospital employees, business was the fastest-growing segment ("Health Promotion Programs," 1985). Survey data from 1987 by the American Hospital Association suggests that the trend continues. Lynn Jones, manager of employee health programs at the Division of Ambulatory Care, Health Promotion, and Women's and Children's Health, stated that there is continuing growth in hospitals offering health promotion to employers, particularly as a component of an industrial medicine product line. (L. Jones, personal communication, February 1988). American business remains interested in purchasing health promotion services and looks to hospitals to provide them.

HEALTH CARE ECONOMICS AND HOSPITAL BUSINESS RELATIONS

Since the enactment of the Tax Equity and Fiscal Responsibility Act (TEFRA) in 1982 and implementation of the Prospective Payment System of Medicare in

1983, hospitals have been in a state of upheaval. Hospital admissions have declined, average length of stay has decreased, and competition among providers has intensified.

Also in this decade there has been a shift in payer mix so that at present, aggregate purchasers of health care exert significant market influence and will do so to an even greater extent in the future. Business is a large group purchaser of health care and will have increasing leverage in the health care marketplace. As an economic buyer, business will make more cost-effective provider choices in the future, which portends a continued increase in the growth rate of managed care products (P. Boland, personal communication, February 1988).

Many hospitals make an entrance into business, facilitating the cross selling of other health care services through health promotion offerings. For example, Methodist Health System of Memphis, Tennessee, has fostered relations with business by providing health promotion. Methodist contracted with a financial services firm to provide healthy lifestyle programs. Later, a comprehensive employee assistance program (EAP) was added. Eventually Methodist arranged a management contract for occupational health services. Finally, in spite of price-competitive intensity, Methodist was successful in maintaining a preferred provider relationship with the firm while other area businesses were shifting loyalties. Hospital and company executives attributed the goodwill between their institutions partially to the quality and responsiveness of Methodist's corporate health services (C. Speros, personal communication, February 1988).

Health Care Cost Containment

Demand and technology have helped to form a delivery system that provides high quality medical services that are available to most United States citizens. In the past, there have been few pressures within the system to limit price or discourage consumption. As a result, the economics of the health care system have combined with the demand and technology, causing constant price escalation. (Spring, 1987, p. 2)

Those few words describe a problem that has been developing for decades and that has finally come home to roost—health care cost containment.

Health promotion has a role in the management of corporate health care costs. Although insurance plan and employee benefit redesign have been the focus of cost containment efforts up to this point, the case for including health promotion in a comprehensive health care cost management program is being made today.

Health Promotion: Present and Future

Worksite health and fitness programs continue to evolve. Employee programs once focused on recreation and featured sport and game activities. Then corporate fitness programs were developed that provided inducements to exercise and principally targeted senior male managers. Now many offerings are centered on health risk appraisal and intervention, featuring assessments, information, education, and behavior modification. Moreover, some programs are expanding to include appropriate health and fitness activities for minor dependents and retirees.

Health care health promotion has changed as well. Hospitals that once offered isolated health education programs free of charge to the community now provide comprehensive "occupational health services" that include a wider array of services and are strategically managed. This chapter discusses the benefits that accrue to the hospital by providing health promotion services to business, particularly when those services are integrated with other health care services and delivery options and are well marketed.

HEALTH CARE COST MANAGEMENT

Data detailing the continuing rise of health care costs are quite prevalent. The decline in Medicare margins (to 9.56% in 1986 from 14.4% in 1985) provides an example. Although it was the first year that the Department of Health and Human Services set the Diagnosis Related Group (DRG) update and the Gramm-Rudman balanced-budget law took effect (both actions lowered Medicare payments to hospitals), others such as Representative Fortney "Pete" Stark (D-California, chairman of the House Ways and Means health subcommittee) blames declining margins on "extraordinary growth in hospital costs" ("PPS Margins," 1988, p. 1).

While the debate over Medicare margins continues (predicted 1987 margin is just 2%), health care inflation continues unabated. In 1987, price increases for overall medical care (commodities, services, and hospitals) amounted to 5.8%, which is 32% greater than the Consumer Price Index of 4.4%. Moreover, spending for health care rose 7.7% in 1987 to $499 billion, representing 11.2% of the nation's gross national product. Spending for 1988 is predicted to increase another 9% to $544 billion.

There are as many "solutions" to the problem of health care cost containment as there are interested companies. Most firms have focused on reducing cash outlay without decreasing incidence of illness or injury. That is, existing cost control programs attempt to reduce the cost of a similar level of medical care or discourage employees from seeking medical care.

Though some care that is provided is assuredly unnecessary, preventive activities have some role in a comprehensive cost management program. Moreover, the primary strategies implemented by business so far merely shift health care costs to the employee. At least in theory, the labor market will respond to decreased employer contribution to benefits by demanding increased wages, resulting in no decrease in health care costs to society nor in employment costs to business.

A Cost Management Program

Comprehensive, integrated strategies for cost management include several components. For example, Dick Hanley (1985) has presented a nine-point cost containment system that provides guidelines that can be adapted for different companies. Hanley recommends that responsibility for health cost management rest with one manager. That person is designated by senior management to have accountability for controlling costs.

Also, the action of business leaders on health activities that occur outside of their own companies affects costs for care in a business community. Participation in health care governance, on health planning agency committees, in health legislation, and with business coalitions on health care can directly impact health care access, quality, and cost.

The most prevalent cost control strategies include activities in a company's internal health management environment, such as insurance plan design and health promotion.

Hay/Huggins (1987) reports that increasing the employee share—through increased health insurance deductibles, copayments, and premium contributions—for health bills remains the primary cost containment strategy among American companies. Also, this survey of 896 business organizations (481 industrial and 415 financial/service) reveals that 78% of companies have health promotion programs to reduce health care cost.

A summary of cost containment program elements recommended by Hanley (1985) begins with senior management program support that draws on resources such as

- health resources planning,
- health provider governance,
- business coalitions on health, and
- legislative surveillance.

These external resources facilitate internal plan design, utilization review, managed care, and health promotion.

The Role of Managed Care

Managed health care programs are increasing in prevalence. Hay/Huggins (1987) reports a continuing strong presence of health maintenance organizations (HMOs) in employer-sponsored health programs, with more than two thirds of survey respondents offering one or more HMO plans.

Preferred provider organizations (PPOs) were offered by 16% of respondents in the Hay/Huggins survey. The PPO market is predicted to grow significantly in the next decade. It is clear that health promotion marketing strategy should consider HMO, PPO, and hybrid products, since more than two thirds of U.S. hospitals' non-Medicare/non-Medicaid revenue will be derived from managed care plan payments by 1990 (P. Boland, personal communication, February, 1988).

More than two thirds of HMOs offer some form of health promotion program because it is expected to lower health care costs and provide a competitive marketing advantage. Partners National Health Plans is the nation's eighth-largest HMO with an enrollment of more than 635,000. Robert Vogel, CEO of Partners National Health Plan of Alabama, cites another reason for HMO providing health promotion: "Attracting a broad subscriber base, and therefore a healthier mix, can result in decreased utilization, enhancing the HMO's financial stability. For example, offering a small dues subsidy for a fitness center may encourage enrollment among those already leading healthier lifestyles" (R. Vogel, personal communication, February 1988).

So, several benefits may accrue to HMOs which offer health promotion, including:

* Retention of members by demonstrating commitment to health enhancement,
* Attracting new members interested in health promotion,
* Increasing visibility of HMO in the community,
* Decreasing health care utilization, and
* Altering case mix by attracting younger, healthier members ("HMOs and Profitability," 1986, pp. 16-20).

According to Neil Sofian of the Group Health Cooperative of Puget Sound, health promotion's role is different for various types of HMOs and for PPOs. For example, the staff-model HMO, which can case-manage more actively, has financial as well as marketing interests in offering health promotion services to members, whereas an independent practice association HMO, like the PPO, has typically included health promotion primarily for public relations value (N. Sofian, personal communication, February 1988).

The marketing challenge to hospital health promotion providers is to form a linkage between their programs and managed care entities to gain a share of the existing market. Of course, hospitals having a proprietary interest in an HMO can market health promotion themselves. Health promotion managers at hospitals that do not own an HMO will have to arrange for outside HMOs to serve as brokers for their products.

Operationally, it is important to realize that health promotion program goals are different in a managed care environment than they are for health promotion in a stand-alone setting. Whereas on its own health promotion may be expected to generate revenue, in an HMO its most important contribution is to plan members' health maintenance.

The Role of Medical Self-Care

It is essential that health promotion offerings to business include market-driven products and services. One requirement of an increasing number of businesses is that health promotion be cost-effective. The health promotion literature suggests that medical self-care, or medical consumerism, may more than pay for itself. A study by the Center for Consumer Health Education showed that members of two large health maintenance organizations who were given medical self-care materials had a 17% reduction in physician visits and a 35% reduction in minor illness visits. The study concluded that for every dollar invested in self-care programs, $2.50 to $3.50 was saved (Vickery et al., 1983).

George Pfeiffer of The Center for Corporate Health Promotion suggests implementation of three concurrent strategies to manage health care cost:

- Health promotion and disease prevention
- Health benefit plan design
- Medical self-care (G. Pfeiffer, personal communication, February 1988)

Cost-Effectiveness

A persistent myth is that employee health promotion programs cannot be implemented cost-effectively. Data suggest that many companies have provided programs that more than pay for themselves. Several books are dedicated to this topic; however, it is worth reviewing some examples of cost-effective programs that have received rigorous analysis. A Prudential study showed that employee fitness level was indirectly related to major medical and disability costs. Johnson & Johnson reported a lower rate of annual inpatient hospital cost increase for employees exposed to its Live for Life program. Also, Blue Cross-Blue Shield of Indiana identified a long-term reduction in average annual health care costs for participants in an employee health promotion program. Finally, Control Data found that long-term health care costs can be reduced through modulation of employees' health risk factors (Elias & Murphy, 1987).

Hospitals have an opportunity to market health promotion services to business and industry on the basis of their contribution to a comprehensive, integrated health care cost management program. As Charles A. McGeorge of Johnson & Johnson Health Management, Inc., reports, "Most of our customers purchase Live for Life because of its cost containment value, and they retain the program because it is also an attractive employee benefit" (C.A. McGeorge, personal communication, February 1988). Moreover, Jeffrey M. Bensky of Price Waterhouse's St. Louis-based Health Care Strategic Management Consulting Group says the next buzzword in health promotion packaging will be "prevention of health care expenditures," a concept that suggests defining health promotion as a cost containment strategy ("Betting on the Future," 1987, p. 27).

DEMAND FOR SERVICES

There is an opportunity for hospitals to provide health promotion services to business since a market already exists. According to a survey sponsored by the U.S. Public Health Service, nearly two thirds (65%) of private worksites with 50 or more employees were supporting at least one health promotion activity. The primary motivation reported for initiating programs was to improve employee health. Moreover, most respondents (81%) indicated that they were extremely or moderately concerned with health care cost management.

Services most in demand according to the Public Health Service survey are

- smoking control (36% of worksites),
- health risk assessment (30%),
- back care (29%),
- stress management (27%),
- employee assistance programs (24%),
- exercise and fitness (22%),
- off-the-job accident prevention (20%),
- nutrition education (17%),
- high blood pressure control (17%), and
- weight control (15%).

Finally, larger worksites (more than 750 employees) are more likely to offer health promotion to employees than smaller companies (fewer than 100 employees).

DIRECT REVENUE

Expansion of hospital health promotion programs at the beginning of this decade was in response to intensified competition among health care providers. Program objectives focused on improving the hospital's image to various publics: community, business, and physicians. Now, the emphasis has shifted to funding programs that can pay for themselves or generate profit.

Few health promotion programs, as defined by Hamilton/KSA, are reporting that they break even. In an exclusive survey conducted for *Hospitals*, responding hospital CEOs reported that wellness and health promotion was the only one of 18 diversification strategies that was not breaking even or better. The survey defined cardiac rehabilitation and sports medicine services as programs separate from wellness and health promotion. "Wellness/health promotion is the only diversification effort that is losing money at more than 50% of the facilities that operate such programs. Although 37.5% of respondents . . . indicate that they break even . . . only 11.5% indicate they make money" ("Diversification," 1988, p. 36).

However, while 50% of the programs may be losing money, the 11.5% of hospitals that are generating positive margins in health promotion offer lessons to others. As Neil Sol accurately suggests in chapter 5 of this book, "The financial return from . . . health promotion . . . is contingent upon appropriate management of the program." Though the commercial fitness industry is fairly mature, it has not benefited from an influx of well-trained professional managers. Moreover, hospital health promotion, newer and more complex than the commercial fitness business, has also lacked an adequately trained pool of managers. It is difficult to locate managers who are sufficiently trained in the variety of business and clinical disciplines— exercise physiology, health education, marketing, accounting, and others—related to successful health promotion management.

Several well-managed programs have produced a positive bottom line. According to Daniel J. Lynch of FitWell Associates, Sinai Fitness, a program of Sinai Hospital of Baltimore, has successfully entered the corporate market by offering a broad spectrum of related services. Included in Sinai's health promotion product group are nutrition programs, aerobic exercise, human performance centers for fitness testing and medical screening, health-fitness facility management, EAPs, and health education classes. The entire group is marketed by a single office, whereas programs are delivered under the direction of a manager for each of the six product lines. Mr. Lynch and FitWell Associates provide management services to Sinai Fitness, which bills more than $400,000 annually for corporate health promotion (D.J. Lynch, personal communication, February 1988).

Sportslife, a health-fitness center owned by the Baptist Medical Centers in Birmingham, Alabama, netted more than $250,000 dollars last year ("Sportslife's Science," 1987). Approximately 15% of Sportslife's business is derived from corporate clients. Bruce Gouin, corporate director of Sportslife, attributes the success to "offering a market-driven menu of services and programs at a reasonable price. We found that our clients wanted sound instruction, a clean facility, and customer-friendly business and hospitality systems. In addition to providing positive health results, every process from monthly billing to member check-in must be efficient and courteous" (B.P. Gouin, personal communication, February 1988).

Carolyn Speros of Methodist Health Systems in Memphis, Tennessee, reports that Methodist provides a significant level of services to area business. Contracts with employers exceeds $350,000 annually and includes clients from a variety of industries: utilities, financial, government, and others (C. Speros, personal communication, February 1988).

Rob Ryder, division director of Profile Systems for Occupational Health, Penrose Health Systems, Colorado Springs, Colorado, reports that Profile's revenues have increased from $40,000 in 1985 to nearly $1 million in 1987. Related statistics include the 22 EAP and 250 occupational medicine clients the company has under contract ("Health Promotion in Ambulatory," 1988).

Barbara Burke of St. Vincent's Hospital in Indianapolis, Indiana, reports that healthy-lifestyle programs are viable in the corporate market. St. Vincent's offers a wide array of wellness programs that include on-site program development and management services, health and medical assessments, risk-reduction and skill-building interventions such as smoking cessation and stress management, program evaluation services, and corporate health culture programs such as policy and facility development.

St. Vincent's corporate wellness offering has been well received in Indianapolis, with billings last year of $150,000. Also, the lifestyle programs are integrated with EAP and occupational medicine in a comprehensive product line offered to area business (B. Burke, personal communication, February 1988).

Neil Sol, medical products president for Nautilus Sports/Medical, believes that market demand is sufficient, but for hospitals to prosper they must (a) define clearly what constitutes "profit," direct and indirect, in health promotion; (b) focus program objectives more sharply, through a strategic profit goal statement; and (c) manage programs accordingly (N. Sol, personal communication, February 1988).

OCCUPATIONAL HEALTH SERVICES

According to L. Jones of the American Hospital Association, "Health promotion programs are increasingly becoming part of a package of services . . . when the target market is business and industry" (L. Jones, personal communication, February 1988). The list of occupational health services may be categorized as including (a) occupational medicine, (b) employee assistance programs, and (c) health promotion.

The development and offering of these services should be market-driven. Of course, what is attractive to an employer varies from one worksite to another. It is incumbent upon the provider to conduct market research to determine the appropriateness of specific services for an industry type (agriculture, heavy manufacturing, mining, financial services, etc.) or a particular company.

The different services (e.g., EAP, health promotion, and occupational medicine) within the occupational health product line should be integrated with one another, and occupational health services should be integrated with other managed care and cost containment efforts. Moreover, occupational health services should be managed as a strategic business unit, not as an add-on to or loss leader for other product lines or the hospital in general.

Occupational Medicine

A significant market exists for hospitals to provide medical services to public and private employers. According to a report of figures provided by the Institute for Rehabilitation and Disability Management, the annual cost of disabled employees to U.S. business is nearly $40 billion— and twice that amount for government-funded programs ("Work Hardening," 1988). While the figures may be debated, it is clear that even a 1% reduction in these costs would save approximately $400 million per year. The area of cost-effective disability management provides a business opportunity for hospitals that can develop services that consider the perspective of employers.

Work hardening is one occupational health service for which there is a market. It is expected that there will be about 3,000 work hardening programs in the U.S.

by the mid-1990s. While the provider base is expanding, demand is just now growing. Presently only 16% of employers are using work hardening to return disabled employees to work sooner, thereby saving health care costs and personnel expenses.

The FIRST (Florida Institute of Rehabilitative Services for the Trades) Work Hardening of Hialeah, Florida, is reported to be one of the largest and most innovative programs in the nation. Housed in a 10,000-square-foot warehouse, FIRST employs a team of rehabilitation specialists, including physical, occupational, and recreation therapists, an exercise physiologist, a registered nurse, a physician, and a physician's assistant. FIRST's market includes bus drivers, dental hygienists, construction workers, and airline employees. The services are typically sold to large employers and insurance companies ("Work Hardening," 1988).

Additional services that have been successfully marketed in some communities include preemployment, preplacement, annual, and executive physicals, and ancillary services such as audiometric, vision, pulmonary, and blood testing.

Employee Assistance Programs

Another product that may be integrated with comprehensive occupational health services is employee assistance programs (EAPs). An employee assistance program is conducted to help business aid employees in resolving problems that negatively affect job performance. Such problems may include drug or alcohol abuse, or family, emotional, legal, or financial problems. Any factor that affects the worker's physical, mental, or spiritual health, thereby reducing productivity, is an EAP target.

EAPs have several marketing advantages over lifestyle programs in selling to business. EAP, particularly the drug assistance component, is generally regarded as cost-effective in the short term. Moreover, comprehensive EAP services can be priced lower ($20 to $30 per capita per annum) than similarly comprehensive lifestyle programs ($30 to $200).

In developing EAPs for business it is important to recognize that an EAP is not synonymous with worksite drug testing. EAP program components include

- policy development,
- supervisor training to recognize performance problems that do not respond to normal corrective supervision,
- counselor training to enable triage of referrals to appropriate level of care,
- identification of referral mechanism and treatment providers,
- effective and economical treatment,
- ongoing program support, and
- program evaluation (American Hospital Association, 1982).

Hospitals can network behavioral medicine and psychiatry departmental resources and medical staff to develop and market cost-effective EAPs to business and industry. Furthermore, EAPs can be an attractive component of an integrated occupational health product line.

Blue-Collar Health Promotion

The literature indicates that blue-collar (blue-collar refers to U.S. Standard Occupational Classification "SOC" definitions) employees have historically received fewer benefits from the expansion of worksite health promotion than have their professional, technical, and management counterparts. This situation may be explained by addressing bias within both the provider and employee components. Health promotion providers (employer and commercial, and, to a lesser extent, hospital and community) have, through policy, program location, promotion strategies, or price, effectively excluded blue-collar employees from participation. Moreover, programs have been structured through type of educational media, supervision, and technology to appeal primarily to white-collar workers.

However, blue-collar employees have also exhibited low receptivity to health promotion offerings. It is widely accepted that higher educated, more affluent management personnel are more receptive to health lifestyle programs than people not possessing those characteristics.

Increasingly, blue-collar workers are being targeted for health lifestyle interventions. Many large corporations that initially offered programs only to management have recently expanded to include the general work force. Companies such as Johnson & Johnson, AT&T, and Tenneco are widely respected for their commitment to total work force health.

SUMMARY

A market exists for those health care providers that can develop well-managed, market-driven health promotion programs. Health promotion is one of several products that may be provided to business as part of a comprehensive occupational health services product line. Occupational health services should be integrated with managed care programs and other health care cost containment strategies.

If health promotion is strategically managed and is marketed as a cost-effective element of a health care cost management program for business, it has profit- and image-enhancing potential for the hospital.

REFERENCES

American Hospital Association. (1979). *The hospital's responsibility for health promotion* [Policy and statement of the American Hospital Association]. Chicago: Author.

American Hospital Association. (1982). *Planning hospital health promotion services for business and industry.* Chicago: American Hospital Publishing.

Betting on the future. (1987, March/April). *Optimal Health,* pp. 24-28.

Diversification: More black ink than red ink. (1988, January 5). *Hospitals,* pp. 36-42.

Elias, W.S., & Murphy, R.J. (1987, September 25). The economic benefits of wellness programs. *HealthAction Managers,* pp. 6-8.

Hanley, D. (1985, October). *The nine point health care cost containment system.* Paper presented at the annual conference of the Association for Employee Health and Fitness (Association for Fitness in Business), Fort Worth, TX.

Hay/Huggins. (1987). *The 1987 Hay/Huggins benefit report.* Philadelphia, PA: Author.

Health promotion in ambulatory care. (1988, January/February). *Optimal Health,* pp. 18-20.

Health promotion programs flourishing: Survey. (1985, August 16). *Hospitals,* pp. 128-135.

HMOs and profitability: Healthier members equal a more robust bottom line. (1986, November/December). *Optimal Health,* pp. 16-20.

PPS margins are down, hospital costs are up. (1988, Feburary 1). *American Hospital Association News,* p. 1.

Smith, J.P. (1984, September/October). Is bad health good business? *Optimal Health,* pp. 14-16.

Sportslife's science of good business. (1987, November/December). *Optimal Health,* pp. 40-42.

Spring, H. (1987). Employer health care: A system in transition. New York: Coopers and Lybrand.

Vickery, D., Kalmer, H., Lowry, D., Constantine, M., Wright, E., & Loren, W. (1983). Effect of a self-care education program on medical visits. *Journal of the American Medical Association, 250,* 2952-2956.

Work hardening: Bridging the gap. (1988, January/February). *Optimal Health,* pp. 42-44.

How Hospitals Engage in Promotion

Many health care institutions have exhibited interest in developing quality health promotion programs. However, they are often at a disadvantage because most administrators and health care professionals are unfamiliar with the structure and utility of these programs.

Health care institutions have historically recruited professionals with experience in acute care and little interest or ability in health promotion. To ensure health promotion success, it is important that programs be designed by people knowledgeable in the field.

Part III provides information about design implementation and market selling of health care/health promotion programs. Chapter 7 discusses developmental issues in relation to comprehensive health promotion programs by incorporating illustrative examples. Chapter 8 deals with developing a market and sales plan and discusses how to sell health promotion services to target markets.

Designing Hospital Health Promotion Programs

Laurie A. Kelley

I have a colleague who owned several health clubs in town, all but one of which he recently shut down. It now appears that he may close the doors on his last club. He called recently because it was rumored that my hospital was building a fitness facility, and he wanted to offer his services as a facility planning consultant. I told him that the rumor was not true—what we were building was a physician office building. With a pensive note in his voice, he said, "You know, I wish I had gotten in on the ground floor of this hospital-based wellness business 5 years ago—it's too hard to make a go of this on your own."

Hospital-based health promotion programs may appear as a plum to those struggling in the health club business, but the key to success is no different than in any new venture—a solid program designed for a specific audience. Successful program designs emanate from creative, informed minds with a foundation in market sensitivity and entrepreneurship. From that base will grow a carefully conceived plan and well-reasoned goals and purposes. This chapter will discuss the process of program design, beginning with generating program ideas by reading, questioning, brainstorming, and otherwise analyzing your environment. Next, the issues of gaining support for your program, determining feasibility, and setting meaningful, achievable goals will be discussed. The nuts and bolts of appropriate organizational structure, intelligent staffing decisions, and adequate financing will be covered as a framework for operation. This will be followed by information gathering that utilizes market research as a tool for product formulation. Consideration of positioning, product, place, and price will round out the final components of program design, guaranteeing the completeness of your venture. Throughout your program design, keep in mind that you are developing a new way of thinking—with a marketing mentality. You are designing a product to meet an audience's needs; you have as your goal delivering that service to your client; and you will judge your success by customer satisfaction.

PROGRAM DESIGN

Generating the ideas for your health promotion program requires the use of your entrepreneurial mind. The three endeavors to become involved in include reading, questioning, and brainstorming. Begin by reading all that is available in trends across the country in program formulation. Resources listed at the end of this chapter and throughout this book will provide more than enough fodder for the creative mind. Expand your reading beyond the traditional health promotion pieces to include business publications, personnel and health care benefits journals, and hospital management articles that discuss current trends in delivery systems. Allow your perspective to expand beyond traditional programmatic thinking like health fairs and Lamaze classes into the broader concerns of the public at large. Then combine your information assimilation with an investigation of programs at other hospitals. Use the director question checklist form supplied here to query others about their programs so you can get a sense of what exists as a possibility. Information like this can spawn creative ideas for your own program, help you avoid pitfalls in future endeavors, and foster a network of colleagues with whom to share ideas.

Additionally, your telephone work should involve a competitive analysis. The following is a list of potential competitors in your community that might be offering health promotion programs.

- Other area hospitals
- Freestanding clinics (e.g., physical therapy, back pain, and home health agencies), laboratories
- Women's centers
- Volunteer agencies (e.g., American Red Cross, American Heart Association, American Cancer Society, and American Lung Association)
- United Way agencies
- YMCA/YWCA
- Health clubs, spas, and gymnasiums
- Exercise studios
- Franchised fitness classes (e.g., Jazzercise)
- Franchised weight loss programs (e.g., Diet Centers and Weight Watchers)
- Community college adult education classes
- Gourmet cooking stores (for cooking classes)
- University-linked research programs on lifestyle diseases (obesity, hypertension, diabetes research).

Find out the range and scope of programming that competitors offer, prices, enrollment, and procedures for registering. Use this information to decide what services and products are already being delivered in your community. Additionally, think about the possibility of joint-venturing with existing programs in your com-

Questions to Ask
Other Health Promotion Program Directors

1. Number of hospital beds: _____   Number of FTEs: _____

   Average occupancy rate: _____

2. Type of hospital (check all that apply):

   _____ Religious affiliation   _____ Community

   _____ National chain   _____ Not for profit

   _____ For profit   _____ Tertiary

3. Approximate population of service area: _____

4. Demographics of audience served (example: blue collar/white collar, industrial/service economy, age, sex, income):

   _____

   _____

5. Type of health promotion offerings (check all that apply):

   _____ Educational classes   _____ Health fairs

   _____ Executive physicals   _____ Written educational
                                              information

   _____ TV shows   _____ EAP

   _____ Dial-a-Nurse   _____ Fitness center

   _____ Health screenings   _____ Occupational
                                              health
                                              programs

   _____ Other _____

   _____

6. Organizationally, where are you located in the hospital?

   _____

7. Number of years programs have existed:_____

8. Most successful endeavors:_____

   _____

9. Least successful endeavors:_____

   _____

munity. (This will be discussed in greater depth later in this chapter.) What do they have that you might need, like instructors, prepared materials, space? What do you have that they might need, such as credibility, advertising funds, medical or technical expertise? Joint-venturing does not necessarily mean a legal agreement but may be something as simple as an informal arrangement to credit the American Heart Association for your CPR class materials or a split on registration fees if you are allowed to use their facility.

Since ideas for your program should address the specifics of your hospital's corporate culture, combine your national search with a careful scrutiny of home base. Read your hospital's mission and role statements, administration's goals and objectives, and any strategic plans (long- and short-range) or annual implementation plans. Look for phrases that indicate a responsibility beyond serving only the needs of the sick. Talk to administrators, physicians, and governing board members and gain a perspective on their thoughts about the hospital's future direction. What are the priorities for your institution? What role does the hospital expect to play in the community? What clinical areas are centers of emphasis? Think creatively about how health promotion can fill a niche in these areas and, by doing so, enhance strategic directions for the future.

GAINING PROGRAM SUPPORT

I was recently reminded of how powerful the harnessed energy of key decision makers can be. Our hospital convened a task force to plan a year-long celebration of its 90th anniversary. In brainstorming a theme for the anniversary, the task force, made up of influential community members, physicians, managers, and employees, continually brought up the idea of a dedication to keeping the community healthy, promoting good health, and being a leader in community service. Even though our hospital is a tertiary care facility, 7 years of dedication to health promotion have given the hospital an image that key decision makers like to see continually at the forefront.

While you generate program ideas and research the environment of the hospital, also begin laying the groundwork for support of your future programming efforts by seeking out the key decision makers—the powerful individuals with influence, personal commitments to health promotion, and a track record of support for entrepreneurial attitudes. Look for champions among the hospital's higher ranks who will stand behind your cause and see it as a hand-in-glove fit with the hospital's mission. Identify their ideas and expectations through extensive one-on-one interviews and provide them with the feedback and information necessary to gain and keep their support. The cases where a convinced physician single-handedly initiates the building of a $1.5-million fitness facility are too numerous to be ignored in the real world of program design.

DETERMINING PROGRAM FEASIBILITY

In some respects, the mechanisms involved in generating ideas and searching out key supporters are similar to doing a feasibility study that helps you decide whether or not to develop and operate a health promotion program. Your hospital may want to hire a consultant to perform a feasibility study, or you and other support staff can perform an informal study. Sol (1986a) makes the point that feasibility studies should not be viewed as a panacea for decision making, nor should they trap you or your administration in "analysis paralysis," which can turn into an excuse for immobility. O'Donnell (1986) advises that a feasibility study should seek answers to questions such as:

- Why do health promotion? What are the reasons, the motives?
- What kind of support will health promotion have from administration?
- How interested will the potential audiences be (community, employees, business and industry)?
- Will there be access to necessary resources?

Some of these answers will come quickly with a great deal of certainty; others will come from best guesses made after carefully considering the environment you have researched. Keep these questions in mind throughout the design process, and remember the importance of using the answers to make the go/no go decision.

SETTING PROGRAM GOALS

Clear goals give you a framework from which the design of the program grows. Begin by using the hospital's mission statement and administrative goals and objectives as guiding tools while you simultaneously ask yourself, "Why will this hypothesized program exist?" Make a list of your answers and then try to categorize those that address similar issues. Longe and Wolf (1984) have found some common reasons:

- To improve the health of the community. Hospitals want to reinvestigate this business of focusing so intensely on the sick, especially with rapidly rising health care costs. They are diversifying towards the continuum of care from optimal health to illness and death.
- To improve the image of the hospital. Hospitals that were once full may now have empty beds and may be losing patients to competitors. There is a desire to reach out to the community to instill or reinstill a favorable image. Hospitals have finally noticed that consumers are exercising their right to choose a facility, and find image enhancement a necessity.

- To change the hospital's service mix. Health promotion is a way to diversify services, either by being a new service itself or by creating market awareness of new services the hospital has diversified into, like obstetrics or gerontology. Diabetic classes are offerings that usually have patient education as an initial goal. Additionally, visibility of that offering in the community creates awareness that clinical services for the diabetic patient are available from your hospital.

- To enter new targeted markets. Hospitals want to tap into new markets like business and industry, senior citizens, young professionals, and others. Offering services to the apparently healthy in those markets could lead them to choose your hospital when medical needs arise.

- To reduce health care costs. medical self-care, disease prevention programs, health screenings for high-risk populations, and occupational health programs at worksites are documenting subsequent reduction in health care costs. Also of importance here is the issue of addressing the hospital employee population, first for the practical reasons mentioned above, and second to set an example for future endeavors in corporate sites.

- To improve productivity. Healthy lifestyle habits may lead to reduced absenteeism, improved attitudes, and lower turnover in employee populations, thereby improving productivity.

The goals for a health promotion program are as numerous and varied as the different programs that exist nationally. Goals structured for success require decisions as to what benefits are to be derived from your program. Your program should then be designed to provide those very benefits. As you set goals, group them according to the following three categories:

- Administrative goals. What does administration expect from you? What are its concerns and visions for the future? What will you pinpoint out of its published goals and objectives? Know what your key decision makers want and then document your achievement of that. Included in this category are goals like improving the hospital's image, changing the hospital's service mix, generating referrals for inpatient or outpatient programs, and entering new target audiences.

- Financial goals. What are you expected to return for the hospital's investment? Examples include being a community service operation (no revenue produced—programs free to the community, businesses, or hospital employees); generating some revenue from fees for services; breaking even and covering costs; generating a profit above the program's operating costs; generating indirect revenues for outpatient diagnostic services; and reducing health care costs for a particular audience.

- Health goals for your audiences. What will your program do for a particular audience's health? Examples of this goal include increasing the community's knowledge of healthy lifestyle habits; reducing the incidence of death due to heart disease in area industries; fostering the adoption of risk-reduction activities by senior citizens; and using screening programs to seek out individuals at high risk for developing heart disease.

Be wary of lofty goals that are difficult to achieve and measure, such as reducing the incidence of death and disability from chronic diseases. This goal would take time, money, energy, and research far beyond the capabilities of most health promotion programs. A recent survey by *Optimal Health* magazine and Price Waterhouse ("Health Promotion," 1987) showed that 69% of hospital health promotion programs measured success by their efficacy as a public relations tool, 66% as a community service tool, and 65% as an image enhancement tool. However, future trends suggest that customer satisfaction combined with bottom-line profitability are rising in importance as goals to be achieved.

A worksheet that can provide a framework for goal clarification is provided on the next two pages.

Use information you have gathered from interviews, administrators, mission statements, etc.

ESTABLISHING AN ORGANIZATIONAL STRUCTURE

According to the *Optimal Health*/Price Waterhouse survey (1987), 21% of health promotion programs report directly to the administrator, 29% to a vice president or line officer, and 42% to a department head. Your place on the hospital's organizational chart is a direct reflection of the level of administrative support. If you report to a coordinator with seven or eight programs, who reports to a department director who in turn is three levels from the hospital administrator, how much support will your new venture realistically receive? Will you be able to stay market-sensitive, instituting change and encouraging growth? Will financial resources be available? Professionals largely believe that the new venture status of health promotion program design requires that you be close to administration, that you be unencumbered by standard operating procedures, and that you have adequate systems support ("Administration: Seeking the Perfect Fit," 1986). In the initial stages, be sure you will get care and feeding from the top, and ensure the formation of formal relationships that are crucial to your success.

Many programs get their start as an administrator's project, often a multidisciplinary task force assigned the job of brainstorming, analyzing resources, determining feasibility, and piloting projects. Once the task force decides that there is a potential audience and deliverable product, the program is staffed and moved to a more permanent place in the hierarchy. Sol (1986b) emphasizes the importance of realizing the limitations of a committee in terms of program management and encourages programs to quickly take the step into hiring dedicated staff.

Some programs are located within another department. Programs move to this place after the "task force period" or begin here as a part of the education, public affairs, marketing, planning, medical affairs, or foundation departments, depending

Goal-Setting Worksheet

Answer these questions:

1. Why was your program/position initiated?

2. What key decision makers in hospital administration have an interest in your program?

   What specifically do they want to see happen?

3. What clinical specialties does your hospital currently emphasize?

   What specialties will they focus on in the next 5 years?

4. Is your hospital recruiting new physicians?

   In what areas?

5. What is your current budget for community education (operating expenses plus salaries)?

6. Do you charge for any of your community education?

   If so, how much revenue do you generate monthly?

7. Do you offer free programs?

If so, what percent does that represent of your total programming?

8. How do you think your hospital is perceived by the community (e.g., for the rich only; serves poor/blue-collar only; only a place to have babies; only in it for profit; caring, returns a lot to the community; old, low-tech; new, high-tech/academic)?

How have you/can you contribute to or change that perception?

9. Do you disseminate health information to the community?

10. Do you provide health screening services for your community?

Use the answers to these questions and guidance from Administration to formulate *program goals*:

Administrative Goals

Financial Goals

Community Health Goals

Other

on the program's goals. This may mean that your program is an important service of the hospital but not a major service. You may vie for funding and recognition with other functions like patient education, nursing education, special events, fund-raising efforts, or staff development.

Health promotion programs with departmental status are becoming increasingly popular, allowing more opportunity for creativity in products, services, staffing, and budgeting. Even though departments in larger hospitals can be buried in the organization by four or more layers, in most instances, this scheme separates the department head by only one to three layers. It speaks powerfully that health promotion is a major service of the hospital.

Spin-off corporate entities have been initiated by some hospitals to endeavor to get health promotion out of the mainstream of red tape by placing it in a separate or already existing corporate entity (the fund-raising entity has provided a home in some hospitals). These corporations can be for-profit or not-for-profit and can allow the accumulation of capital outside the patient care realm. Diversifying into a new service area and protecting income from the calculation of reimbursement rates are reasons for new corporate entities. Additionally, health promotion programs may be generating income unrelated to the services on which the tax-free status of an institution is based, like charitable services and medical education. The accumulation of unrelated business income can jeopardize tax-free status and thus become a major reason for corporate spin-off.

FINANCING YOUR PROGRAM

Assuming that your hospital has made a commitment to offering health promotion, program funding will most likely come from the hospital's general operating fund. Other potential sources include grant moneys from the hospital foundation or other national, regional, or local agencies, fund-raising endeavors, donations, and fees paid for your products or services. Whatever your sources, a clearly outlined budget is necessary to drive spending decisions and track revenue. Accountability without a budget is virtually impossible as is evidenced by the number of unbudgeted programs that are "called on the carpet" and scrutinized for overspending after the first year.

Instead of being a chore to accomplish annually, your budget can be a valuable business tool. Tracking monthly expenses in specific categories puts you in touch with the ebb and flow of business transactions. Tying expenses directly to the revenues that they bring in is the best way to measure the cost-effectiveness of your program.

If your program does not have any historical expense data, begin with a zero-based budget, building expense projections based on known needs and costs. While this is a time-consuming and detailed task, it is a valuable investment in a strong base for future budgets and provides you with a realistic picture of what you need, from the number of pencils and pens to hours of contract labor.

A sample line-item budget is provided for your examination.

Sample Health Promotion
Annual Budget Figures*

Subaccount categories	Annual budget amount
Salaries—director, coordinator, fitness specialist, secretary	$110,528
Consulting fees—advertising agency, market research	29,000
Office supplies	12,000
Printing—brochures (4 times/year)	64,000
Minor equipment**—answering machine, calculator, hand weights, blood pressure cuff	1,500
Books—wellness resources for staff	300
Promotional supplies—T-shirts, stress cards, sweatbands	5,000
Purchased repairs—typewriter repair	100
Contract labor—instructors, health fair staff, student interns	24,000
Building rental—classrooms	450
Dues/subscriptions	500
Advertising—newspaper, radio	30,000
Transferred labor—Lab blood work, pulmonary function test	18,000
Dietary transfer—snacks for classes	90
Total	$295,468

*Beginning program with community education and corporate wellness programs

**Does not account for starting and stocking a fitness center, which can add $100,000-$600,000, or repair of fitness equipment, which can add $5,000-$15,000. For a brief review of fitness center budgets, see Bellingham and Tager (1986) and Howell (1987).

The following guidelines will aid you in the budgeting process.

Get a "chart of accounts" from your accounting department. Find out what subaccounts you need as line items in your budget. Be sure you are aware of any subaccounts that require special approval to use, such as transferred medical or pharmaceutical supplies. If you have special needs that do not fit into the available categories, ask about creating special subaccounts. For example, my program uses a large number of promotional items, like T-shirts. Since these are not a typical departmental expense, I created a special subaccount to hold budgeted funds for those items. Also, subaccounts can be created for special events, like a health fair, community screening, or television show.

Find out what things cost. Talk to equipment vendors; know what your costs will be for conferences, subscriptions, and office supplies. Especially important is knowing the cost of items or services that you will transfer into your department from other hospital departments, like plant services, dietary, pharmacy, laboratory, respiratory care, medical illustration, and mail room. Uneducated guesses may leave you with unexplained budget variances that reflect negatively on your management capabilities.

Use a 12-month spread sheet to project monthly revenues and each individual subaccount's expenses. Know what months you will pay for advertising, printed brochures, equipment purchase and repair, and subscriptions. Discuss billing with vendors so that your funds are available to match their billing cycles. To avoid large monthly variances, find out if accounting charges your account for goods when they are received or when they are billed. Instead of taking the annual estimated expense for a line item and dividing it by 12 to complete your monthly spread sheet, make educated projections about your revenue and expense peaks and valleys. Rarely does any program have a consistent level of activity.

Learn how to budget within the health care system. Health promotion program managers are frequently frustrated by the requirement that their budgets be based on hospital parameters like cost per equivalent admission. If your budget is based on patient care indicators, learn what those indicators are and how to use them for maximum flexibility. For instance, if your total budget figure must be calculated mathematically to meet a standard set by the finance office, use your creativity to distribute the funds between line items, giving more money to crucial line items and cutting back on those of marginal necessity. If the brochures you print for your program are vitally important to product sales, you may be willing to cut back on office supplies and books to maintain your printing at an optimal level.

Develop a narrative to accompany your budget that names items, services, activities, dollar amounts, and dates. This will serve as a plan that you can refer to when questions of priority spending arise, or simply when you have forgotten how much you budgeted for newspaper advertising.

Establish documentation systems before your budget is implemented. Common indices to track include monthly and year-to-date figures for actual and budgeted revenues by subaccount, as well as expenses. Report any variances from budgeted amounts, either positive or negative. Additionally, calculate the monthly and year-to-date percentage of expenses that have been covered by revenues (expenses/revenue x 100). For programs that have one budget for all expenses, it is often useful to use tracking mechanisms for the costs incurred by specific programs like community education classes. Mechanisms like these ensure an awareness of expense that will enable you to make decisions based on cost-effectiveness. A sample format for documenting expenses related to a health education seminar is provided for your use (p. 110). Consult your line officer on the level of detail required in a reporting mechanism and follow it religiously. A well-documented, consistent budget report will ensure that there are no questions about your accountability.

The question frequently arises as to how many budgets a health promotion department should have. Your options are to have one budget and one account number for the entire department, or to have a different budget and account number for each specific program you offer. For example, Health Promotion Department A is responsible for community health education classes, cardiac rehabilitation, and occupational health for business and industry. It has three budgets, each prepared by the individual program coordinator for the expenses related directly to each service. On the other hand, Health Promotion Department B offers a wide variety of programs—community health education classes, wellness programs for hospital employees and business and industry, and community service programs for the indigent. Because its resources are shared among so many offerings with varying levels of activity, it chose to have one budget with one account number and has developed tracking systems that monitor expenses by program.

The system that you set up will be based on the following:

- Your hospital's chief of finance and accounting system—what guidelines do they typically follow for new program design?
- The size of your program—you may start with one budget and, as your department grows, expand into multiple budgets for specific programs.
- Your financial goals—programs expecting an immediate return on investment may begin with a more detailed, sophisticated budgeting system.

DEVELOPING ADEQUATE AND APPROPRIATE STAFFING

Most programs function with five or fewer full-time employees, though a few have up to 45. The determining factor in staffing is usually the rate of program growth, based on a response to audience needs and opportunities. Programs that started with as few as two employees have grown in 3 years to 15 employees. Frequently, the administrative response to increasing staff for an existing program is "Do the work first, demonstrate the need, collect the revenue, and then ask for the position." This can create a condition of chronic overwork or apathy in the program director. These guidelines will help in making staffing decisions.

Seminar Expense Summary

Seminar _____   Date _____

Expenses

Account	Category	Description	Amount
.6600	Instructor pay		
.6600	Contract labor		
.8900	Food		
.4600	Office supplies		
.4630	Print purchased		
.5145	Promo supplies		
.7500	Building rent		
.9300	Transfer labor		
.8810	Travel		
	Miscellaneous		
	Other		

Total expenses

Revenues

Cash in: _____

Sales: _____

_____

Gross revenue _____

Net revenue _____

Director approval _____

Use your "honeymoon" period wisely. Create and fund critical positions like secretary, exercise specialist, and salesperson. Requests are usually honored more quickly and with less red tape during the first year of program start-up.

Be creative in your staffing. If necessary, find departments willing to share positions like secretary, exercise physiologist, nutritionist, psychologist, and salesperson. Look to the community for professional contract labor, persons who will carry out specific responsibilities (like teaching) for an hourly rate. Put in a request to your volunteer office for extra help. Contact local schools and universities about providing placement opportunities for student interns. Roberts (1987) feels that student internship programs are an opportunity for young professionals with "untarnished ideals, fresh ideas, and boundless enthusiasm" (p. 1) to get quality work experience. Internal research at my hospital turned up a summer internship program for students interested in any aspect of health care, an internship that was fully funded by the hospital's foundation. At one time, that program brought four full-time, paid students into my department.

Consider job requirements carefully. Health promotion is an innovator's field that frequently functions as a small business or new venture and, because of that, requires a unique staff. The educational preparation of the originating director usually influences the type of services offered. An exercise physiologist may develop a program with a strong physical fitness component, while a nurse director may present a strong clinical focus. If careful scrutiny of your goals points to a very diverse program emphasis with multiple product lines, consider hiring staff with liberal, well-rounded backgrounds including education, marketing, business, public relations, accounting, sales, and any mix of wellness training. Clearly define expectations for jobs that combine management and technical expertise. Do you expect the program coordinator to teach stress management and manage the aerobic instructors? If so, chances are you will sacrifice either management or technical skills, unless you make a concerted effort to develop one or both. Recent informal research (Sol, 1987) shows that health promotion professionals have a variety of titles and chains of command within administration, a reflection of the confusion in a growing field. Initial work on a job description that delineates functions and responsibilities will spare you staffing problems later on.

The final but perhaps most important comment on staffing addresses the issue of medical expertise. What role will physicians play in your design scheme? Possible options include a medical director (paid position), either for your department exclusively or shared with another department; a medical advisor (unpaid); or a medical advisory committee, made up of supportive physicians. A physician component to your program has the following advantages:

- It provides medical credibility.
- A physician can order tests that require physician orders such as blood work and stress tests.

- A physician can review abnormal test results and executive summary reports on corporate health programs.
- A physician can sign policies and procedures that address medical issues.
- A physician can support programs that require physical assessments, such as executive physicals, preseason athletic exams, and preemployment assessments for business and industry.
- A physician can champion your causes with the hospital's medical staff (Powell and Brownson, 1986).

There are disadvantages as well:

- Medical review of your policies and procedures may impede your program's progress.
- An unavailable or busy physician cannot adequately address your needs.
- A conservative medical environment is unsupportive of some health promotion aspects and may not be market sensitive.
- Your program ideas may not coincide with those of your medical director.

However, the advantages of medical support for a hospital health promotion program usually outweigh the disadvantages. The key to success is selecting the mechanism for support (director, advisor, committee) that best suits your political environment, program design, and budget. For an in-depth discussion on this issue, please refer to chapter 9, "The Physician's Role Health Promotion."

GATHERING MARKET INFORMATION

The "I-know-what-is-best-for-you" philosophy can undermine even the most meticulously planned program. Recent research conducted by Oakwood Hospital in Dearborn, Michigan, showed that consumers and health care professionals do not necessarily agree on the focus of hospital health promotion programs (Bills, 1986). When asked to identify health topics that should be addressed by hospitals for consumers, professionals ranked smoking as number one, while consumers rated it 18th in importance. Similarly, while professionals ranked heart disease as the disease topic that would be of most interest to consumers, the consumers' priority list was topped by cancer. Testing your "best guesses" about audiences' needs by investigating their perceptions and desires before you select specific program components is insurance against program failure.

Decision makers partake of health promotion services and purchase health promotion products for numerous reasons—to look better, to feel better, to perform better, to meet people, to reduce company health care expenses. Thus, the program you design must suit the needs of your market. Mechanisms to discover those needs and desires can run the gamut from simply collecting available data to hiring a consultant for market research. Whatever methods you use, confidence about knowledge of your market is your goal. A service designed to meet specific needs will virtually sell itself.

During the idea-generation phase of program design, you collected information on health promotion by reading, questioning, and brainstorming. Continue that process on a national and local level by searching popular health and women's magazines (like *American Health* and *Redbook)* for health topics, watching local and national television talk shows and health news segments (like "Donahue" and Cable Health Network), and scanning your local newspaper for health stories by the medical reporter or lifestyle editor. This process should synthesize an awareness of national trends with a sensitivity to local interest. For example, the latest self-care concept may be massage therapy, but if your local newspaper is conducting investigative reporting on massage parlors, then that course should not be among your first selections for community education. Similarly, if AIDS is a major issue in your community, educational endeavors combined with testing may be a lucrative project.

Gathering available information about your community enables you to segment, or divide, that market into groups or parts that are meaningful to you. Begin by gathering information from available sources. Several such sources follow.

- Patient origin data. Your marketing, admissions, medical records, or information systems department can provide you with this data. This is a demographic description of hospital patients, type of reimbursements, and discharge diagnoses. It is helpful to discuss with decision makers at the hospital the issue of using health promotion programs to reach either current users or nonusers of hospital services.
- Demographic data by census tracts. This data has been correlated with consumer preferences by market researchers for years. The Chamber of Commerce can provide this data, which includes items such as age, sex, income, race, occupation, number of years in the community, family size, and marital status. Census tract data can be clustered to match zip codes in your community. Future direct mail campaigns can then be targeted to zip codes that match your audience demographics.
- Business data. This data is also available from the Chamber of Commerce, as a profile of the business community, including types of businesses and number of employees. Chamber of Commerce directories are useful for mailings to businesses and telephone interviews with business executives.
- Health statistics. These are available from national, state, and local health agencies and include such measurements as disease rates and morbidity/mortality statistics.
- Hospital employee data. Your personnel department can provide information on employee absenteeism, turnover, insurance claims, and accident/safety records.

Now that you have information about your audience, brainstorm ways to divide them into segments, such as by the following:

- Geography—neighborhoods, zip codes, suburbs, towns, and counties.
- Demographics (as discussed previously). Demographic groups receiving recent attention include Yuppies (young urban professionals), Sinks (singles with no kids), Dinks (double income households with no kids), Woofs (well-off older folks), and empty nesters (older adults whose children have left home).
- Psychographics. This segmentation is based on lifestyle habits, values, attitudes, and motivations. Groups can be differentiated by adjectives such as conservative, liberal, upscale, patriotic, fashion-conscious, ambitious, sophisticated, price-conscious, and old-fashioned. Information on psychographic groups in your community usually has to be generated by original research; however, it may be available free of charge from your advertising agency or from local television stations that are using it as a marketing tool in the sales department.
- Behavior. When are people most apt to act on information, to purchase your product or service? Are they unaware, aware, informed, interested, ready to buy? How will their stage of readiness affect their involvement? A prime example of this is the promotion of weight loss and fitness classes after the first of the year, when consumers may have made resolutions to lose weight and shape up.
- Decision-making role. Who makes the decision to buy your services? If you decide to sell executive physicals, do you market your product to executives, their spouses, or benefit managers of local businesses?
- Specialty groups. Is there a subsegment of business that needs your service to help meet OSHA standards? Can you target dental office staffs for CPR classes? Will bereaved family members attend grief workshops?

Targeting the segmented audience with the best potential return is your next step. Pick a large enough audience, with decision-making power, that is ready to become involved (unless you are willing to make a long-term investment in changing the level of awareness). For example, if Hospital Y is developing a clinical emphasis in orthopedic surgery and sports medicine, it might be health promotion's job to develop a program that markets that new emphasis. Hospital Y's predominantly young, family-oriented audience has a number of public and private schools that are heavily engaged in sports teams. A Sports Injury Prevention Workshop is developed and advertised to all area coaches, who have repeatedly expressed their concerns about star players becoming "walking wounded." For Hospital X, which has the same clinical emphasis but a large community of young professionals and double-income families, the program consists of a weekend walk-in clinic. "Weekend athletes" are able to get immediate medical attention for and education about injuries, thereby alleviating the waiting time and expense of an emergency room visit and acquainting them with Hospital X's new service.

MARKET RESEARCH

In addition to gathering available information for market analysis, you can conduct original research to test your hypotheses about what your audience will purchase. Research can create new ideas for products, refine ideas you already have, or pinpoint problems that have arisen in your program. Moosbrugger (1986) relates the story of one hospital that, through an analysis of patient origin data, found that its admissions had 25% more seniors than the national norm. A strategic decision was made to develop health promotion products for this promising market segment. Original research queried caregivers, physicians, and seniors from the area about possible products. Findings showed that caregivers of elderly adults, not the elderly themselves, were the ones in need of programming on issues such as coping with the daily needs of aging family members and cooking for special diets.

Table 7.1 lists the types of market research typically used in new product design and refinement with strengths, weaknesses, and their best uses.

For new services, most market research consultants recommend that you invest up to 10% of your proposed first year's budget for the new service on research. One hospital decided to test the potential for employee assistance programs (EAPs)

Table 7.1 Types of Market Research

Qualitative research focus group ($1,000–$4,000)		
Strengths	**Limitations**	**Purpose**
Quick	Small sample	Explore areas where decisions are made in social contact
Flexible	Results not conclusive	
Immediacy	Few market segments	
Brings issues out		Learn WHY
Learn consumer language		Sharpen product design
Inexpensive		Refine position

(Cont.)

Table 7.1   (Continued)

Qualitative individual interviews ($500–$750)

Strengths	Limitations	Purpose
Flexible	Expensive	Include busy respondents
Can show product	Not anonymous	Include respondents spread out geographically
Allow indepth exploration	Time-consuming	Explore private, individual decisions

Quantitative mail survey ($5,000–$15,000)

Strengths	Limitations	Purpose
Wide distribution	Nonresponse bias	Survey entire population/group
Low cost	No open-ended questions	Survey groups that would be eager to respond
Time	Time-consuming	Explore sensitive issues
Anonymous	Errors in tallying	
No interview bias		

Quantitative telephone survey ($10,000-$20,000)

Strengths	Limitations	Purpose
Quick	Can't show product/concept	Track awareness, use, preference, interest
Random sample		Learning how many are interested
Good for busy group		
Wide geographic reach		

Quantitative person on the street survey ($10,000-$20,000)

Strengths	Limitations	Purpose
Quick reaction Can show product Allow probing Cost-efficient	Sample not projectable Won't locate hard-to-find respondents	Test communications (ads, descriptions) Test product

with local business and industry since national trends demonstrated a tremendous market for these services. Additionally, on the local level, the hospital felt that there was a market for a cost-effective program. Research costing $10,000 was conducted on the proposed $250,000 EAP program, only to show that area business was satisfied with current resources and apathetic about cost-effectiveness issues. Thus, the likelihood for failure of the proposed program was very high. A substantial investment in program design was saved by checking the readiness of the audience to purchase the proposed service.

Finally, remember that there is research that can be performed without hiring a market research firm, such as employee interest and current lifestyle habit surveys, informal focus groups, surveys of captive audiences that already exist (like cardiac rehabilitation outpatients), and individual interviews. In your market analysis, be sure you follow this checklist:

1. Start with your customer; know your market size and preferences.
2. Segment your market.
3. Select the segment with the most potential for return.
4. Do enough research to develop a sound working hypothesis.
5. Make sure the features of your product match the benefits your audience wants.

This will ensure that you obtain the most accurate information possible.

POSITIONING

The next phase of program design involves positioning your program, developing your product(s), making space and facility decisions, and dealing with pricing issues.

Aurin (1986) claims that the fundamental mistake health promotion programs make is failure to clearly define their position in the marketplace. Positioning is simply establishing an identity for your program. This involves writing several paragraphs detailing what the program is, who the audience is, the needs the program serves, and the benefits consumers will receive. This positioning statement serves as the foundation upon which everything else rests. You will refer to it when you make product development decisions and write advertising copy, asking yourself if your choices are made on the basis of your position. Guidelines for positioning follow.

Stand apart from the crowd by differentiating yourself. Focus on the unique aspects of your program.

Be the leader in what you are doing, if possible. Honestly ask yourself if you are a carbon copy of other programs in the area.

If your program is similar to others in the area, juxtapose yourself against them as something unique or better. Avis car rental has used this strategy in the promotional slogan, "We try harder." Obviously, there are many companies in the car rental business, but Avis wants us to know that they are different because they try harder than the competition.

Choose a name and theme line that reflect your position. A theme line turns your positioning statement into a few succinct words that should be repeated in all communications with the public (Aurin, 1986). Examples are: "Because you are your own best medicine;" "Because your good health matters;" "Bringing good health to your neighborhood;" "We're at the heart of your good health;" "Because your employees' health is the best investment;" "Answering your health care cost concerns." When choosing a name, select one that is simple to remember. Many programs have found that leaving out any reference to "hospital" reinforces the wellness concept and removes the stigma of sick care.

Be aware of what special niche will perk your audience's interest. Examples include location (neighborhood, convenience), service (fitness testing, special classes), staff (experts, caring people), history (oldest institution, only religious hospital), audience (seniors, family), initiative (innovators, first in town), or size (biggest, largest variety, small and personal). Talk about your niche in the positioning statement and address it in your theme line.

PRODUCT DETERMINATION

Your products and services will be determined by the audience you target. Product lines and service options will be different for each targeted audience—community members, hospital employees, and business and industry—and the subsegments within those audiences will challenge your product development creativity. Seniors within the community market may want health risk screenings; nurses within the hospital environment may want stress management and grief workshops; businesses with fewer than 500 employees may want individualized fitness testing and contractual EAP services. A manager who uses creative thinking, knows the targeted audience, and seeks out flexible resources will be positioned to deliver what the audience wants.

Products range from health fairs and classes to dial-a-nurse telephone services and drug screening for business and industry. There are even a number of packaged programs available on risk reduction topics, like weight management and smoking cessation, that include prepared materials, instructor training, and franchise rights. Bills and Sherman (1985) and Powell (1985) discuss considerations for selecting packaged programs.

Basically, most products can be divided into three groups:

- Products that enhance awareness—these products can range from a simple information delivery system like paycheck stuffers to a complex screening program. The purpose of these products is to increase the audience's level of awareness (bringing them through the different stages from unaware to ready to buy), increase their interest in the product, and increase knowledge of their individual health status. Examples are newsletters, teaser campaigns at the worksite that arouse interest, posters, flyers, educational literature, health fairs, educational classes, health screenings, and television shows.

- Products that promote behavior change—these teach and encourage lifestyle change. Awareness products act as a direct feeder to lifestyle change products in the sense that only the aware, interested audience is going to invest in intervention. Examples are health education workbooks, computer-assisted learning modules, health screenings with counseling, behavior modification classes (usually long-term—6 to 12 weeks), individual counseling (EAP, fitness assessments, nutritional counseling, biofeedback), and inpatient and outpatient programs (cardiac rehabilitation and mental health).

- Products that provide support—these products encourage long-term maintenance of lifestyle changes. Products include ongoing fitness classes, support groups, therapy groups, automatic retesting and callbacks (for fitness assessments and cholesterol checks), incentive programs (earning dollars for miles walked), walking clubs, and corporate culture changes (changing cafeteria foods and vending machines to encourage healthier selection).

Naturally, these are not definitive areas and your products will frequently cross the line between each of the groups mentioned. But the segregation of product types can help make your initial selection easier.

CONTRACTING LABOR

Perhaps one of the most frequent concerns of program managers is staffing their programs with qualified teachers. The answer for almost all successful programs has been the development of a system of contract instructors. Contract labor can be made up of experts from the community and the hospital who are paid on an hourly basis to prepare and present educational programs. Issues to address include recruitment, selection criteria, agreements, pay, and quality control.

Possible sources for recruiting qualified professionals include your own hospital staff (key departments are usually education, respiratory therapy, physical therapy, dietary, and nursing), schools and universities, professional organizations (United Way agencies, mental health clinics), private practitioners (licensed clinical social workers, psychologists, physicians), and your competition (attend their offerings when possible).

You will want potential instructors to fill out a resumé and a program outline similar to the program outline included here for your use.

Begin your selection process by looking for the following criteria:

- Certification, if required for the proposed course
- Reputation—How well known are the candidates in their fields?
- Degree(s)—Do the candidates have the necessary academic preparation?
- Affiliations with well-known agencies or groups
- Variety indicated in selected teaching tools
- Specific training in health fields related to the course
- Types of handouts proposed for use
- Flexibility in time and travel
- Outgoing personality
- Prior related experience and references

The agreement that you establish with your instructors can be a formal, written contract; an informal, verbal agreement; or a letter of agreement. Whatever method you choose, be sure you address issues such as required handouts, minimum and maximum course enrollments, cancellation notice, reimbursements for materials, and audiovisual requirements. The most important part of the agreement will be the pay, which can be any of the following variations:

- Hourly rate for teaching
- Hourly rate for teaching, preparation, and course planning (used if your program wants to "own" the course)
- Percentage split of registration fees
- Percentage split of net profit (after paying class costs)
- Fee per person attending class or event (often used with aerobics instructors)

Nationally, rates vary from $5 to $75 per hour, and the hourly rate mechanism is the most frequently used payment method.

Program managers usually develop quality control measures for their programs. Some offer continuing education for instructors in areas such as speaking skills

Program Outline

Name _____

Phone (Office) _____

(Home) _____

I. Program

• Title _____

• Behavioral objectives (audience will be able to do, know, identify, etc.):

• Class content and activities—list by session, if desired. Attach handouts:

• Audiovisual/equipment needs—list by session:

(Cont.)

II. Audience
- Describe target audience:

- Class size: Min. _____ Max. _____
- Class format: No. of sessions _____   No. of hr/session _____
- Can you lengthen/shorten program if needed?

- Class setup (tables, chairs, arrangement):

III. Instructor
- Attach resume
- How will you determine of your class is successful?

and communication; others use written evaluations from the audience or mail surveys to selected clients. Wainer (1986) suggests that the most valuable and least expensive tool is visiting classes and events, watching instructors, and listening to the reactions of the audience.

To summarize, Longe (1986) states that utilizing contract staff offers your program the following:

- Access to expertise
- Wider range of programming
- Flexible staffing levels (especially in large projects like employee wellness fairs)
- Savings on salary
- Easier hiring and firing

Contract labor is not without its disadvantages. Staff is contracted to perform specific duties, like teaching, so you can make few other demands unless they are agreed upon. There are no guarantees that your labor will be loyal to you— quitting is as easy for them as firing is for you. You may also find a lack of consistency in teaching styles, as well as with the image that each instructor projects for your institution. But, for the capable manager, these obstacles can be overcome with clear communication of expectations, making contract labor a valuable asset to any program.

LOCATION/FACILITY

There are almost as many choices in locations and facilities as there are in products, and, as it was for product selection, location depends largely on your targeted audience.

The place you do a program is important to consider by itself; factors like convenience and image may help consumers make their choice. Additionally, the location is the vessel, package, container—it is what contains or holds the programs you are offering and, instead of being considered as a decision separate from your products, should be an integral part of the product determination. In some instances, such as the opening of a fitness facility, your place is one of your products and takes on twice as much meaning in the scheme of program design.

Products of an educational and informational nature targeted for the community at large, such as seminars and health fairs, are best held in community locations, especially if your goals are to reach out to the community and create awareness of your hospital. Potential sites include churches and synagogues, parks and recreation facilities, apartment complex club rooms, meeting rooms in shopping malls, cooking stores with demonstration kitchens, schools and universities, and restaurants. Locations at community sites have the following advantages:

- Low cost or free rental
- Accessibility to community members
- No upkeep required
- Potential new audience from group that uses facility
- Free advertising through facility's newsletter or bulletin board
- Nonthreatening, "nonsick" environment

The space that you use also reaps the benefits of offering additional services to current clientele (you may offer incentive discounts to apartment complex dwellers or church members) and receiving free advertisement and recognition for supporting your program. However, using community facilities can have drawbacks, especially if your program management is remiss about checking the facility regularly. You may have little control over cleanliness, comfort, and room design; audiovisual equipment may not be available, necessitating that the instructor transport whatever is needed; registrants may need written directions to the location; and getting approval for use of the facility may be a lengthy process. Written agreements, searches for facility space well before scheduled program dates, use of portable audiovisual equipment, and spot checks of the facility can prevent problems and maintain quality programming.

Corporate clients as an audience typically prefer programs for their employees to be held on-site, meaning that your program has to be mobile and flexible. A specific facility, other than an administrative office, is not necessary. However, there may be a need to provide certain clinical testing on the hospital campus for corporate clients. In that case, sharing resources found in different departments is frequently cost-effective ("Facility Design," 1986). For example, exercise testing equipment used by cardiac rehabilitation, respiratory therapy, and health promotion can be clustered for space savings, convenience, and optimal use of equipment.

The most recent trend in locations is a wellness center, a relatively new strategy for the health care industry (Clair, 1987). Consultants in the field estimate that there are probably several hundred facilities, from 3,000- to 5,000-square-foot fitness and education centers housed in hospitals to 50,000-square-foot fitness complexes that copy commercial health clubs ("Administration: Experts," 1987). Those currently available usually fall into one of the following categories (Howell, 1987).

- Storefront health education centers. These are usually in heavily trafficked areas like shopping malls. Compared to other types of centers, these are usually low cost with minimal staffing, negligible equipment, and rental payments as the largest upkeep cost. Additionally, they create a strong community presence with good visibility.
- Centers inside a hospital. These were either added during a construction

project or provided a new way to use an empty wing. Usually they have up to 3,000 square feet and are inexpensive with minimal exercise equipment and a focus on being an employee benefit.

- Centers separate from the hospital but still in the campus. Although requiring major capital investments in equipment and construction, the center does not require the investment in land acquisition. Sales and marketing efforts lead to revenue generation, but limited access (location, parking) can deter customers. Physician referrals are a major audience because of convenience to patients and physician comfort with physical proximity of the center to the hospital.

- Centers built in a community location. These centers are expensive (some costing over $3 billion) because of the requisite land purchase, but they do increase the awareness of the hospital in other areas and may provide easier access for customers, thus generating more revenue and profit. Targeted locations are usually high-growth areas with discretionary income, although "medical malls," one-stop shopping centers for various health care needs, may be the location of the future.

The last category frequently includes joint ventures with existing commercial clubs, YMCAs, or even other hospitals. Woods (1987) claims that these can be healthy marriages for hospitals, achieving cost-effectiveness while maintaining a cutting edge in program design. Howell (1987) suggests that joint venturing is only one of a number of ways that wellness centers should strive to keep costs down. Additionally, he suggests sharing staff, facilities, and equipment with other related areas (cardiac rehabilitation, respiratory therapy, sports medicine, physical therapy) as was mentioned above in serving the corporate client; seeking out programs that are less technology-intensive, developing more on-site programs for corporations, increasing sales staff, and increasing the offering of recreation programs to avoid client burnout.

For the wellness center manager, the effect of today's growing restrictions on reimbursements coupled with the tremendous start-up costs of a full-service center indicate a need for accountability. Financial indicators, such as return on investment, revenue, and expense ratios; personnel indicators, such as staffing, intensity, and productivity; and utilization and sale indicators are terms and calculations that good business management demands. Clair (1987) outlines the potential implications of using these criteria and indicates that developing such standards of measurement is the best format for measuring achievement of program objectives and assuring program longevity.

PRICING HEALTH PROMOTION PRODUCTS

Pricing is an issue that many health promoters are uncomfortable addressing, mainly because of the business/marketing orientation that the decision requires and the newness of health promotion products. It would be simple if your program could be priced according to a set formula or a quick glance at your competition; but careful pricing requires a variety of approaches.

The first and most important factor to consider is your financial goal. If your financial goal is to be a community service and achieve high volume, your prices will probably be set low or free of charge. Remember, though, your audience will place more value on your programs, develop a more vested interest, and be more likely to maintain commitments (like registering and attending a course) if they pay a minimal fee. It is also easier later to institute price increases if you have established a pattern of charging fees than if your programs are always free.

A financial goal of breaking even requires that you calculate those points in your intended product sales. The direct and indirect costs of a program should be logged into an accounting mechanism (similar to Form 7.4) and totaled. Dividing that total cost by realistic participation projections will then give you an idea of the pricing required by your program to break even. Similarly, a goal of profit generation will have a percentage margin built in over and above the break-even cost.

When pricing your program, consider what the audience will receive for its money and be careful of sacrificing quality for volume. Your constituency may be willing to pay $15 for a CPR class if they receive quality instruction, handouts, thorough preparation for the certification test, snacks, and sterile equipment to practice on. Of course, the willingness to pay for quality must come from an audience that is ready to purchase. Bringing an audience from the stage of unaware to ready to buy can be accomplished through a front-end investment in low-cost or free programs that generate volume. That audience will then be your potential purchaser of quality-priced products.

Many managers claim that their programs are low-cost or free because they are acting as "loss leaders." Loss leaders are not merely programs that lose money, which is how some managers tend to define the term. They usually have one or two purposes within the organization. The first purpose is to use the initial underpricing to attract a large market. Once the audience is hooked, prices are increased to repay the front-end investment. The second purpose is for the underpricing to attract an audience that is subsequently fed into a service that has greater revenue potential, like physician practices or hospital diagnostic services. For example, a low-priced or free cholesterol screening may be considered a loss leader because the high-risk clients who are without a family physician will be fed into your hospital's physician referral network. The trickle-down effect may be strategically planned to impact the hospital's laboratory, from whom physicians may order lipid profiles for the referred clients, and dietary services, from whom they may order nutritional counseling. Eventually, a small percentage of these clients may become hospital patients to be treated for heart disease. Loss-leader services should equip themselves with tracking mechanisms that validate their effectiveness as a feeder.

The analysis that you performed earlier on your competitors will give you specific information on their products and corresponding fees, which are the next factors to consider in pricing. Beware of setting your prices at the same level as your competitors, unless there is a very large audience for the product. The risk here is in splitting an already small market and having a lower turnout than you anticipated.

Knowing competitors' fees can also be useful in performing pricing research. An informal research strategy is to take a captive audience and test its reactions to your product's planned price, which you set between the lowest-priced competitor and the highest-priced one. If the research indicates that the mid-range price you tested is too high, then there is room to move the price lower without matching the lowest-priced product. If research indicates that the selected price is overwhelmingly acceptable, then the price can be inched upward without topping the highest-priced product. For example, if you find that fitness assessments in your community range from the local YMCA charges of $40 to the local health club charges of $15, you could test a price of $30 with an available audience (an existing exercise class, hospital managers, or health fair participants). If a large majority respond positively, consider a price closer to $35. If the response does not indicate the volume you desire, move it closer to $25.

SUMMARY

Successful hospital health promotion programs, regardless of their focus—wellness center, community education, occupational health, or cardiac rehabilitation—have given top priority to making program design comprehensive and responsive to their audience's needs. Recognizing that your audience is your hospital administration as well as the purchasers of your service means that goal setting, corporate culture analysis, support seeking, and financial accountability are as important as position, product, price, and place. Utilizing the tools you have available, such as existing data, other hospital departments, and your own creativity, will be the base for a sound program design driven by a professional staff with market sensitivity and a clear sense of your program's position in the marketplace. Your carefully designed program will then contribute to the longevity of health promotion as a career field and to its permanence in the structure of health care organizations of the future.

REFERENCES

Administration: Experts are bullish on wellness centers. (1987). *Optimal Health*, **4**(2), 20-24.

Administration: Seeking the perfect fit: Hospitals and health promotion. (1986). *Optimal Health*, **2**(6), 14-18.

Aurin, R. (1986). The major mistakes programs make in advertising health promotion. *Promoting Health*, **7**(2), 1-3, 8.

Bellingham, R., & Tager, M. (1986). *Designing effective health promotion programs: The 20 skills for success.* Chicago: Great Performance.

Bills, S.S. (1986). Assessment project seeks better ways to identify consumer needs, interests. *Promoting Health,* 7(2), 4-9.

Bills, S.S., & Sherman, S.L. (1985). Packaged programs: Where to find them and what to consider in choosing one. *Promoting Health,* 6(4), 1-3, 10.

Clair, K.M. (1987). Wellness center management: Operating standards define effectiveness. *Optimal Health,* 3(6), 52-58.

Facility design: Clustered services are more efficient, save money. (1986). *Optimal Health,* 2(6), 14-18.

Health promotion young, but growing: *Optimal Health*/Price Waterhouse health promotion survey. (1987, July/August). *Optimal Health,* pp. 22-24.

Howell, P. (1987). Facility design: Strategic innovations in wellness centers. *Optimal Health,* 3(4), 48-54.

Longe, M.E. (1986). Working with contract staff. *Promoting Health,* 7(5), 4, 5, 10, 11.

Longe, M.E., & Wolf, A. (1984). *Promoting community health through innovative hospital-based programs.* Chicago: American Hospital Publishing.

Moosbrugger, M.C. (1986). Market research helps manage the risk of product development. *Promoting Health,* 7(5), 4, 5, 10, 11.

O'Donnell, M.P. (1986). *Design of workplace health promotion programs.* Royal Oak, MI: American Journal of Health Promotion.

Powell, D.R. (1985). Sizing up the packaged product. *Promoting Health,* 6(4), 4, 5, 11.

Powell, D.R., & Brownson, J. (1986). How to win friends among physicians. *Optimal Health,* 2(4), 36-39.

Roberts, N. (1987). Student internships provide extra hands, enhanced credibility for health promotion. *Promoting Health,* 8(2), 1-3.

Sol, N. (1986a). The feasibility of feasibility studies. *Optimal Health,* 3(2), 3.

Sol, N. (1986b). Professional management for a professional program. *Optimal Health,* 3(4), 13.

Sol, N. (1987). A peek at our profession. *Optimal Health,* 3(4), 13.

Wainer, N. (1986). Willingness to experiment creates financially viable community program. *Promoting Health,* 7(4), 1-3.

Woods, K.M. (1987). Creating a healthy marriage between hospital and commercial health club. *Promoting Health,* 8(4), 4-11.

CHAPTER 8

Marketing and Selling Hospital-Based Health Promotion

Jeffrey M. Bensky

A traditional approach to this topic might include discussions about the "four Ps of marketing" or "selling intangible services to consumers." However, a case can be made for approaching this chapter from a different perspective. It might be helpful to view marketing and sales from a strategic management perspective. An attempt has been made in this chapter to sequence a series of explanations to better prepare you to market and sell health promotion and related services from a business perspective. In fact, the purpose of this chapter is to assist you in thinking about improving your competitive position today and over the long term. Accordingly, this chapter will be organized by three issues:

- Understanding the strategic management process in developing your marketing plan
- Developing successful marketing strategies for health promotion and related services
- Executing the sales component of your marketing plan

A few caveats about what you should assume prior to reading this chapter: First, there are no answers to the marketing question. There are processes, and those will be reviewed here. Second, a more thorough understanding of the strategic issues attached to marketing will be helpful to understanding the business of marketing.

UNDERSTANDING THE STRATEGIC MANAGEMENT PROCESS

We all want to do the best we can in marketing our products and resources. However, it is important to first ask what are our strategies to accomplish this; more importantly, do our individual business unit's strategies fit our organization's strategies and goals? Clearly many United States businesses (including hospital-based health promotion) fall into the same traps. One critique of business planning weaknesses, *Steimers Report Card*, points to several pitfalls that have direct implications for your business. Those business weaknesses included, among others, the lack of

- clear identification of purpose,
- creative and strategic thinking,
- linkage to capital allocation, and
- acceptance and involvement of middle management.

Clearly, putting together marketing strategies, given the above weaknesses, will require a coordinated effort over time. Where does one begin? Keeping it simple will help.

Probably the best place to begin would be with an understanding of the definition of strategy. Strategic management simply means developing an integrated set of activities or actions aimed at achieving sustainable, competitive advantages for your business unit—that is, figuring out what will make you unique and distinctive in your marketplace so you can beat the competition today and in the future. A key attribute of developing successful marketing strategies is perspective. Most of our jobs continually emphasize helping others challenge certain lifestyle assumptions that they have held for many years. Changing assumption, beliefs, perspectives, and behaviors is, in large part, a critical factor in determining our eventual program success. It is also true that in developing marketing strategies, altering our business perspectives will assist us in achieving those sustainable competitive advantages.

In our business, market planning perspectives have traditionally assumed a view of the world the way we would like it to be. For the most part, marketing and market planning has been very experiential (how we feel the market will react), judgmental, and short-term (what we need to do to make our budget); has had limited participation in its own development (either the plan was given to us, or we developed it in a one-day retreat); and is internally focused (what capabilities we have). This is not to say that all hospital-based health promotion efforts have this perspective. But the development in this business area and other non–health promotion businesses suggest this planning process to be fairly typical.

In contrast, a strategic management perspective for market planning should include a view of the world the way it actually exists. This approach emphasizes a new perspective on marketing and market planning. This process is very dynamic and open to change, analytical and factual (marketing decisions are based upon different forms of research data), and it is long-term in orientation with input from a variety of participants. Most importantly, it is externally focused. That is, it is market-driven—based upon various factors that are currently present or will be present in the marketplace. The lifestyle analogies are very clear; when assisting someone to lose weight, change diets, or start an exercise program, we provide factual, analytical data that is open to change and long-term oriented. We know the results when we work with a person who has only short-term goals and is totally internally focused only on judgments and feelings. Similarly, strategic management helps people gain a perspective that is especially important for marketing their businesses. As depicted in Figure 8.1, strategic management provides a very high external focus with a long-term horizon. This, compared to an annual budgeting exercise, requires a lot more long-term thinking and planning.

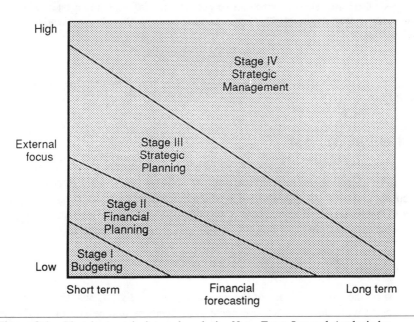

Figure 8.1. Planning matrix internal analysis. *Note.* From Internal Analysis by Price Waterhouse, 1987. Copyright 1987 by Price Waterhouse. Reprinted by permission.

Achieving the plane of strategic management requires an understanding of the ongoing processes. Figure 8.2 demonstrates this process in detail. The following paragraphs provide and explain the components and key issues in this process.

Strategic Role and Objectives

It is important that the business unit have a clear understanding of its role. It is best to start with this definition to orient the business objectives. Usually this

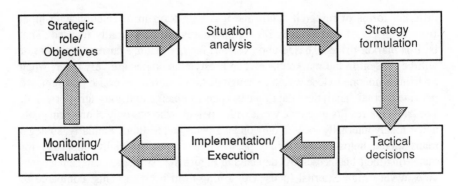

Figure 8.2. Strategic management versus strategic planning. This ongoing process suggests there are relative boundaries between the stages. *Note*. From Internal Analysis by Price Waterhouse, 1987. Copyright 1987 by Price Waterhouse. Reprinted by permission.

role is adjusted to meet the external perspective. It will include high-level goals and objectives.

Situation Analysis

Traditionally, this component has included many different tasks. Generally, it includes assessing the internal (capabilities and resources) and external (market demand and competition) factors that will help a business achieve sustainable competitive advantages. The outcome of this component is a thorough understanding of what is happening in the marketplace and what it will take to win there.

Strategy Formulation

Based on thorough analyses of the data and ongoing discussions, the marketing strategies will address what will make your business unique and distinctive in the marketplace and what it will take to sustain your competitive advantages over time. Obviously, these strategies will not just "appear;" they require some creative problem solving.

Tactical Decisions

Based upon your chosen strategies, what are the tactics necessary to achieve success? This area is commonly the one most people incorrectly address first. It needs to be based on the first three issues listed above. It is the implementation planning of who, what, when, where, and how. It is deciding which strategy will have the best cost/benefit ratio.

Implementation and Execution

Obviously, the best test of your strategies and tactics is whether they stand up in the marketplace. Implement and execute as soon as it is reasonable to test your strategies.

Monitoring and Evaluating

Especially in the marketing area, it is of crucial importance in any business to measure your effectiveness in an ongoing manner. Adjustments can be made to the strategic role, strategies, and tactics through objective measurement. As suggested in the preceding descriptions, this strategic management process is ongoing. It is dynamic and open to change through all types of data and information. The key to successful implementation of marketing strategies is measurement, consistency, and maintenance of an external perspective.

Applying strategic management principles to the hospital health promotion business would require many more pages than allotted here. What is important is focusing on specific marketing and sales issues.

DEVELOPING SUCCESSFUL MARKETING STRATEGIES FOR HEALTH PROMOTION

To begin to build your marketing strategies it is assumed you have answered the following questions:

* How does my parent organization strategically position my business unit?
* What are we all about as a business unit?
* What is going on in the market?

There are many important variables that affect the answers to these questions. For example, knowing your hospital's strategic plan as it applies to your business unit and related services is a critical area of analysis. Does your hospital's plan refer directly or indirectly to your business unit? If so, how? If not, what are the implications? The answers to these and related questions will obviously have a direct impact on how you will strategically define your business unit's role and objectives.

Knowing what is going on in your market includes first understanding your existing competition but also becoming aware of potential competition that might arise from new entrants (as a result of creating an attractive business), bargaining abilities of the suppliers and buyers of your services, as well as determining whether substitutes for your services are possible. In short, it is understanding the economic forces driving your business and your competitors. It is not sufficient to superficially understand what your competition is doing; you must know what they will do in response to your marketing strategies and how you will be affected by any of the four factors mentioned previously. (For a more detailed discussion of these factors, please review *Competitive Advantage: Creating and Sustaining Superior Performance*, by Michael E. Porter, published by The Free Press, 1985.)

After thoroughly understanding your competition, the understanding of your market then dictates knowing what the key business factors are for each identified, target-market segment—in other words, understanding what values will motivate a buyer to purchase your services or products. The process of assessing these factors and values can be one of the most important determinants of your success over the long term. It directly impacts your advertising and direct sales efforts. However, before identifying the key buying factors, it is important to identify your target market segments. Traditionally, these target market segments are drawn from demographic analyses (i.e., understanding population trends in your marketplace, especially as they affect purchasing decisions) and sometimes from primary market research (i.e., directly asking your marketplace, through phone surveys, face-to-face interviews, mailed questionnaires, or focus groups, a series of questions designed to answer how they make purchasing decisions). An example of developing this consumer decision model for various target market segments is shown in Figures 8.3 and 8.4. These figures are from actual models

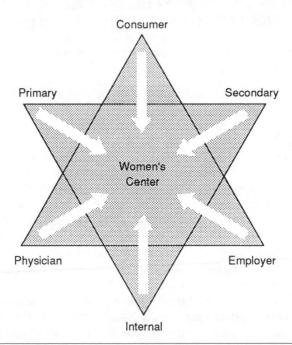

Figure 8.3.   Proprietary model of how data impacts decision making. *Note.* From *Proprietary Model* by National Research Corporation, 1986, Lincoln, NE: Author. Copyright 1986 by National Research Corporation. Reprinted by permission.

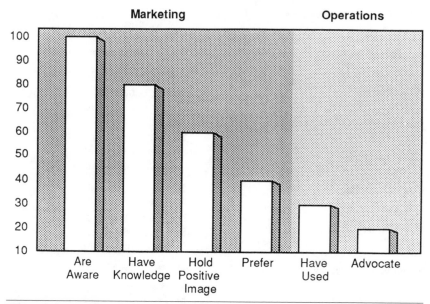

Figure 8.4. Proprietary model of consumer health decisions based on thousands of consumer interviews. *Note.* From *Proprietary Model* by National Research Corporation, 1986, Lincoln, NE: Author. Copyright 1986 by National Research Corporation. Reprinted by permission.

used by a leading health care marketing research firm, National Research Corporation of Lincoln, Nebraska. Figure 8.3 depicts how different sources of data affect the decision about a particular issue. Figure 8.4 depicts NRC's health care consumer decision model based upon thousands of consumer interviews. This model clearly demonstrates the marketing implications of collecting market research data (e.g., if you know a certain percentage of a group is aware of a service but a smaller-than-depicted average holds a positive image of or prefers that service, the marketing implications are clear).

Knowing your target markets has clear advantages. In a recent *Optimal Health*/Price Waterhouse survey, hospital-based health promotion managers were asked to list their target market segments and the related products and services they were purchasing. Table 8.1 depicts this information. What is most important to note is, though there are common products for different targets, purchasing motives can be and are different.

If you have made it this far in answering the first three questions outlined in the beginning of this section, then you can now proceed to actually determining the development of your marketing strategies. The key questions to answer in developing your strategies are, What are your options? What options should you pursue, and how?

With respect to the first question, there are four possible answers. These are depicted in Figure 8.5 (page 137). Again, adapted from Porter (1985), these

Table 8.1   Target Markets

Target markets	Related products
Corporations	Health education Health risk appraisal (HRA) Screening Smoking cessation Stress management⎤ Tie Occupational health⎦
General public	Health education Fitness Nutrition/Weight control Smoking cessation Stress management
Employees/Sr. citizens	Health education Fitness Screening Nutrition/Weight control Smoking cessation
Women	Health education ⎤ Tie Nutrition/Weight control⎦ OB/GYN⎤ Screening⎥ Tie Fitness⎦ Prenatal Birthing Osteoporosis

Note. From "Health Promotion Young, But Growing: The *Optimal Health*/Price Waterhouse Health Promotion Survey," 1987 (July/August), *Optimal Health*, pp. 22-24. Copyright 1987 by *Optimal Health* and Price Waterhouse. Reprinted by permission.

marketing strategies suggest that positioning your business depends upon first, how broad your scope of competition will be, and second, what will give you the most competitive advantages—cost leadership or differentiation.

Table 8.2 (p. 138) reviews some of the issues that can assist you in making those decisions. Closely analyzing the required skills, resources, and organization's variables will direct your overall marketing strategies. Some additional comments might be helpful.

Cost leadership as a strategy requires skills, resources, and organizational standards typically not found in hospital-based health promotion businesses. Cost

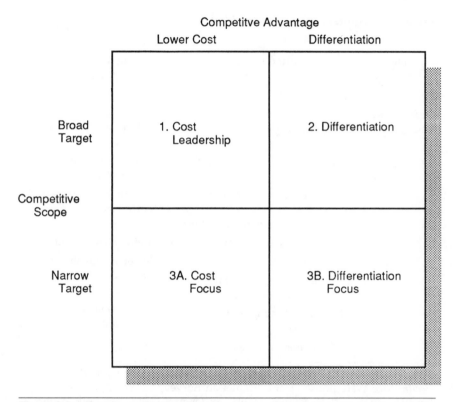

Figure 8.5. Generic competitive strategies. *Note.* Adapted from *Competitive Advantage: Creating and Sustaining Superior Performance* (p. 12) by M. Porter, 1985, New York: MacMillan.

leadership means more than cutting your prices. It means having the ability to lower operating costs more than your competitors. Do you know your exact operating costs by product line? Can you control them? Can you sustain yourself within a competitive marketplace where marginal pricing leads to increased price competition, lower profits, or even losses? If you can answer yes to these questions, as well as positively address the skills, resources, and organizational requirement issues, then cost leadership might be your marketing strategy.

The other marketing strategy is achieved by being unique and distinctive in the marketplace. Can you market unique value(s) in your market? The skills, resources, and organizational requirements more closely resemble a hospital and hospital-based health promotion business unit. However, several critical variables remain. Can you identify specific values that people will buy? (This assumes the customers can actually differentiate products and services based upon value.) For example, IBM, Rolex, and Audi make judgments regarding values on which customers base their purchasing decisions. These values affect their product design,

Table 8.2   Requirements of Generic Strategies

Generic strategy	Required skills and resources	Organizational requirements
Overall cost leadership	□ A lot of capital	□ Tight cost controls and systems
	□ Intense labor supervision	□ Highly structured organization
	□ Easy-to-assemble products	□ Quantitative targets and incentives
	□ Low cost-distribution system	
Differentiation	□ Strong marketing capabilities	□ Highly coordinated
	□ Creative R&D	□ Subjective/Qualitative measures versus quantitative
	□ Longstanding corporate reputation for quality	
	□ Strong cooperation from channels	□ Highly skilled professionals
Focus	□ Combination of above	□ Combination of above

Note. From "Health Promotion Young, But Growing: The *Optimal Health*/Price Waterhouse Health Promotion Survey," 1987 (July/August), *Optimal Health*, pp. 22-24. Copyright 1987 by *Optimal Health* and Price Waterhouse. Reprinted by permission.

production, marketing, and distribution. They have a highly coordinated effort with highly skilled professionals delivering their products. They also assume that people will pay for these values (and they do!). Can you make the same assumptions about health promotion and related services? Probably not. That is why a more focused approach to marketing strategies for hospital-based health promotion is more reasonable.

It may not be impossible to assume a cost leadership or differentiation marketing strategy, but given the turmoil in health care and hospital-based business units such as health promotion, a more focused approach is more likely to succeed. Specifically, focusing on a narrow target market segment and attempting to assume cost leadership and differentiation goals has a higher probability of success. As a business you will be more likely to meet these requirements:

• Better labor supervision
• Tighter cost controls
• Stronger marketing capabilities
• Better use of corporate reputation for quality

- Better coordination
- Use of highly skilled professionals

This does not mean a hospital-based health promotion business cannot assume a cost or differentiation strategy. Rather, it means your target markets may not be able to differentiate upon value across the continuum of services you have to offer, and your business probably cannot assume a cost leadership across the array of target markets available. The time has come for hospital-based health promotion businesses to prove their worth as profitable businesses. Starting with achievable marketing strategies may be a step in the right direction. Here is a checklist of questions that are important in developing your marketing strategies.

- What will make us unique and distinctive?
- What will give us sustainable competitive advantages?
- What are the key buying factors of our target markets?
- How do our targets respond to different channels?
- How can we be cost-effective and achieve economies of scale for our product line?

The key to a successful marketing strategy is taking the time to collect the information necessary to answer these important questions.

EXECUTING THE MARKETING PLAN THROUGH DIRECT SALES

Now that your planning process has been completed (including the development of a tactically oriented implementation plan), it is time to make it happen. There are many aspects of execution, including advertisement, promotions, and public relations. However, it is clear that one of the most effective means of generating revenues for this type of business (intangible services) is that of direct sales. Thousands of pages have been written on the aspects of the direct sales process (techniques for selling, managing the sales process, etc.). The intent of this section is to provide a brief overview of this process and to emphasize its importance. Currently, the perception of the field suggests that direct sales is an important variable in the success of a health promotion business. As Table 8.3 demonstrates, based upon the recent *Optimal Health*/Price Waterhouse survey, salespeople are involved, but the business and marketing planning processes might not be up to date to direct their efforts.

We know the people are out selling, but they may not be receiving the necessary planning support. Furthermore, as Table 8.4 suggests (again from the *Optimal Health*/Price Waterhouse survey), other forms of support to the direct sales approach are available but are relatively limited in terms of marketing dollars allocated. From any perspective, the development of a direct sales component will

Table 8.3 Business/Marketing Planning and Sales

Hospital size	Percent employing salespeople	Average number of salespeople	Percent of hospitals with a business plan	Percent of business plans developed within the past 2 years	Percent of hospitals with a marketing plan	Percent of marketing plans developed within the past 2 years
Fewer than 100 beds	10	2	24	62	34	9
100-299 beds	21	1	39	48	49	9
300-499 beds	29	1	38	39	49	9
500-749 beds	45	2	57	43	76	10
750 or more beds	20	10	30	0	40	25

Note. From "Health Promotion Young, But Growing: The *Optimal Health*/Price Waterhouse Health Promotion Survey," 1987 (July/August), *Optimal Health*, pp. 22-24. Copyright 1987 by *Optimal Health* and Price Waterhouse. Reprinted by permission.

Table 8.4 Marketing and Sales

Media and planning sources	Average dollars spent annually	% of marketing budget
Television	11,130	25
Radio ads	6,870	13
Magazine ads	10,024	12
Newspaper ads	8,987	43
Public relations/Promotions	8,991	26
In-house	2,478	16
Planning	4,872	9
Agency fees	9,760	13

Note. From "Health Promotion Young, But Growing: The *Optimal Health*/Price Waterhouse Health Promotion Survey," 1987 (July/August), *Optimal Health*, pp. 22-24. Copyright 1987 by *Optimal Health* and Price Waterhouse. Reprinted by permission.

significantly add to the overall marketing process but, more importantly, will provide a linkage among business units and product lines, and will be able to make tangible most of the services being offered.

To establish a direct sales approach also takes some planning and understanding of several important principles:

- Understanding the planned sales call
- Sales planning and management
- Personalities and types within sales

Sales has a variety of connotations. Though you won't find these definitions in the dictionary, sales is

- Behavioral engineering—managing a variety of behaviors over time to reach a variety of mutually beneficial goals,
- Persuasive communications—the ability to give logical reasons through the five senses regarding identified values for purchasing a service, and
- Mind share—the ability to ''capture'' a portion of a person's brain that will categorize your product as unique and distinctive.

For the purpose of this chapter and hospital-based health promotion services, we will assume a consulting sales model. That is, the salesperson is a consultant who is required to ask more questions than provide solutions to problems in an active problem-solving approach. The planned sales call can assist a buyer to move along the motivational continuum from nonawareness to awareness to interest to positive attitude for the service to commitment for and finally to executing the buying decision. Obviously, a coordinated effort among the other aspects of tactical marketing (advertisement, promotions, and public relations) will assist the direct sales call. The mind-set of the buyer will also influence the process; however, it is the direct sales effort that links these efforts and provides some connection to a typically intangible service. For example, direct sales helps a buyer to understand and see the values of looking better, feeling better, and having more energy. Mention has been made several times of the concept of a planned sales call. The exact steps of this model are as follows:

- Contact and qualify
- Entry
- Proposed presentation and negotiation
- Close

In general there are several factors that influence these steps. First, 64% of all sales calls in the service business are made to the wrong person. Second, in health promotion the final sale takes an average of 6 months and five to seven meetings. Understanding and managing the above steps can significantly increase your effectiveness and efficiency.

The first step of contacting and qualifying is generally known as lead generation. There are a variety of methods to generate leads, and they all have their advantages. It is important to note, however, that these methods should be coordinated and carefully tracked. They include

- lists and books;
- networking;
- speeches and seminars presented to groups, clubs, and organizations;
- advertising, promotion, and publicity; and
- in-house/image campaign/word-of-mouth.

Once leads are generated, it is important to qualify them by noting where they are on the motivational continuum (e.g., are they aware of or interested in your service, and are they the "right" people to be talking with about your services?). For example, are you talking with an ally (someone within the company who will support your efforts but will not make the decision) or the decision maker? Do you need to go through the ally first before getting to the decision maker? It is important to determine this during the initial step. There are a variety of methods of accomplishing this tactic, including qualifying phone calls and planned social contacts. What is key to this step is your need to know as much as possible about the group or company and individual decision makers *prior* to talking with them. An informed salesperson can more easily qualify the potential customer!

This step can and should take some time to carefully investigate and understand your customer.

Assuming you have qualified your potential customer, the next step is entry. The goals of this step are fairly straightforward:

- Explain the concept behind your services.
- Assess needs.
- Elicit a request for a proposal.

Though simple in theory, in practice the ability to connect the three objectives in a smooth, flowing process is the challenge. Several important issues require explanation. First, the products and services we are "selling" are mostly intangible. Therefore, explaining the "concepts" of these services requires an understanding of perceived value. Since the service or product is intangible, the sales process must help the buyer to understand its more tangible aspects. One can make intangible services tangible by connecting the specific service or product with a perceived touch or actual visualization. For example, how would you make exercises or weight loss tangible? Can you state these products or services so someone can touch the results? Most often when explaining services and products, salespeople in health promotion use terms that depict the features (characteristics of the product or service), advantages (how a feature will help them), and benefits (depends upon the explicit need of the customer). What is important is that during any explanation, the salesperson accomplish two goals: Make the service or product tangible in terms the buyer can identify, and match the service or product to the buyer's explicit needs.

Ultimately your sales ability and results will depend upon accomplishing many tasks. However, clearly your ability to ask the right questions to assess a need and then match the appropriate service or product to that need will be critical. There are a variety of questions that can elicit responses regarding a customer's needs:

- Situation questions—these will uncover implied needs about the customer situation. What in your current corporate climate will support these kinds of services?

- Problem questions—these will encourage the customer to state implied needs. Is the incidence of cardiovascular disease in your company higher than your industry norm?

- Implication questions—these will help the customer make extrinsic any implied need. What would happen if we identified 30% of your work force as smokers?

- Need/payoff questions—these will help the customer to state desired solutions. What type of results would you envision if we intervened to address this identified problem?

There are many different categories and types of questions. The key is to be able to assess potential customer needs from a variety of perspectives. The third objective of this step is to match services and products to the customer's explicit needs. This part of step two requires handling objectives and using persuasive communication to demonstrate your problem-solving approach. The goal of having the customer ask for a proposal is not as difficult to achieve as making sure the proposal will meet the customer's internal and external needs. Sometimes, a customer will ask for a proposal just to put you off. In this case you may not have elicited all the needs or handled the objections appropriately. When handling objections there are four principles to observe: always listen, ask questions, restate the objection, and always "get in step."

There is nothing wrong with objections; in fact, they usually assist both parties in understanding more clearly each other's perspective. It is how you manage the objection that matters. If you have done your job and matched the customer's needs with the appropriate service or product, it is time for the next step—negotiation.

Several books have been written about negotiation, so it will not be covered here. However, as in the entry stage, communication (understanding and meeting implied needs) will cue your success. Communication through a proposal is usually the way services are offered. Your proposal can take several forms but in general should

- reflect the data collected to date about the customer's needs and characteristics;
- provide conclusions regarding needs and problems;
- detail an approach to solving the problems and meeting the needs;
- provide a summary of recommended alternatives to select from within budget considerations; and
- provide the professional arrangements you will use to implement the solutions (staff, timing, fees, etc.).

Negotiating the details of this proposal occurs during and after a presentation, formal or informal. It is critical to directly attack the problems and answer them honestly and fairly.

The final step in the planned sales call—closing the sale—can happen at any time but should be consciously planned. The most successful method of closing is to make a request for commitment or consent to go forward. The related questions usually follow an ongoing summary of needs matched to recommendations. It is critical at this step not to be perceived as too "pushy" or too "meek." Rather, a proactive and positive approach will be helpful. Questions such as how and when will the decision to purchase these products be made will enhance your understanding of when to ask for the business. Expecting customers to close the deal on their own probably will not be as successful as assisting them directly. For example, asking the question, "What will it take for you to make a positive decision?" might be an avenue for exploration.

There are several thoughts that are important to reemphasize before reviewing some of the key characteristics for sales success. First, the model and approaches presented are fluid (i.e., the steps interact with each other but do not necessarily always occur in this order). Second, your ability to tailor this process to fit your own needs and style will be important for success. We encourage active participation in sales training to fine-tune your skills. Experience and time are your biggest allies in the sales process. Use them!

Related issues are important to note briefly because of their impact on the planned sales call: tracking and accountability, and personality/types.

With respect to sales planning and management, one of the most critical issues is tracking your efforts in the most concrete manner feasible for your situation. Minimally, three objectives should be written for each client (primary, secondary, and tertiary), and ongoing notes should be made as to your accomplishment or modification of these goals. Meeting dates, times, and names of people involved will assist you in ascertaining trends and achievement of goals and objectives. Prior to implementing any sales system, it is important to plan the system and develop a tracking method.

There are literally hundreds of books written on personality and types as related to the sales process. There are many personality variables that will directly affect your success. Two such factors are these: First, you will be relating to, discovering, advocating, and supporting various people with various needs; successful attributes include establishing credibility, being empathetic, active listening, honesty, and problem solving. Second, there are a variety of different types of people. Do you know what your type is and how you interact with other types? There are a variety of tests designed to assist people in understanding their types. One such test, the Myers-Briggs Type Indicator (Myers-Briggs & McCaulley, 1985) has identified four interactive variables with thousands of permutations and implications. The variables are

- perception (sensing, intuition),
- judgment (thinking, feeling),
- attitudes (extraversion-introversion), and
- dealing with the outer world (judgment, perception).

Space does not permit detailed elaboration here. However, it should be clear that identifying your type and how you interact with others will enhance your sales abilities.

SUMMARY

What began with a theoretical discussion of strategic management as applied to marketing has ended with a technical description of execution. Throughout the entire chapter several themes have been emphasized:

- Action without planning is fatal; planning without action is futile.

- An external perception (the world as it really exists) with a dynamic, fact-based planning process that involves others will directly affect your success.
- Strategic marketing means designing a set of activities that will sustain your competitive advantages over the long term.
- Know what targets you can reasonably and profitably attract. Included in this are understanding your target's key buying factors and your capabilities of delivering the right services while sustaining your competitive advantages.
- Execution through a planned consulting sales process will be the thread that holds together your marketing plan.
- Remember, we continually deal with assumptions and beliefs as they relate to lifestyle and health promotion. Do you know what your strategic assumptions are for success?

BIBLIOGRAPHY

Health promotion young, but growing: *Optimal Health*/Price Waterhouse health promotion survey. (1987, July/August). *Optimal Health,* pp. 22-24.

Myers-Briggs, I., & McCaulley, M.H. (1985). *Manual: A guide to the development and use of the Myers-Briggs Type Indicator.* Palo Alto, CA: Consulting Psychologists Press.

National Research Corporation. (1986). *Proprietary model.* Lincoln, NE: Author.

Porter, M. (1985). *Competitive advantage: Creating and sustaining superior performance.* New York: Macmillan.

PART IV

The Multidisciplinary Approach to Hospital Health Promotion

Health promotion programs by their very nature involve a great many disciplines. These programs must attend to unhealthy behaviors that have nutritional, medical, physiological, psychological, and social implications. Providing a comprehensive health program to any group or individual requires involvement of a variety of experts. For this reason hospitals are probably the best program providers. They are endowed with a complement of medical and allied health professionals with expertise in every area of health promotion. No other program provider has these resources. No other provider can meet the need for comprehensive, multidisciplinary health promotion delivery as competently as hospitals.

Chapter 9 explores the physician's critical role in health promotion and hospital use of health promotion. Chapter 10 discusses the nurse's role as the key professional historically responsible for providing health promotion. Chapter 10 reviews how this role has evolved and how it is changing. Chapter 11 describes the role of administrators and shows how their perceptions and requirements have dictated the process of health care and health promotion. Chapter 12 examines the contribution of the many other medical and allied health professionals and shows how these professionals make the hospital uniquely useful in health promotion.

CHAPTER 9

The Physician's Role in Health Promotion

Stephen M. Schmitz

Physicians have made numerous valuable contributions to the study and practice of health promotion. These contributions have occurred in the areas of scientific research, public health, health policy, and patient care. Many of these contributions have gone unrecognized by other health promotion providers who in fact utilize much of the scientific research in their work. Physicians will continue to make major contributions to the health promotion field, and their role will expand in the future.

Although physicians have made important contributions to health promotion, many physicians currently have little or no involvement in it. The two major reasons for this are physician training and the health care system's expectations. Physician training occurs almost exclusively in the mechanistic, disease-treatment model, and most physicians have limited knowledge and experience in the delivery of health promotion. The health care system, including hospitals, patients, the reimbursement system, and the media, regularly acknowledges and rewards successes in the disease-treatment realm. As long as physicians are educated and rewarded preferentially in the disease-treatment mode, only small gains can be expected in physicians' delivery of health promotion.

Tremendous potential does exist for changing the limited contributions of many physicians. Major changes are now occurring that make this next decade an excellent one for the growth of the discipline of health promotion. Interest in health promotion is high for many reasons, including personal, financial, and societal. Because physicians are perceived as the best single source of health information, they are in an excellent position to facilitate the spread of health promotion to a large population. Most physicians are interested in learning how to influence the health lifestyles of their patients and are optimistic about their ability to do so.

It is vital to capitalize on this physician interest in health promotion. However, physicians need more than excellent learning opportunities to practice health promotion. They need to practice in an environment that encourages and rewards the learning and delivery of health promotion. This environment is attainable and is the optimal environment for the proliferation of the field.

HEALTH PROMOTION AND DISEASE PREVENTION DEFINED

When discussing the role of physicians in health promotion, it is important to make the distinction between health promotion and disease prevention. These definitions were used in chapter 1: "Health promotion is the maintenance and enhancement of existing levels of health through the implementation of effective programs, services, and policies" (Goodstadt, Simpson, & Loranger, 1987, p. 61); and "Preventive medicine is the application of biomedical and epidemiological science to the promotion of health and to the elimination or early detection of disease in populations and individuals" (Jonas, 1981, p. 9). Although some argue that there is a large difference between health promotion and preventive medicine, the similarities are far more numerous than the differences. The prime focus of preventive medicine is risk reduction, which is based on a disease model of health care. The predominant focus of health promotion is health enhancement, which is valuable aside from its obvious effect on disease prevention.

The disease prevention model and the health promotion model overlap at numerous points. For example, health promotion would advocate regular aerobic exercise as a means of enhancing health in many areas, while preventive medicine would encourage it in order to prevent cardiovascular disease, obesity, and osteoporosis. The rationale for preventive medicine is perceived as "negative," or disease-oriented, while health promotion is "positive," or health-oriented. While this may be so, the outcome of practices in both disciplines is often the same.

Rather than focusing on the differences between health promotion and disease prevention, it is better to emphasize the similarities. It is important to realize that the continuum of our health care system includes disease treatment, disease prevention, and health promotion, and that disease treatment is in the preeminent position. Before the health care system becomes more health promotion-oriented, it must become more disease prevention-oriented. This is no small task, but is an important one for the evolution of health promotion. Recognizing and expanding the discipline of preventive medicine will only help this evolution.

TRADITIONAL AREAS OF PHYSICIAN CONTRIBUTIONS

When analyzing the current role of physicians in health promotion, it is important to recognize that their contributions have come from different areas of the health care setting. Physicians are actively involved in research, public health, academic, and clinical practice. Clinicians are typically involved with individual patients, and the medical setting is often an office, clinic, or hospital. In this setting, the primary focus is the specific problem of a particular individual. Physicians engaged in research, academia, or public health are involved with large populations. They are more concerned with epidemiology, risk factor stratification, and long-term effects of certain interventions. While clinicians are engaged mostly in the present, public health physicians attempt to deal with the future. There are numerous opportunities to practice health promotion in both settings, though the approaches are sometimes quite different.

Public health physicians have made many significant contributions to health care in this country. These include the discovery and advocacy of measures that have improved food and water supplies, sanitation practices, and nutrition. Medical research led to the discovery of vaccines and antibiotics, which dramatically decreased morbidity and mortality from infectious diseases. These discoveries are largely responsible for the increase in life expectancy that has occurred over the past 80 years. Physicians have played key roles in the discoveries, and their implementation of policies have made them available to large numbers of people.

Physicians have spearheaded numerous research studies that form the scientific basis for health promotion. The Framingham study (Kannel & Gordon, 1974), the Alameda County study (Belloc & Breslow, 1972), the Stanford Three Community study (Farquhar, 1978), the Multiple Risk Factor Intervention Trial (MRFIT) study (1982), and the Pooling Project Research Group (1978) are just a small number of studies that physician-researchers have initiated. These studies are vital to both preventive medicine and health promotion, and future research will heavily influence the success of both.

Physicians involved in academia are actively engaged in research and the education of medical students and physicians. In this capacity, these physicians influence the practices of the 15,000 new physicians who graduate from medical schools each year. The success of the effort to integrate preventive medicine and health promotion into the medical curriculum is limited by the health care system's bias toward disease treatment. Despite this, efforts are ongoing to improve the undergraduate and postgraduate teaching of preventive medicine, and significant gains in physicians' practice of health promotion are expected.

A small number of physicians have played important roles since the growth of the wellness movement. Halbert Dunn, a retired public health physician, is credited with initiating the movement with a series of lectures and the book, *High Level Wellness*, that for the first time viewed health as more than the absence of disease. John Travis, who was inspired by Dunn's work, created the Wellness Resource Center in Mill Valley, California. Travis is especially committed to helping educate physicians and other health care professionals about wellness. William Hettler has been instrumental in the development of the National Wellness Institute and of a university-based wellness model now used in different parts of the country. These physicians have stepped beyond traditional physician roles, and their success in these roles will help pave the way for additional physician involvement.

THE UNREALIZED POTENTIAL OF PHYSICIANS IN HEALTH ADVOCACY

Improvement in the health promotion skills of practicing physicians has great potential for influencing the health practices of the populace. Physicians are perceived as the single most reliable and credible source of health information. Physicians see large numbers of patients daily, and these patients often have a heightened receptivity to recommendations during this time of illness. Physicians as a group are excellent role models, having made impressive lifestyle changes within the past 20 years.

In spite of this, the advocacy of health promotion by practicing physicians is disappointing. Physicians frequently underestimate their impact on their patients' lifestyles. A study by Russell, Wilson, Taylor, and Baker (1979) on smoking cessation recommendations by general practitioners revealed that a single 2-minute verbal intervention combined with the distribution of a pamphlet resulted in a 5% one-year smoking cessation rate. Studies on breast self-exam practices show that physician instruction is instrumental in women's attitudes toward and practice of breast self-exam (Baines, 1984). If every physician involved in patient care consistently inquired about health lifestyle practices, an incredible impact could be made on the health of this country.

Perceptions of Ineffectiveness

However, most practicing physicians do not consistently ask questions in the health promotion area. The reasons are manifold and are related to physicians' beliefs about health promotion. Studies by Sobal, Valente, Muncie, Levine, and DeForge (1985); Collins (1986); Valente, Sobal, Muncie, Levine, & Antlitz (1986); and Wechsler, Levine, Idelson, Rohman, and Taylor (1983) have examined in detail physicians' beliefs about health promotion. These studies indicate that there is fairly good agreement across specialties when rating the importance of certain health behaviors. Physicians consistently rated eliminating cigarette smoking, wearing protective equipment, avoiding excess caloric intake, eating a balanced diet, and always wearing seat belts as most important (see Table 9.1). Interestingly, these five behaviors are dependent upon individual behavior and, until morbidity or mortality occur, are unrelated to the typical patient encounter. Although 97% of physicians routinely gather information on smoking, alcohol, drugs, stress, exercise, and diet, only 27% routinely ask about all these behaviors.

Only 3% to 8% of physicians feel "very successful" and 40% to 57% "somewhat successful" when trying to help their patients make behavior changes (see Table 9.2). Collins (1986) found similar overall results with Tennessee physicians,

Table 9.1 Physicians' Beliefs About the Importance of 25 Health Behaviors for Promoting the Health of the Average Person

Health behavior	Very important (%)	Important (%)	Unimportant (%)	Very unimportant (%)
Eliminate cigarette smoking	94	6	0	0
Protective equipment/clothing around harmful substances	82	15	1	0
Avoid excess caloric intake	73	24	2	0
Eat a balanced diet	68	29	3	1
Always use seat belts	67	26	6	1
Knowledge about drug contents	59	33	7	1
Avoid unnecessary x-rays	52	39	7	2
Avoid saturated fat foods	52	42	6	1
Drink alcohol moderately	52	31	12	5
Eliminate cigar smoking	43	46	10	2
Avoid undue stress	42	48	9	1
Decrease salt consumption	41	50	7	2
Avoid high-cholesterol foods	41	46	11	2
Eliminate pipe smoking	40	47	12	2
Eat breakfast every morning	33	40	21	6

(Cont.)

Table 9.1 (Continued)

Health behavior	Very important (%)	Important (%)	Unimportant (%)	Very unimportant (%)
Get 7 hours sleep each night	30	46	20	4
Limit daily caffeine intake	23	54	19	4
Annual physical examination	28	41	25	5
Aerobic activity 3 times/week	27	45	22	7
Practice relaxation methods	20	47	26	8
Minimize sugar intake	15	47	30	8
Baseline exercise test	12	33	36	19
Drink no alcohol at all	15	21	32	33
Annual exercise test	6	23	39	33
Take vitamin supplements	6	21	40	34
Mean for all 25 behaviors	41	36	16	7

Note. From ''Physicians' Beliefs About the Importance of 25 Health Promoting Behaviors'' by J. Sobal, C.M. Valente, H.L. Muncie, D.M. Levine, and B.R. LeForge, 1985, *American Journal of Public Health*, **75**, p. 1427. Copyright 1985 by *American Public Health Association*. Used with permission.

and found that for certain interventions, namely blood pressure control, physicians felt "very successful" more than 34% of the time. The confidence that physicians have in their ability to deal with behavior change will affect their willingness to work with patients on behavior change issues. Confidence varies, depending on the type of intervention, with physicians feeling "very prepared" to counsel patients most often on smoking habits and least often on stress issues (see Table 9.2).

Table 9.2 Percentage of Physicians Expressing High Levels of Confidence in Dealing with Behavior Change

Behavior	"Very prepared" to counsel patients (N ~ 430)	Currently "very successful" in helping patients (N ~ 427)
Smoking	58	3
Alcohol use	46	3
Exercise	40	8
Diet	35	7
Drug use	31	5
Stress	29	4

Note. From "The Physician's Role in Health Promotion—A Survey of Primary-Care Practitioners" by H. Wechsler, S. Levine, R.R. Idelson, M. Rohman, and J.O. Taylor. Reprinted with permission from *The New England Journal of Medicine*, **308**(2), p. 98, 1983. Copyright 1983.

Low confidence in the ability to facilitate behavior change is only one reason that physicians do not give advice on healthier lifestyle practice. Cummings, Giovino, Sciandra, Koeningsberg, and Emont (1987) examined physician advice for smoking cessation and found other reasons for not giving advice. These included

- the belief that the patient does not wish to quit,
- previous failures to persuade,
- preoccupation with other problems,
- lack of time, and
- the belief that smoking poses no immediate danger to a patient's health.

In addition, physicians who doubted that a patient would heed advice to stop smoking were less likely to counsel the patient. Physicians were more likely to give advice to heavy smokers or those who had recently experienced a serious illness related to cigarette smoking. Physicians were less likely to give advice to new patients, perhaps out of fear of offending the patients and discouraging them from returning to the office.

Knowledge of Prevention Varied

Like many other professionals, physicians prefer to succeed. In order to succeed more often, it is crucial that physicians be prepared with both the knowledge and the skills to succeed. Knowledge of preventive medicine measures is strikingly variable, and there is a marked discrepancy between physician prevention recommendations and the previous recommendations of national organizations. Gemson and Elinson (1986) found that physicians overwhelmingly supported the concept of preventive medicine, but there was significant variability of prevention practices among different groups of physicians. Many physicians felt that preventive recommendations were not clear, and nearly 80% felt that a task force was needed to clarify the recommendations.

The source of physician information for recommendations for asymptomatic patients also varies. The sources included clinical judgment (98%), professional experience (98%), medical journals (85%), continuing medical education (84%), the American Cancer Society (71%), and other physicians (48%). Although 71% of physicians identified the American Cancer Society as a source of knowledge, Gemson and Elinson (1986) found that more than half of those physicians were "not familiar" with the cancer-related checkup, and only 4% were "very familiar."

Despite this lack of familiarity with preventive recommendations, physicians are very interested in learning more about preventive medicine and health promotion and almost unanimously believe they should try to modify their patients' behavior. The type of assistance physicians desire includes videotapes, physician and staff training, information on where to refer patients, patient education literature, and more (see Table 9.3).

Valente et al. (1986) found that, given appropriate support, practicing primary care physicians believed they could be up to six times more successful in influencing behavior change. Given that 70% to 80% of adults in the United States visit a physician at least once per year, the potential impact of health-promoting physicians is great.

ADVOCACY EDUCATION FOR PHYSICIANS

Education at the undergraduate and postgraduate levels is the only realistic means of producing practicing physicians who strongly and consistently advocate health promotion. Jonas (1987a) suggests that the current model of medical education must be broken and that medical schools and their faculties realize that the way in which they were taught, with nearly exclusive disease-treatment orientation,

Table 9.3   Percent of Responses on Types of Assistance Reported as Being "Valuable" or "Very Valuable" in Working with Patients on Health Promotion

Types of assistance	Percent response
Literature	89.6
Information on where to refer patients	84.7
Health risk appraisals	82.8
Training for support staff	75.6
Reimbursement	72.8
Reimbursement for staff	71.5
Physician training	71.3
Training in behavior modification	68.4
Videotapes	68.2

Note. From *Health Promotion Profile of Beliefs, Attitudes, and Activities of Tennessee Primary Care Physicians* (p. 69) by C.A. Collins, 1986, unpublished doctoral dissertation, University of Tennessee-Knoxville. Reprinted by permission.

is not necessarily the best way. As with other medical disciplines, preventive medicine needs a clinical focus to be taught effectively in medical school. Preventive medicine has an identifiable body of knowledge, skills, values, and attitudes that are necessary for its effective implementation in clincial practice. The Association of Teachers of Preventive Medicine (1987) recently developed a task list for preventive medicine in clinical evaluation. With some variation by specialty, it is as follows:

- Health risk appraisal
- Social and family history, including psychosocial factors
- Occupational history
- Psychological profile
- Regular monitoring of immune status
- Nutritional history
- Routine application of screening tests on a regular schedule by age, sex, and risk status

The association also recommended personalized intervention programs to promote health and prevent disease, including

- cigarette smoking cessation, substance abuse control, and weight loss services as needed;

- nutritional counseling;
- stress management;
- exercise promotion;
- immune status management;
- occupational risk counseling;
- maternal and child health services; and
- tertiary prevention, as in the effective long-term management of hypertension and diabetes

Finally, the association stressed communication, education, and motivational skills as essential in personal preventive medicine. To practice prevention effectively, physicians also must be able to

- make referrals to and work with other health professionals;
- identify, evaluate, and make appropriate referrals to specific community-based health promotion and disease prevention resources;
- use epidemiological skills to evaluate their own practices so as to identify and keep track of persons at risk; and
- create and use health-oriented, as well as problem-oriented, medical records

Jonas (1987b) notes, "In order to effectively teach clinical medicine, both personal and community, medical schools should have one or more 'model practices' in which clinical preventive medicine is effectively practiced and integrated with curative medicine" (p. 237).

Lane and Varma (1986) underscore the need for a formalized postgraduate training approach. Most physicians engage in continuing medical education opportunities of a variety of types, and preventive medicine must become a subject for postgraduate study. In addition to educational opportunities, trained medical leadership is necessary to accomplish enhanced physician education in preventive medicine. Practicing physicians must view preventive medicine measures as seriously as they do the latest anti-hypertensive medication. Now is the time to "achieve a proper balance in medical education between attention to health and attention to disease" (p. 218).

PHYSICIANS AS ROLE MODELS AND HEALTH PROMOTERS

A curious imbalance also exists between the physician as role model and the physician as health promoter. Physicians as a group have made many healthy lifestyle changes so that today, for example, fewer than 10% of physicians smoke. Young physicians and medical students are doing even better. Thus, although physicians have apparently discovered the secrets of good health, they are hesitant or ineffective in sharing them. Dismuke and Miller (1983) believe this is due mainly to the medical education system, residency training, and the lack of incontrovertible evidence for prevention. They also add that physicians are unaware of the impact they can make on a patient's health behavior. Numerous behavior modification techniques exist and can be utilized by physicians or their staffs, and "because of contact with people during times of crisis, the physician is in a unique position to help patients take advantage of an illness to modify their long-term behavior" (p. 3183).

This time of crisis has been called the "teachable moment" and represents a brief period of heightened receptivity to health information. A smoker who is experiencing a particularly troublesome bout of bronchitis may be uniquely receptive to smoking cessation advice and help. A myocardial infarction may not only be a good time to suggest lifestyle changes for the affected patient, but also to ask questions of the family and possibly ascertain their cardiovascular risks. Physicians must be attentive to their patients, for the teachable moment may be just that—a moment, which may pass as quickly as it materialized. Physicians must take advantage of these unusual opportunities.

Maximizing such opportunities requires certain skills, in some of which the physician has little or no training. The most important skill is listening, which, though apparently simple and straightforward, is often overlooked. Patients often give valuable information that can be utilized by an alert physician to increase the likelihood of behavior change. Knowing that a patient's spouse smokes will make smoking cessation a more difficult task. Counseling a patient who is not the family cook on the merits of a low-cholesterol diet may be of little or no use. Realizing that an individual is going through an extremely stressful period may modify a physician's recommendation to change a significant health behavior. Asking a patient to name a favorite exercise and encouraging participation will be more effective than merely recommending regular exercise. This personalized approach requires slightly more time, and physicians in a hurry to conclude the patient visit will be less likely to listen.

Familiarity with basic behavior modification techniques will be useful for addressing a wide variety of health behaviors. Physicians can help patients analyze their present health behaviors, generate a behavioral plan, motivate a patient, and help with implementation. Awareness of the concepts of substitution, stimulus control, environmental engineering, cognitive restructuring, positive and negative consequences, and aversive conditioning can be quite helpful to the physician interested in working with patients in behavior modification. Physicians can also facilitate referral to a psychologist, psychiatrist, or other health professional for more extensive behavior modification approaches.

THE REFERRAL NETWORK AS ADVOCACY TOOL

The referral network is an important ally to physicians interested in promoting the health of their patients. Referrals can be made to a physician's staff, which may include nurses, dietitians, physical therapists, or others. Or the physician may refer to outside consultants, such as psychologists, dietitians, or fitness specialists, or to centers, such as weight loss, smoking cessation, and behavior modification clinics. Referring physicians must be wary of the staff of some centers, particularly weight loss centers, because medically unsafe practices are not rare.

Many hospitals are developing health promotion programs, and thus the likelihood of finding a hospital-based program is high. Referring physicians should expect regular follow-up from the referral consultant or center, and if they do not receive it, they should reconsider future referrals. Referral centers and consultants can be of great assistance to a physician, particularly one who does not have the interest or does not wish to devote considerable time to these areas.

HEALTH PROMOTION OPPORTUNITIES IN THE OFFICE SETTING

Opportunities to integrate health promotion and disease prevention into the practice of medicine are nearly as varied as the reasons patients go to physicians' offices. The typical office or clinical visit can be categorized as

- periodic examination,
- acute illness of potentially serious consequences,
- acute illness of a benign nature, or
- chronic illness.

Each of these settings provides an opportunity to incorporate health promotion into the office encounter.

Periodic Examinations

Periodic examinations include physical examinations, Pap tests and breast exams, well-child care, and others. The patient generally comes to the visit without symptoms and hopes to leave with a clean bill of health. The yearly physical examination, once thought to be useful, has come under scrutiny and criticism in the past several years. Breslow and Somers (1977), the Canadian Task Force on the Periodic Health Examination (1984), Frame (1986a-d), and the American College of Physicians have decried the yearly physical and replaced it with an examination targeted to specific age groups, at specified time intervals, which takes into account relative risk of illness and which is aimed at early detection and treatment of disease. Such examinations are ideal for exploring lifestyle practices in many areas and making recommendations for improvement and enhancement of health.

Acute Illnesses

Acute illness of a potentially serious nature is unusual, but when it does occur, it is rather impressive. It often presents the physician with a "teachable moment," especially if the patient's illness is related to a current lifestyle practice. The physician can also influence family members' lifestyle practices as well as enlist the help of the family in modifying the patient's unhealthy lifestyle practice.

Acute illness of a benign nature is probably the most common type of visit to a primary care physician. It has been estimated that 75% of all visits to primary care physicians are for self-limited illnesses, namely illnesses that will resolve in the near future, with or without treatment. Such illnesses include viral infections, musculoskeletal injuries, headaches, and others. Unfortunately, patients are often overwhelmingly interested in symptom control, and physicians usually comply, turning quickly and efficiently to their pharmaceutical armamentarium. Such quick visits are satisfying to both parties but represent missed opportunities to discuss lifestyle practices.

Chronic Illnesses

Chronic illnesses, such as diabetes mellitus, obesity, cardiovascular disease, hypertension, and many others, are diseases that often involve periodic office visits. At each such visit, the current status of the patient and the progression of the illness are monitored. Medication may be added, discontinued, or modified. Chronic illnesses ultimately contribute to the leading causes of death in this country, and lifestyle practices strongly influence both the morbidity and mortality. Because of this and the frequency of the visits, physicians can consistently and frequently encourage healthy lifestyle practices that can minimize illness-related disability and enhance overall health.

Both physicians and patients benefit from the practice of health promotion. Patients, if able to adopt healthier lifestyles, will benefit in manifold ways, including not only decreased morbidity and mortality, but also an enhanced quality of life. Physicians will benefit by having a healthier, more informed patient population. The small amount of extra time spent communicating with the patient about health promotion and disease prevention will usually translate into an improved doctor-patient relationship and increased patient loyalty. As Mechanic (1985) has pointed out, this is especially important in today's cost-conscious medical environment, in which changes in finances will shift the physician's role from one of patient advocacy to one in which the physician shares greater responsibility for allocating fixed budgets. If trust between physician and patient is to remain strong, physicians must become better communicators and educators, and be not only empathetic and medically proficient, but informative as well.

ADDITIONAL ROLES FOR PHYSICIANS

Physicians can become involved with health promotion and disease prevention at more than the individual patient level. As the Simons-Mortons (1987) have pointed out, physicians can also work at organizational, community, and governmental levels. At the organizational level, they can consult, help set policies, and serve on committees. At the community level, they can serve on task forces, publish articles, appear on radio and television, and participate in social action. At the governmental level, they can vote, lobby, contribute money, write letters, testify, and meet with government officials. By becoming involved at these levels, physicians can have a greater voice in positively influencing the health of this country.

IMPEDIMENTS TO HEALTH PROMOTION

A number of impediments serve to limit physicians' practice of health promotion. These factors must be taken into account when working with physicians, and they include

- the medical education system;
- the expectations of patients, physicians, and the health care system;
- limited reimbursement for health promotion services;
- shortage of time;
- unfamiliarity with the scientific basis of health promotion;
- lack of confidence in the methods of health promotion and in the physician's own skills;
- low status of health promotion and disease prevention among the medical profession; and
- fear of loss of control of patient care.

Each of these factors will be examined in the following sections.

The Medical Education System

The undergraduate and postgraduate levels of education emphasize disease treatment, not disease prevention and health promotion. Little attention is paid to clinical models for disease prevention, and thus clinician role models are uncommon. Like most other professionals, physicians practice what they are trained to practice, and until the system provides educational training and hands-on clinical experience in health promotion and disease prevention, gains in physician practice of health promotion will be slow.

Present Expectations

In our present health care system, physicians are expected to practice disease-care medicine. This powerful expectation comes not only from the medical educational system, but also from the reimbursement system and patients themselves. Patients usually visit physicians during illness, not health, and often expect some type of symptom-relieving treatment, either medicinal or otherwise. Physicians are partly responsible for training patients to rely upon them for "cures," but patients, too, are responsible for training their physicians to deliver the magical treatment. Collins (1986) makes an excellent point when she writes, "One must question just how much of a role the physician can have in health promotion if the society is unwilling or unable to take responsibility for the lifestyle choices that are available" (pp. 86-87). However, if patients begin to expect their physicians to practice health promotion, many physicians will respond by adopting a more health promotion-related practice.

The Reimbursement System

The reimbursement system's failure to reimburse health promotion and disease prevention services sends out a strong message to physicians—namely, that the service is not valuable. Ordering a baseline mammogram, counseling on breast self-exam, or devoting an office visit to developing an exercise and weight loss plan will not be reimbursed by the majority of insurance companies. Though such companies will not deny that these services are useful, they will not pay for them. Although improving reimbursement practices for health promotion services does not guarantee that physicians will order them, it is highly likely to improve physician practice of such valuable services.

Shortage of Time

Practicing health promotion demands time. It takes far less time to see a patient with a sprained ankle or a minor laceration than it does to counsel an obese patient on ways to lose weight. This time demand is compounded by the reimbursement system's failure to pay for such services. The time spent in practicing health promotion can be well spent, as the study by Russell et al. (1979) on physician's recommendations for smoking cessation showed. Physicians do not necessarily need to get intimately involved in all aspects of health promotion, but can delegate some of this responsibility to their own staff or to a consultant. Improving physician skills in health promotion and integrating the referral network will greatly enhance the clinical practice of health promotion.

Lack of Familiarity and Confidence

The scientific basis for health promotion is relatively new, at least compared to the scientific basis for the practice of clinical medicine. Additionally, the results of health promotion and disease prevention studies do not always appear in the "right" journals; that is, the ones most frequently read by practicing physicians. This unfamiliarity with the science of health promotion lessens the likelihood that physicians will be enthusiastic advocates of its tenets. This difficulty can be assuaged by incorporating health promotion into the continuing medical education curricula and by publishing studies in journals more widely read by practicing physicians.

Because of limited education, training, and experience in health promotion and the lack of familiarity with the scientific basis for health promotion, many physicians lack confidence not only in the methods of health promotion, but also in their own skills in delivering health promotion. With additional training, many physicians believe that their ability to deliver health promotion can improve dramatically. When physicians receive this training and begin incorporating health promotion into their practices, confidence will grow, thus facilitating future physician advocacy and practice of health promotion.

Low Status and Loss of Patient Control

The practice of health promotion and disease prevention does not have tremendous status or visibility within the medical profession. Jonas (1987a) and others have recently proposed development of a clinical specialty of preventive medicine that would serve as a referral source for other physicians. This fascinating and controversial "new" specialty would meet a number of currently unmet patient needs. It would also add more credibility to disease prevention and health promotion among all physicians.

Many physicians feel ultimately responsible for all the needs of the patients in their practices and are not entirely comfortable making referrals for health promotion services, even if they are not providing the services themselves. Providers of health promotion must be sensitive to this and consult the referring physician when appropriate. Most physicians will appreciate regular follow-up, for it keeps them informed and allows them to feel that they are still actively involved in all aspects of patient care.

WORKING WITH PHYSICIANS IN HEALTH PROMOTION

The rapid growth of health promotion within the past 10 years has resulted in the development of many health promotion providers. Hospitals are among the most prominent of these providers and are also the providers with which physicians feel most comfortable. If hospital-based programs are to be optimally successful, they must work cooperatively with physicians on the medical staff (Kernaghan & Giloth, 1983).

Programs must market themselves to physicians who can serve as excellent referral sources for a variety of health promotion programs. Physicians in turn can receive referrals from the programs, which can effectively identify patients who have no regular physician. The relationship between provider and physician must be grounded in a spirit of cooperation, and facilitated by clear and frequent communication. The relationship is a long-term one, built upon mutual trust and benefit.

Working with physicians is not as difficult as it sometimes seems, and physicians can be great allies for a health promotion program. It is important to keep the following in mind when working with physicians:

1. **Think before acting**. Before launching a major program, speak with and survey the physicians on your staff. Find out if there is a perceived need from physicians, and in what particular areas. Are there specific programs that physicians would find particularly useful for their patients? What is the specialty mix at your hospital? Primary care physicians are the most likely to refer patients to a program. If physicians seem especially resistant to a new program, find out why before going ahead. Physician resistance is insufficient reason not to go ahead, but knowing the reasons why can help you formulate a strategy to lessen resistance.

2. **Pick a physician ally carefully**. A primary care physician is preferable, particularly one who is active on the medical staff and who makes a practice of personal health promotion. Such a physician will favorably reflect the program in public and among colleagues and will most likely integrate health promotion into his or her practice. Programs should help with this integration by providing support and additional training and should also consider sending most "undoctored" patients to this physician.

3. **Sell physicians on the program**. Physicians need to be convinced of the benefits of your program. In this competitive health care environment, physicians are leery of potential competitors. Most programs do not directly compete with physicians, but physicians may not be aware of this. Present your program as complementary to their practices, and show how your program can actually enhance physician practices. Make presentations to physicians at routine medical staff meetings as well as part of their continuing medical education.

4. **Make it easy for physicians to refer to your program**. This may involve working with a physician and the physician's staff on the optimal mechanism for patient referral. Check back with the physician and staff to make certain that the process is working smoothly.

5. **Provide physicians with ongoing assistance**. This includes patient education materials, audiovisual assistance, referral information, and other such assistance. When physicians make special requests, try to be accommodating, for such efforts will likely pay off in the long run.

6. **Reward physicians for their support**. Such rewards include referrals, tokens of appreciation, and regular follow-up. It makes sense to send patients to the physicians who support your program. Though it may not be politically expedient or practical to refer all patients to a small number of physician-supporters, it is certainly reasonable to preferentially refer patients to those physicians who are advocates of your program. Physicians, like most other people, enjoy receiving tokens of appreciation for their support, and a thank-you card can go a long way. Finally, regular

follow-up with a physician can be rewarding, for it reminds a physician of the progress that has been made as a result of a referral.

The time spent fostering relationships with physicians is rarely wasted. Physicians can be intimidating, however, and sometimes appear set on obstructing the progress of a newly developing health promotion program. Before giving up on a program because of physician resistance, explore the reasons for it in light of other factors in your environment. Physician opinion is only one factor influencing the success of your program, but it is an important one. Try at all times to maintain an optimistic and cooperative attitude when working with physicians. Their support can be a tremendous boon to a program.

CONCLUSION

Physicians to date have played a role in health promotion. Physicians engaged in public health and preventive medicine have been instrumental in systematically improving public health measures, formulating health policy, and training medical school graduates. Many practicing physicians have integrated certain aspects of health promotion into their practices, although not in a systematic fashion. The involvement of physicians in health promotion is strongly influenced by the disease care model, and thus physicians are more involved in disease prevention than in health promotion. In many ways health promotion and disease prevention are quite similar, and it is important to focus on the similarities. Our current health care system is disease treatment-oriented, and if significant movement toward health promotion is to occur within the medical profession, the system must move first toward a disease prevention model.

Numerous opportunities exist for the expansion of the role of the physician. For this to happen, impediments must be overcome and incentives instituted. Changes in the reimbursement and medical education systems, altered societal and professional expectations, and improved collaborative relationships with health promotion providers will help expedite the incorporation of health promotion into the practice of medicine. Innovative models are developing for the creation of a clinical specialty of preventive medicine and for the incorporation of the preventive approach to patient care.

Major improvements in physicians' practice of health promotion cannot occur without the support of other health promotion providers. Such providers must realize that physicians can be tremendous allies whose support can be instrumental in a program's success. Fostering positive relationships with physicians is an ongoing, long-term process, well worth the time and effort it requires. The potential impact patients' physicians can have through health promotion and disease prevention is great, but can be realized only by a thoughtful, coordinated, and cooperative approach.

BIBLIOGRAPHY

Association of Teachers of Preventive Medicine. (1987). The Association of Teachers of Preventive Medicine: An inventory of knowledge and skills related to health promotion and disease prevention. *Perspectives in Prevention,* **1**(2), 14.

Altekruse, J.M. (1987). Viewpoint: President's message. *Perspectives on Prevention,* **1**(2), 4.

Baines, C.J. (1984, March). Breast self-examination: The doctor's role. *Hospital Practice,* pp. 120-127.

Belloc, N.B., & Breslow, L. (1972). Relationship of physical health status and health practices. *Preventive Medicine,* **1**, 409-421.

Blum, A. (1982). Medical activism. In R.B. Taylor, J.R. Ureda, & J.W. Denham (Eds.), *Health promotion: Principles and clinical applications* (pp. 373-391). Norwalk, CT: Appleton-Century-Crofts.

Breslow, L., & Somers, A.R. (1977). The lifetime health monitoring program: A practical approach to preventive medicine. *New England Journal of Medicine,* **269**, 601-608.

Bridges, W.F. (1987). The independent specialty practice of preventive medicine (Editorial). *Perspectives on Prevention,* **1**(3), 8.

Canadian Task Force on the Periodic Health Examination. (1984). The periodic health examination—A report of the Canadian Task Force on the Periodic Health Examination. *Canadian Medical Journal,* **130**, 1-16.

Collins, C.A. (1986). *Health promotion profile of beliefs, attitudes, and activities of Tennessee primary care physicians.* Unpublished doctoral dissertation, University of Tennessee-Knoxville.

Conger, B., et al. (1987). Effectiveness of physician anti-smoking advice. *American Journal of Preventive Medicine,* **3**(4), 223-226.

Cummings, K.M., Giovino, G., Sciandra, R., Koeningsberg, M., & Emont, S.L. (1987). Physician advice to quit smoking: Who gets it and who doesn't. *American Journal of Preventive Medicine,* **3**(2), 69-75.

Currie, B.F., & Beasley, J.W. (1982). Health promotion in the medical encounter. In R.B. Taylor, J.R. Ureda, & J.W. Denham (Eds.), *Health promotion: Principles and clinical applications* (pp. 143-160). Norwalk, CT: Appleton-Century-Crofts.

Dismuke, S.E., & Miller, S.T. (1983). Why not share the secrets of good health? The physician's role in health promotion. *Journal of the American Medical Association,* **244**, 3181-3183.

Doll, R. (1983). Prospects for prevention. *British Medical Journal,* **286**, 445-453.

Dunn, H.L. (1961). *High level wellness.* Arlington, VA: R.W. Beatty.

Eisenberg, L. (1977). The perils of prevention: A cautionary note. *New England Journal of Medicine,* **297**, 1230-1232.

Farquhar, J.W. (1978). The community-based model of lifestyle intervention trials. *American Journal of Epidemiology,* **108**, 103-111.

Fletcher, D.J. (1985). Periodic health monitoring: How to help patients stay well. *Postgraduate Medicine,* **78**(5), 305-317.

Fletcher, D.J. (1986). Periodic health monitoring revisited. *Postgraduate Medicine,* **80**(5), 145-160.

Frame, P.S. (1986a). A critical review of adult health maintenance: 1. Prevention of atherosclerotic diseases. *Journal of Family Practice,* **22**, 341-346.

Frame, P.S. (1986b). A critical review of adult health maintenance: 2. Prevention of infectious diseases. *Journal of Family Practice,* **22**, 417-422.

Frame, P.S. (1986c). A critical review of adult health maintenance: 3. Prevention of cancer. *Journal of Family Practice,* **22**, 511-520.

Frame, P.S. (1986d). A critical review of adult health maintenance: 4. Prevention of metabolic, behavioral, and miscellaneous conditions. *Journal of Family Practice,* **23**, 29-39.

Gemson, D.H., & Elinson, J. (1986). Prevention in primary care: Variability in physician practice patterns in New York City. *American Journal of Preventive Medicine,* **2**(4), 226-234.

Goldberg, R.J., DeCosimo, D., St. Louis, P., et al. (1985). Physicians' attitudes and practices toward CPR training in family members of patients with coronary heart disease. *American Journal of Public Health,* **75**(3), 281-283.

Goodstadt, M.S., Simpson, R.I., & Loranger, P.D. (1987). Health promotion: A Conceptual Integration. *American Journal of Health Promotion,* **1**(3), 58-63.

Hettler, W. (1980). Wellness promotion on a university campus. *The Journal of Health Promotion and Maintenance,* **3**(1).

Jonas, S. (1981, March). Prevention: Helping patients 'upfront.' *Colloquy,* pp. 9-12.

Jonas, S. (1987a). The clinical preventive medicine specialist: A proposed model. *Perspectives on Prevention,* **2**(1), 17-19.

Jonas, S. (1987b). Implementing the recommendations of the GPEP report pertaining to preventive medicine. *American Journal of Preventive Medicine,* **3**(4), 233-238.

Kannel, W.B., & Gordon, B. (1974). The Framingham study: An epidemiological investigation of cardiovascular disease (Section 30). *Some characteristics related to the incidence of cardiovascular disease and death: The Framingham study 18-year follow-up* (DHEW Publication No. NIH 74-599). Washington, DC: U.S. Government Printing Office.

Kernaghan, S.G., & Giloth, B.E. (1983). *Working with physicians in health promotion: A key to successful programs.* Chicago: American Hospital Publishing.

Lane, D.S., & Varma, A.A.O. (1986). The postgraduate education of physicians in preventive medicine. *American Journal of Preventive Medicine,* **2**(4), 216-229.

Mechanic, D. (1985). Public perceptions of medicine. *New England Journal of Medicine*, **312**, 181-183.

Multiple risk factor intervention trial research group: Multiple risk factor intervention trial—Risk factor changes and mortality results. (1982). *Journal of the American Medical Association*, **248**, 1465-1477.

Oppenheim, M. (1980). Healers. *New England Journal of Medicine*, **30**, 1117-1120.

Paffenbarger, R.S., Hyde, R.T., Wing, A.L., & Hsieh, C.C. (1986). Physical activity, all-cause mortality, and longevity of college alumni. *New England Journal of Medicine*, **314**, 605-613.

Pooling Project Research Group. (1978). Relationship of blood pressure, serum cholesterol, smoking habit, relative weight and ECG abnormalities to incidence of major coronary events: Final report of the Pooling Project. *Journal of Chronic Disease*, **31**, 201-306.

Powell, D.R., & Brownson, J. (1986, March/April). How to win friends among physicians. *Optimal Health*, pp. 36-39.

Russell, M.A., Wilson, C., Taylor, C., & Baker, D.C. (1979). Effect of general practitioners' advice against smoking. *British Medical Journal*, **2**, 231-235.

Sands, M.J., Osborn, R.R., Leach, C.N., & Lachman, A.S. (1984). Industrial fitness programs: The physician's role. *Connecticut Medicine*, **98**(1), 1-5.

Sheriden, D.P., & Winogond, I.R. (1987). *The preventive approach to patient care*. New York: Elsevier.

Simons-Morton, D.G., & Simons-Morton, B.G. (1987). Health promotion and disease promotion: Roles for the primary care physician. *Postgraduate Medicine*, **81**(3), 235-242.

Sobal, J., Valente, C.M., Muncie, H.L., Levine, D.M., & DeForge, B.R. (1985). Physicians' beliefs about the importance of 25 health promoting behaviors. *American Journal of Preventive Medicine*, **75**, 1427-1428.

Somers, A.R. (1978). Perils of prevention (Letter to the editor). *New England Journal of Medicine*, **298**, 746-747.

Stokes, J. (1983). Why not rate health and life insurance premiums by risks? *New England Journal of Medicine*, **308**, 393-395.

Taylor, R.B. (1981). Health promotion: Can it succeed in the office? *Preventive Medicine*, **10**, 258-262.

Valente, C.M., Sobal, J., Muncie, H.L., Levine, D.M., & Antlitz, A.M. (1986). Health promotion: Physicians' beliefs, attitudes and practices. *American Journal of Preventive Medicine* **2**(2), 82-88.

Wartman, S.A., Morlock, L.L., Malitz, F.E., & Palm, E. (1981). Do prescriptions adversely affect doctor-patient interactions? *American Journal of Preventive Medicine*, **71**, 1358-1361.

Wechsler, H., Levine, S., Idelson, R.R., Rohman, M., & Taylor, J.O. (1983). The physician's role in health promotion—a survey of primary-care practitioners. *New England Journal of Medicine*, **308**, 97-100.

Wyshak, G., Lamb, G.A., Lawrence, R.S., & Curran, W.J. (1980). A profile of the health-promoting behaviors of physicians and lawyers. *New England Journal of Medicine*, **303**, 104-107.

CHAPTER 10

The Nurse's Role in Health Promotion

Carolyn I. Speros

A s a profession, nursing has maintained an orientation toward health promotion and disease prevention since its early beginnings. However, a variety of forces within our society have prompted nurses of late to focus less on health and more on illness care and cure of disease.

Nursing responds to trends within a society in an effort to meet the perceived health needs of the culture within which it exists (Moore & Williamson, 1984). The interrelationship between health status, lifestyle behaviors, and the condition of the environment has increasingly been demonstrated in public health research of the past decades. National emphasis has been given to health promotion through the setting of objectives for improving the health status of the entire nation. Appropriately, the traditional practice of nursing is being reevaluated to assess its ability to function effectively given these trends. The role that nurses can play in the emerging arena of health promotion and wellness will be the focus of this chapter.

HISTORIC INTEREST IN HEALTH PROMOTION

The concern for health promotion and disease prevention is fundamental to the practice of nursing despite its strong and traditional links with the provision of hospital care.

In 1859, Florence Nightingale wrote the following:

I use the word nursing for want of a better. It has been limited to signify little more than the administration of medicines and the application of poultices. It ought to signify the proper use of fresh air, light, warmth, cleanliness, quiet, and the proper choosing and giving of diet. (Nightingale, 1859/1946, p. 6)

As early as the 1800s Nightingale recognized the relationship between an individual's health, the environment, and nutritional status. The standard of nursing practice in her day assumed that nurses would assure that basic human needs were met to strengthen the diseased body, restore health, and prevent further illness.

Later, in Nightingale's *Notes on Nursing* (1859), she defined nursing as that care which places a person in the best possible condition for nature to restore or preserve health, and to prevent or to cure disease or injury. Certainly, the roots of nursing are entrenched in the belief that nurses play an essential role in health teaching, assuring healthy environments for the people with whom they work, and guiding individuals to attain the highest level of well-being possible.

It is important to define the current state of nursing practice in relationship to the broad concept of "health." The World Health Organization's definition of health as a "state of complete physical, mental, and social well-being and not merely the absence of disease or infirmity" (1960, p.1) seems to be the most appropriate definition within which to practice nursing. In this context, nursing can be seen as the process of assisting individuals to overcome illness and achieve a higher level of well-being, facilitating their move toward an optimal state of health.

The International Council of Nursing, in 1973, defined a nurse in the following manner:

A nurse is a person who has completed a program of basic nursing education and is qualified and authorized in his/her country to provide responsible and competent service for: the promotion of health, the prevention of illness, the care of the sick, and rehabilitation. (p. 61)

NURSING MODELS
OF HEALTH PROMOTION

Until recently, very little nursing literature has focused on the practical or applied aspects of health promotion in nursing practice. Nursing texts typically follow the medical or illness model, focusing on diagnosis, treatment, and restorative care. Two nursing authors warrant examination. Each has explored extensively the concept of health promotion as a basis for nursing theory, applied practice, and research.

Brubaker (1983) attempts to answer the question, When is health care health promotion? Her premise is that health promotion is a "specific area of health care" (p. 9). According to Brubaker's definition of health promotion, health promotion strategies are applicable only after the health status is stable. She rejects the idea that just staying alive or moving to a non-ill state is health promotion.

Accepting any movement upward on the health continuum as health promotion, no matter where the starting point . . . is thus rejected. Otherwise most health care would be health promotion (p. 12).

Within this context, the health promotion arena becomes more focused on the apparently well, and nursing activities directed at those individuals without active disease constitute health promotion nursing practice.

Pender (1987) defines health promotion as "activities directed toward increasing the level of well-being and actualizing the health potential of individuals, families, communities, and society" (p.4). Health-promoting behavior always has as its goal the maintenance of current health status or movement toward a more desirable level of health. The primary examples of health-promoting behaviors cited by Pender are good nutrition, physical exercise, and development of social support systems when done to enhance the sense of well-being or to maximize one's potential. The motivation of individuals to action distinguishes such activity from a health-protecting behavior.

Whether the action is a health promotion or health protection one, it is an essential nursing intervention in the plan of care. Pender discusses in detail the skills necessary for effective function as a health promotion nurse. The models proposed by Pender can be used as a framework for further nursing research into health promotion and illness prevention.

Achieving a more focused definition of health promotion nursing can aid those within the profession in identifying the body of knowledge and skills needed to assume a role in this emerging field of specialty. At that point, responsibilities and accountabilities can be more easily understood by health professionals and the public.

NURSING'S CURRENT ROLE
IN HEALTH PROMOTION

Nurses are in an ideal position to assume a leadership role in the promotion of health among individuals, families, and the community at large. Their recognized expertise and close, frequent contact with their clients afford them the unique opportunity to work with a variety of populations concerned about their health.

A variety of settings are targeted for wellness or health promotion activities today. Many of these settings offer nurses the opportunity to apply their assessment, interpersonal, and evaluative skills in working with individuals or groups. Typically, health promotion efforts have targeted the community at large and the worksite in servicing aggregate populations. In addition to these settings, however, opportunities for health promotion nursing practice exist in the acute-care setting, as well as the outpatient and ambulatory centers affiliated with many hospitals today.

In Community-Based Settings

Community-based health promotion programs capitalize on the growing consumer interest in wellness and the individual's desire for convenience and accessibility.

Nurses can enhance the quality of a community campaign by participating in the assessment, planning, and intervention phases of the effort. Conducting health screenings, assessing the physical health status of individuals, and making appropriate referrals for treatment if indicated are very necessary services that a nurse can provide. In many states, a licensed nurse is required to perform many of the clinical tests conducted in multiphasic screening programs. Certainly, the nurse's knowledge of public health issues and problems is a valuable addition to a community-based health promotion effort.

As consumer interest in health continues to rise, the demand for health information and education increases. Nurses are called upon frequently to speak to community groups on a variety of health-related topics. The nurse's knowledge of behavior modification principles and experience with individuals suffering from the consequences of unhealthy lifestyle practices are good preparation for effecting change in people contacted in the community.

In Worksite Health Promotion Programs

The private sector's concern about rising health care costs has precipitated great interest in worksite health promotion programs. By expanding the scope of services typically provided by the occupational health nurse or the traditional "industrial" nurse, hiring a health promotion nurse can be a sound investment for companies committed to containing their costs associated with accidents, illness, and absence. In addition to the traditional responsibilities for industrial safety and OSHA compliance in the role of the occupational health nurse, the health promotion nurse can assess the employees' risks for disease and initiate a comprehensive plan for intervention at the worksite. Incorporating fitness and lifestyle assessments into employee and executive physicals, conducting health awareness campaigns, leading a variety of lifestyle classes related to risk factor reduction and fitness, and targeting high-risk groups of employees and dependents with special programs are some of the many ways that occupational health nurses can expand their role into health promotion at the worksite. An understanding of the employee's state of health as a factor of environment and lifestyle is central to the practice of the occupational health promotion nurse.

In Acute-Care Settings

Nurses practicing in the acute-care setting have an even greater opportunity to practice health promotion nursing if the concept of health is viewed in the broadest sense. If a focus on health promotion, rather than curing disease, becomes the outcome of care, then nurses in the hospital setting are in a unique position to positively influence the health-promoting behaviors of individuals with whom they come in contact.

Certainly, increased consumer demand for health information has precipitated unprecedented emphasis on self-care and patient education in hospitals today.

Teaching and counseling are considered integral components of nursing care. Although time to teach is an important issue, as inpatients are more acutely ill and are discharged earlier, staff nurses have a professional obligation to do all they can to ensure that patients and their families are appropriately prepared to manage their own care upon their return home (American Nurse's Association, 1973). The health promotion nurse in the hospital setting can incorporate the strategies of lifestyle assessment, health teaching, role modeling, and effective communication in day-to-day practice to promote the health of patients. In addition, attention to the health needs of family members affected by the illness of a loved one must be given high priority by the health promotion nurse in the hospital.

A variety of settings exist that afford nurses many opportunities to expand their role into health promotion. Caution must be taken, however, that traditional skills and illness-focused nursing are altered to address the real health needs of those being served in the community, worksite, or hospital. Illness care in innovative and nontraditional settings is *not* health promotion nursing practice.

UNDERSTANDING THE DEMANDS OF TRADITIONAL NURSING

Often, lack of cooperation from nursing is cited as an obstacle to moving forward in a hospital-based health promotion effort. In many instances, non-nurses fail to appreciate the overwhelming demands placed on nurses both in the hospital and in the community. Non-nurses feel that nursing is obligated to cooperate, when in fact nurses' job functions are typically very well defined around illness care.

Motivational Forces

In order to elicit nursing's support for and participation in the health promotion program, it is helpful to explore those factors that motivate individuals to enter nursing. In that way, strategies to nurture cooperation can be developed that satisfy the intrinsic needs of nurses.

A market research project was conducted in Memphis, Tennessee (Cox & Kenny, 1983), that explored rational and emotional motivators for individuals choosing nursing as a career. The study found that, in addition to the expected rational motivators for entering nursing, such as job security, career opportunities, salary, and recommendations by friends, individuals selected nursing as a career to meet their emotional needs for control and to be needed by others.

"Need for control" was the most frequent emotional motivator for individuals entering nursing. This need relates to the need for structure in and control over one's life. Nursing affords individuals structure, as typically seen in clearly defined hierarchies, distinct areas of authority, and a body of knowledge that is well defined and concrete. Individuals motivated by this need for control enjoy managing others, taking charge, and being the "expert."

In working with individuals with this need, health promotion specialists would be wise to build in avenues for input from nursing, so that nurses feel that they are involved and respected for their expertise. Encouraging an ally who maintains a health promotion orientation to chair a working task force or develop a health promotion product in some area of nursing expertise would go a long way in nurturing support from those in need of control.

The second emotional motivator most frequently identified was a need to be needed by others. Individuals motivated by this need want to be loved and appreciated. When these individuals receive positive feedback from others, they feel a sense of purpose in their lives. People with this need go into nursing because they feel that they will be able to serve patients and will be loved and respected by those for whom they provide care.

The altruistic benefit of health promotion, enhancing the quality of the lives of those involved, is highly appealing to nurses with this need to be needed. These nurses receive a great deal of intrinsic reward in serving individuals in mass screenings, health fairs, and other activities that put them in direct contact with people in need. It is very difficult for nurses motivated by this need to deal with the economic realities of health care because of the satisfaction they experience from providing a service to others.

Nurses relate best to other nurses. In securing nursing's support for health promotion, a wise program manager identifies nursing allies who emulate the ideals their programs espouse. Nurses who are well respected by their peers can be effective advocates within nursing and often garner support that a non-nurse may be less successful in securing.

SUMMARY

In 1976, the Board of Directors of the Registered Nurses Association of British Columbia adopted a position paper (since withdrawn, due to outdated material) entitled, "The Nurse's Role in Health Assessment and Promotion" (Registered Nurses Association of British Columbia, 1976). In it, standards related to health promotion nursing practices are outlined (see Table 10.1). All practicing registered nurses are expected to perform the following functions related to health promotion:

"Be a role-model of health; act as a change agent with/for patients; encourage lifestyle activities compatible with optimal health; collaborate with other health workers in providing health oriented care; [and] support those policies, procedures and activities [that] promote health" (p. 9). It is time for all nurses to embrace similar standards for health promotion nursing practice.

Nurses have an unprecedented opportunity to take a leadership role in the emerging field of health promotion. Nola Pender (1987) wrote, "Providing health care in a societal context that places primary emphasis on health promotion rather than

Table 10.1   Standards Related to Health Promotion Nursing Practices

1.   **Be a role model for health**
1.1   Maintain physical health
   a. Undertake an appropriate physical activity program
   b. Cope with stress
   c. Avoid harmful products and circumstances
   d. Ensure proper nutrition
   e. Keep immunization current
   f. Have regular checkups
   g. Plan for relaxation and sleep
1.2   Maintain psychosocial health
   a. Strive for positive interpersonal relationships
   b. Increase self-esteem
   c. Avoid harmful circumstances
   d. Select healthy role models
   e. Have regular checkups
   f. Anticipate developmental tasks rather than just living in the here and now
1.3   Adopt a healthy lifestyle
   a. Cope with stress
   b. Avoid harmful products and circumstances
   c. Adjust own concepts of health and fitness
   d. Set realistic goals, priorities, guidelines
   e. Assume accountability for own health
2.   **Act as a change agent with/for patients**
2.1   Use appropriate motivational approaches
   a. Establish a trusting relationship
   b. Increase client's self-esteem
   c. Identify and enlist support of significant others
   d. Contact
   e. Participate
   f. Reduce anxiety and/or guilt
2.2   Get patient commitment to change
2.3   Assist in the formulation of realistic goals and priorities
2.4   Reinforce health responses
2.5   Provide anticipatory guidance for each life stage
3.   **Encourage lifestyle activities compatible with optimal health**
   a. Appropriate physical activity program
   b. Adequate rest and relaxation
   c. Avoidance of harmful products and circumstances
   d. Identify and cope with stress
   e. Regular checkups

(Cont.)

Table 10.1   (Continued)

---

   f. Fluoridation
   g. Good hygiene
   h. Proper nutrition
   i. Current immunization
   j. Appropriate management of chronic disorders
   k. Appropriate use of community resources
   l. Accountability for health maintenance

4.   **Collaborate with other health workers in providing health-oriented care**

   a. Know own role and limitations
   b. Refer appropriately
   c. Cooperate

5.   **Support those policies, procedures, and activities that promote health**

   a. Health-oriented institutional philosophies
   b. Health standards and guidelines
   c. Health-oriented institutional policies, procedures, and routines
   d. Health-oriented evaluation procedures and criteria
   e. Health-oriented community and political involvement

Note. From "The Nurse's Role in Health Assessment and Promotion" by the Registered Nurses Association of British Columbia, 1976, *RNABC News,* November, p. 9. Copyright 1976 by the Registered Nurses Association of British Columbia. Reprinted by permission.

treatment of illness is an exciting challenge to the nursing profession" (p. 11). Health promotion nurses will have a definitive place in the health care system of the future if they respond to the challenge of viewing health in its broadest sense and embrace a health promotion orientation in their practice.

REFERENCES

American Nurse's Association. (1973). *Standards of nursing practice.* Kansas City, MO: American Nurse's Association.

Brubaker, B. (1983). Health promotion: A linguistic analysis. *Advances in Nursing Science, 5,* 1-14.

Cox, S., & Kenny, C. (1983). *A study in motivation: Nursing as a career choice.* Memphis, TN: Message Factors.

International Council of Nursing. (1973). Nurses and nursing. *International Nursing Review,* pp. 20, 61.

Moore, P., & Williamson, J.C. (1984). Health promotion: Evolution of a concept. *Nursing Clinics of North America, 19,* 195-206.

Nightingale, F. (1946). *Notes on nursing.* Philadelphia: J.B. Lippincott. (Original work published 1859)

Pender, N.J. (1987). *Health promotion in nursing practice.* Norwalk, CT: Appleton and Lange.

Registered Nurses Association of British Columbia. (1976, November). The nurse's role in health assessment and promotion. *RNABC News,* pp. 7-9.

World Health Organization. (1960). *Constitution.* Geneva: Palais des Nations.

CHAPTER 11

The Administrator's Role in Health Promotion: Preparing a Broader Perspective for the Future

Jeffrey M. Bensky

Daniel J. Bonk

Clearly one of the most important issues influencing the success of a hospital-based health promotion program is the level of understanding and support provided by administration. It is the intent of this chapter to depict the program administrator's current role and how that role can prepare a broader perspective for a successful future. This chapter will present three sets of issues that we believe are critical to the overall business and administrative success of hospital-based health promotion:

- Understanding how business complexity is increasing for hospital-based health promotion
- Reviewing what management issues will affect the future
- Understanding the broader management perspectives required to meet the new "business" challenges

UNDERSTANDING THE COMPLEXITY OF BUSINESS

It is obvious that the business complexity of hospital-based health promotion has dramatically increased. What was perceived as a public relations activity in the

181

late seventies and early eighties is now viewed from a direct revenue-expense perspective. Having one or two products in the past has been replaced by offering an integrated continuum of services with multiple goals and objectives. How did all this transpire? Much of the complexity can be traced to increased technological sophistication of both providers and consumers of these services. Also, as this product market has matured, a more businesslike orientation has developed. However, a major factor that has driven the changes can be reflected in the way the entire health care industry has restructured and will continue to be reshaped in the future. For example, changes that are apparent today and will continue through the early nineties reflect the following:

- The health care industry is being defined by financial changes of the move from acute- to managed-care, hospital consolidations and alliances, the changing physician marketplace, and specialty and niche product lines.
- Quality delivery systems at the local level will be as important as national and regional capabilities.
- Successful health care providers are becoming more consumer-driven, market-sensitive, and therefore somewhat more commercial.

It should be obvious that these and other issues directly affect health promotion and related product lines. In fact, these issues have created a rather turbulent upheaval in many health care product lines, including our own. In addition, new technologies, shifting demographics, maturing markets, and many competitive dynamics are creating a more complex health care environment and therefore are also increasing the business complexity of health promotion. The business of health promotion is in the process of dramatically shifting, and many are not prepared for these changes or for the future. For example, how many times have you had to financially justify an activity in your business and could not because of your inability to account for all of your costs? Or how many of your colleagues have not been able to meet the challenges and are now in different jobs, different fields, or not working? The challenges brought to us by our sponsor—business complexity—clearly are requiring everyone to learn new skills and confront new issues. What is important to realize is that it is happening now! Some of the business complexities facing health promotion today will be discussed in greater detail.

Establishing and Reaching New Strategic Goals Related to Financial Viability

As shown in Table 11.1, according to the recent *Optimal Health*/Price Waterhouse survey, the financial goals of hospital-based health promotion seem to be public relations- or service-oriented (as perceived by the providers and managers of services).

Clearly this is counter to all we know regarding what heath care as a business

Table 11.1   Financial Goals

Financial goals for all hospital respondents	Percent responding
Public relations	62
Service	53
Break even	39
Profit	29
Loss leader	10

Note. From "Health Promotion Young, But Growing: The *Optimal Health/* Price Waterhouse Health Promotion Survey," 1987 (July/August), *Optimal Health,* pp. 22-24. Copyright 1987 by *Optimal Health* and Price Waterhouse. Reprinted by permission.

Table 11.2   Budget Experiences

Hospital size	Median revenues	Median expenses
Fewer than 100 beds	$50,000 or less	$50,000 or less
100-299 beds	$50,000 or less	$50,000-$149,999
300-499 beds	$50,001-$149,999	$150,000-$249,999
500-749 beds	$150,000-$249,999	$150,000-$249,999
750 or more beds	$350,000-$449,999	$250,000-$349,999

Note. From "Health Promotion Young, But Growing: The *Optimal Health*/Price Waterhouse Health Promotion Survey," 1987 (July/August), *Optimal Health,* pp. 22-24. Copyright 1987 by *Optimal Health* and Price Waterhouse. Reprinted by permission.

is facing. Moreover, as Table 11.2 shows, the budget experiences of hospital-based health promotion providers are not on the profit side.

In fact, we face the entry of low-cost competitors on a daily basis. This will obviously lead to marginal pricing and increased price competition, even lower industry profitability, and the eventual exit of some of the more marginal players. Will that be you? As an administrator or manager, the strategic questions you will be asking yourself in this area will relate to the financial viability of your business. Obviously this complexity is influenced by many variables that require a thorough analysis.

Establishing the Basis
of an External, Market-Driven Perspective

One of the more entertaining complexities facing administrators with health promotion responsibilities includes how to establish a market-driven perspective. This
obviously requires a more external perspective and sophisticated systems and
methodologies to more effectively market your products and services. As reviewed
in chapter 8, planning your marketing efforts and connecting them with the overall
hospital mission and goals will be important for your success. Even more important
is having the means and resources needed to be in touch with your marketplace.
As previously mentioned, financial viability will be a critical variable. One method
of improving your financial picture is through revenue generation. This is directly
tied to becoming market-driven. Untangling the complexities related to this area
can be achieved only through proper planning.

Coping With New Operational Demands

How one operates a business is directly tied to many different assumptions. As
has been stated many times, these assumptions are changing as the environment
we operate in changes. Some of the newer operational issues confronting management follow.

Integrating and Cross-Marketing Related Services

As hospitals attempt to reduce their overall operating costs, economies of scale
will be sought. Additionally, increased marketing effectiveness and efficiency
will be the option of choice. Integrating services, in some cases, may create health
promotion as a lead service intended to achieve different goals than other more
profitable services.

Creating the New Positives of Health Promotion

As has been mentioned in other parts of this book, justifying your existence can
be achieved in many direct and indirect ways. There are many "internal positives"
of health promotion, but these may have to be repositioned through more clearly
identifying and defining the strategic role of health promotion, given the realities
of the marketplace. Obviously measuring your success through inpatient utilization
is one new positive; accurately tracking it and measuring other "soft" indicators
of the positive impact will be the challenge.

MANAGEMENT ISSUES
IMPACTING THE FUTURE

There are a variety of management issues that will impact the future. For example, how one determines or measures success in this business will most likely
be a pressing issue in the future. As noted in Table 11.3, the hospitals surveyed

Table 11.3 Success Factors

Factors determining success	Percent responding
Public relations	69
Community service	66
Image enhancement	65
Customer satisfaction	62
Behavior change	48
Patient referral	41
Profitability	39
Other department support	25

Note. From "Health Promotion Young, But Growing: The *Optimal Health*/Price Waterhouse Health Promotion Survey," 1987 (July/August), *Optimal Health,* pp. 22-24. Copyright 1987 by *Optimal Health* and Price Waterhouse. Reprinted by permission.

by *Optimal Health*/Price Waterhouse indicated that their success, for the most part, was still measured in subjective ways.

The more objective (albeit difficult) determinants of success, profitability and patient referral, are still not perceived as important by those surveyed. More importantly, critical success factors mentioned most often by respondents appear to indicate a possible shift in determinants. The following were most often mentioned:

- Responsive, results-oriented quality programming
- Marketing and communications
- Management and physician support
- Customer satisfaction

What all this appears to mean is that the way success is being measured is different from the perceived critical success factor for hospital-based health promotion. If this trend continues, clearly the mechanisms necessary to objectively measure success will also need to change. Attacking the management issues for the future might best be accomplished via the elements described in the following sections.

Defining Your Future Success

As mentioned previously, how one defines success will be paramount to your effectiveness. Included in this definition are many other organizational and operational variables. For example, how you define your role and responsibilities will

Table 11.4   Future Resource Breakdown

Resources to do a better job	Percent responding
More staff	39
Equipment/Facilities	13
Strategic planning/ Management support	11
Marketing assistance	11
Additional funding	11
Time	4

Note. From "Health Promotion Young, But Growing: The *Optimal Health*/Price Waterhouse Health Promotion Survey," 1987 (July/August), *Optimal Health*, pp. 22-24. Copyright 1987 by *Optimal Health* and Price Waterhouse. Reprinted by permission.

Table 11.5   Future Issues of Importance

1 year from now	Percent responding
Marketing	53
New programs/Coordination	25
Developing relationships	7
Funding	3

3 years from now	Percent responding
New programs/Expansion	47
Marketing/Planning	24
Profit	4

Note. From "Health Promotion Young, But Growing: The *Optimal Health*/Price Waterhouse Health Promotion Survey," 1987 (July/August), *Optimal Health*, pp. 22-24. Copyright 1987 by *Optimal Health* and Price Waterhouse. Reprinted by permission.

directly affect your definition of success. Additionally, as pointed out in Table 11.4, the survey respondents listed resources they felt will be needed to do a better job in the future. Unfortunately, the first two items represent expenses that in turn might negatively impact your success. How you tie these resources to good business management will be a key variable.

Other issues relevant to the definition of success relate to Table 11.5; when asked about probable issues of importance 1 and 3 years from now, the survey respondents identified issues related to many of the critical success factors previously highlighted.

Table 11.6 also highlights some of the future management problems anticipated for this business.

As previously identified, bottom-line contribution will be a significant problem to resolve.

Understanding What Differentiates
The Winners From the Losers

As Table 11.7 depicts, there are some very tangible items that differentiate the winners in hospital-based health promotion from the losers. Clearly, structuring the business from a for-profit, market-sensitive perspective with a continuum of services is the key to success. Just as important is the use of finely tuned financial systems to manage the business. As part of your management checklist, establishing these areas in a coordinated, planned fashion is more advisable than implementing in a shotgun approach.

Proactively Managing the Future

There are several tasks that administrators can undertake immediately as they begin to manage the future (rather than letting the future manage them). One is to determine the financial worth of the business. What is the financial value of the direct and indirect benefits of the business? How much is this business really worth to the hospital? This will assist everyone in making informed decisions about the business. Second, can your hospital begin managing the business by

- cross-marketing for profitability,
- increasing efficiencies through economies of scale, and
- measuring and tracking patients and inpatient utilization?

We know that the hospitals with successful health promotion businesses have attempted this. Finally, have you addressed how this business unit fits the overall strategic plan of the hospital? As Table 11.8 demonstrates, hospital administrator perspectives on this question lead to the interpretation that the full impact of health promotion has not been realized, planned for, or anticipated.

Table 11.6 Problems to Solve for Present and Future Success

Present problems	Percent responding	Future areas of concern	Percent responding
☐ Program coordination/selection	16	☐ Bottom-line contribution	12
☐ Bottom-line contribution	12	☐ Cost containment	11
☐ Cost containment	12	☐ Reimbursement	9
☐ Meeting community needs/Market sensitivity	7	☐ Program development/design	9
☐ Quality/Participant satisfaction	6	☐ Competition	8

Note. From ''Health Promotion Young, But Growing: The *Optimal Health*/Price Waterhouse Health Promotion Survey,'' 1987 (July/August), *Optimal Health*, pp. 22-24. Copyright 1987 by *Optimal Health* and Price Waterhouse. Reprinted by permission.

Table 11.7 Observations About Providers Doing Well in Hospital-Based Health Promotion

Business area	Observation
Management and structure	Designed as a business with profit centers and proactive leaders
Market strategy	Market driven—image, diversification, pricing, referral network
Service delivery model	Convenient, tailored continuum, MIS-driven
Financial systems and performance	Budgets used for planning and control; understand economic forces

Note. From *Internal Analysis* by Price Waterhouse, 1987. Reprinted by permission.

The administrators' perception that health promotion contributes very little to revenue diversification, referral networks, and alternative delivery services points to the fact that perhaps communication of the full benefits of health promotion has not been sufficiently integrated into the business plan. More importantly, when reviewing how administrators view health promotion contributing to the strategic plan (Table 11.8), there are contradictory reasons as to the future success factors of bottom-line contribution. Obviously the connections will need to be made for the future survival of these businesses. This will most likely come from connecting the strategic plan of the hospital directly to the goals of this business.

BROADER MANAGEMENT PERSPECTIVES

As has been mentioned throughout this chapter, management issues regarding the hospital-based health promotion business are undergoing change as the business complexity increases and future issues of survival become more apparent. What will become important from an administrative perspective is the ability of management to meet the challenges of integrating strategic, organizational, and operational issues, as described in Table 11.9.

Addressing these issues in an interactive manner, building from strategic to organizational to operational, will ensure that from an administrative perspective the necessary challenges and issues are met, leaving little room for anything to fall between the cracks.

Table 11.8   Health Promotion Contributions to Strategic Plan

Very important contribution	Percent responding	Contributes very little	Percent responding
☐ Image enhancement in the larger community	55	☐ Referral network	55
☐ Quality service	51	☐ Revenue diversification	53
☐ Enhancing corporate relationships	48	☐ Supplement/Complement alternative delivery services	51
		☐ Patient utilization	48
		☐ Provision of full services	48

Note. From "Health Promotion Young, But Growing: The *Optimal Health*/Price Waterhouse Health Promotion Survey," 1987 (July/August), *Optimal Health*, pp. 22-24. Copyright 1987 by *Optimal Health* and Price Waterhouse. Reprinted by permission.

Table 11.9   Administrative Challenges and Issues

Challenges	Specific issues
Strategic	There are three major issues related to the strategic area. Ensuring the fulfillment of the strategic role and objectives as defined by the hospital is of prime importance. Next, defining how you will beat the competition today and in the future needs to be addressed. Finally, focus on how you will sustain your competitive advantages over time.
Organizational	There are many issues that require attention in this area. Any product line development effort similar to health promotion efforts like these require the organization to • build institutional culture that will support this business unit; and • align key organizational support elements to insure efficiency and effectiveness. Addressing this area will obviously impact decision making, reporting relationships, and staffing needs.
Operational	The overall theme for this area is to address functional performance factors. Issues such as how to ensure operating effectiveness/scale (information systems, communication, customer service, etc.) and steps to manage down costs will be critical.

SUMMARY

Adopting a broader perspective in managing hospital-based health promotion businesses requires attention to several key variables:

• Defining your role and responsibilities administratively
• Using vision to plan and address the future of your business
• Knowing "when to hold and when to fold"
• Organizationally, being able to balance turfs and egos for efficiency
• Knowing the importance of consistent measurement and tracking of results

There are no simple solutions to the future of managing these product lines. However it should be noted that the future *is* bright for an integrated health promotion business, and that this business can be developed as an asset to the hospital.

CHAPTER 12

The Roles of Other Professionals in Hospital Health Promotion

Philip K. Wilson

M any professionals are considered part of the "wellness team," in addition to the administrator, physician, and nurse. The exercise physiologist (exercise leader or fitness instructor), health educator, nutritionist, and in some cases, physical therapists and recreational specialists are all important members of the team. A final member of the team, likely to have a specialty in possibly any of the aforementioned areas, is the program director. Accordingly, the following is a description of the responsibilities of the program director, followed by discussions of specific members of the team (excluding the administrator, physician, and nurse, as these have been discussed in previous chapters).

THE PROGRAM DIRECTOR

The program director is the key to an efficient and effective wellness program (Abbott, 1988; Sawyer, 1986; Wilson & Hall, 1984). The program director functions as the hands-on leader of the program, and as the "day-to-day, nuts-and-bolts" person. As the individual responsible for daily operation and reporting to an assigned manager in the hospitals' administrative structure, the program director must have the ability to operate the unit successfully. Attributes of the successful program director are knowledge of the field, confidence, fairness, flexibility, and the ability to delegate responsibility.

Knowledge

The program director must be knowledgeable about and well acquainted with all aspects of the program. Although it is not necessary to be expert in every facet of the program, the director should have access to other individuals with the appropriate expertise. The staff's confidence in administrative decisions is greatly enhanced when the director is knowledgeable. In addition, a director who knows what is right and what works can simplify and save time in the decision-making process.

Confidence

In addition to being knowledgeable, the program director must have confidence in all areas of management. This confidence must be apparent to the staff in the decisions that are made and the actions that are taken. Often, a decision may not immediately appear to be correct and, at times, may even prove to be incorrect. In these circumstances, the director must be able to admit mistakes. This is the true test of the confidence of the program director.

Fairness

Another important attribute of a good director is fairness. Inexperienced program directors often display favoritism to some employees and ignore the accomplishments of others. The director must be fair and equally attentive to all staff members regardless of personal feelings. The ultimate evaluation of the merits and worth of an employee must be based on productivity and performance, not on favoritism or friendship. Every employee should feel special.

Flexibility

There may be several ways to accomplish a particular task. In these circumstances, flexibility is an important trait for administrators. Experienced program directors realize that they do not always know the best way to complete a task. Flexibility allows them to shift gears in the middle of a task and try an alternative method.

Delegating Responsibility

One of the most important characteristics of a good program director is the ability to delegate responsibility and authority. Inexperienced administrators often delegate but are hesitant to give the authority necessary to complete the task. One must delegate, provide direction, and then allow the individual to work on the task without interference. A good administrator does not hesitate to delegate responsibility and authority, and when doing so, should expect and accept mistakes. Ultimately, the program director is responsible for task performance and the overall conduct of the program.

Additional Management Concerns

One of the most difficult and stressful management skills concerns how to approach incompetent employees. Employees should be made aware of their responsibilities through job descriptions. Then, if the employee is unable to accomplish a particular job-task, either the job is too complex or the individual is not capable. The program director should carefully review the job description and resolve the problem. If incompetence is the case, the responsibilities of the position must be documented in writing and the individual informed that a performance review is being undertaken. A reasonable time period must then be established, after which the individual's performance is evaluated again. If the employee is still performing unsatisfactorily, then that person must either be reassigned to another position or released. The retention of incompetent employees can be detrimental to other employees as well as to the entire program. A mistake often made is to reassign some of the incompetent employee's responsibilities to another person. This usually results in a good employee having to complete the tasks of two people and often has a negative impact on the morale of the entire staff.

Although dealing with incompetent employees is difficult for a program director, the management of good employees is often ignored. An employee who performs well must be recognized and sufficiently rewarded. When good work goes unrewarded, the results can be equally demoralizing to the program staff. Unfortunately, one cannot always reward with promotions, since a position for promotion must be vacant, and the promotion must be well deserved.

Finally, administrators must examine their own personalities in order to develop management techniques and styles with which they are comfortable and that result in a productive and loyal staff who enjoy their work. Not all program directors have the personality required to be well liked. Most, however, have the ability to be good administrators respected by their staff. The "good guy" image is a trap into which many inexperienced administrators unknowingly fall. All administrators must know their own qualities and how they can best perform as an integral part of the overall program.

One method of determining effectiveness as a program director is to create both informal and formal mechanisms for staff input and performance review. Although not all program directors are capable of doing this on an informal basis, there is no excuse for failure to create a formal review process. Everyone on the staff should have the opportunity to evaluate the performance of the supervisors, as they, in turn, expect to be evaluated by them.

ADDITIONAL STAFF

Additional staff of the program can include an exercise physiologist, a health educator, a nutritionist, and possibly a physical therapist and a recreational specialist.

Exercise Physiologist

The exercise physiologist is the person most likely to be found on a wellness staff,
if a broad definition of exercise physiologist is used. There is no universally accepted definition of an exercise physiologist, and accordingly anyone who deals
with an individual in an exercise setting can be called an exercise physiologist.
However, the most common field from which exercise physiologists emerge is
physical education (Stoedefalke, 1973). Most state-of-the-art undergraduate physical education programs have emphasis areas in fitness leadership, corporate fitness,
or adult fitness (Wilson & Hall, 1984). Graduates of these areas are employed
in exercise programs based in communities, hospitals, or corporations. (Oldridge,
1977; Christina, 1982). Many of the more aggressive young professionals soon
enter graduate schools where similar programs exist.

Responsibilities of the exercise physiologist will vary from those of a fitness
instructor to, in many cases, those of a program director. With the tremendous
variance in job responsibility, it is extremely important to assess the abilities and
background of the individual and assign responsibilities as appropriate. The American College of Sports Medicine (ACSM) has developed a certification program
for exercise physiology personnel (1986). Various levels of certification are offered

Figure 12.1. American College of Sports Medicine (ACSM) preventive/rehabilita-
tive certification, as developed and maintained by the ACSM Preventive/Rehabilita-
tive Exercise Program Committee.

within both the rehabilitation and prevention fields, and include exercise test technologist, exercise specialist, exercise leader, fitness director, and program director. Figure 12.1 illustrates this certification process; Figure 12.2 illustrates, in detail, the preventive area.

Each certification level is developed according to specific behavioral objectives and requires passing a written and practical examination. Over 1,500 professionals have been certified by the ACSM since 1975.

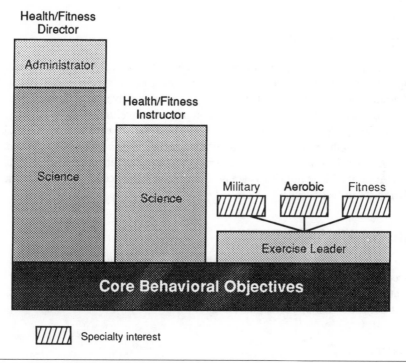

Figure 12.2. ACSM certification preventive tract, 1987.

Health Educator

The health educator position is extremely important and has responsibility for the many behavioral changes required of participants in the program. Health educators can be prepared at either the undergraduate or graduate level, as many university programs now specialize in developing individuals for placement in wellness and adult fitness programs based in hospitals, communities, and corporations. The health educator is responsible for stress reduction programs, weight loss and nutritional diet programs, smoking cessation programs, and other offerings intended to improve the health of program participants.

Nutritionist

Nutrition specialists or dietitians are important members of the wellness team. These individuals may work on a one-on-one basis with participants, or they may teach classes. The Sports and Cardiovascular Nutritionists (SCAN) section of the American Dietetic Association (ADA) is a dietetic practice group dedicated to professional efforts toward weight loss and management of participants involved in exercise, wellness, and, in a general term, sports medicine-type programs (Marcus, 1986).

Physical Therapist

In many programs, the physical therapist is an important component of the team. Sports medicine as a specialty is an emphasis area of the American Physical Therapy Association (APTA). In addition, a subspecialty area of cardiovascular disease of the APTA offers a certification program involving 5 years of practice in the field, 3 years of which must be full-time patient care in cardiovascular disease of both an acute and rehabilitative nature (*Cardiopulmonary Specialty Council*, 1984). Many programs consider cardiac rehabilitation and the care and treatment of athletic injuries as areas of emphasis in service and employ physical therapists in that service capacity.

Recreation Specialist

An extensive recreation program is often a service of a wellness program, and accordingly, a recreation specialist is employed to conduct this service. The recreation specialist is usually a graduate of an undergraduate program in recreation and parks service or recreation therapy.

Other Staff

Other staff may consist of secretarial and clerical personnel, and possibly volunteers. The secretarial and clerical duties may be performed by part-time staff for a small program or full-time personnel for a larger program. Receptionist and telephone duties are usually a part of this position. It is extremely important that these individuals be good role models for health and physical fitness. Program participants must always be reminded of the need for personal fitness, and the good example of all staff members is important.

Volunteers can also play a significant role as program staff. Lay personnel with significant interest and reasonable understanding of the program area can become very important in provided services. Students in various curricula in the area can also be of assistance to a program. Most important with volunteers is a clear understanding of the limitations of their assignments. Volunteers must understand their abilities and not extend beyond them.

OTHER CERTIFICATIONS

Additional certifications, dependent upon services provided and related staff, must be considered. Exercise sessions with an emphasis on dance are often popular offerings. Several dance associations offer certification programs that should be considered for assigned program staff (International Dance Exercise Association, 1986; "Basic Facts," 1985). Certainly, a certification requirement for all staff is the American Heart Association (AHA) basic cardiac life support (BCLS). In addition, the AHA has also developed advanced cardiac life support (ACLS) certification, which includes intubation, defibrillation, intravenous techniques, recognition and treatment of cardiac arrhythmias, and acid-base management ("Standard and Guidelines," 1986). Though the course is very advanced, a portion of the wellness staff should be ACLS certified.

CONCLUSION

The staff of a program will vary greatly dependent upon the goals, objectives, and resulting services offered. Proper staff is unquestionably the number-one priority for an effective and efficient program. It is the responsibility of the involved hospital administration, the assigned administrator of the program, and the program director to always place quality staff as an absolute requirement. Nothing is more essential to a quality program than a quality staff.

ACKNOWLEDGMENT

Portions of this chapter have been adapted from Chapter 10, "Personnel," also by Philip K. Wilson, in *Cardiac Rehabilitation, Adult Fitness, and Exercise Testing* by P. Fardy, F. Yanowitz, and P. Wilson, 1988, Philadelphia: Lea and Febiger.

REFERENCES

Abbott, R. (1988). Who should administer the cardiac rehabilitation program: Exercise physiologist, nurse, physical therapist, physician. In L.K. Hall & C. Meyer (Eds.), *Cardiac rehabilitation, exercise testing and prescription: Vol. 2* (pp. 3-43). Champaign, IL: Life Enhancement Publications.

American College of Sports Medicine. (1986). *Guidelines for graded exercise testing and exercise prescription* (3rd ed.). Philadelphia: Lea and Febiger.

Basic facts on forty-seven training organizations. (1985, January/February). *Dance Exercise Today*, p. 42.

Cardiopulmonary Specialty Council, Board for Certification of Advanced Clinical Competence. (1984). Alexandria, VA: American Physical Therapy Association.

Christina, J. (1982, July). The fitness professional: What to look for in a qualified director. *Athletic Purchasing and Facilities*, p. 38.

International Dance Exercise Association. (1986). *Industry and certification examination* (Bulletin of Information). San Diego: Author.

Marcus, J.B. (1986). *Sports nutrition: A guide for the professional working with active people*. Chicago: American Dietetic Association.

Oldridge, N.B. (1977). What to look for in an exercise class leader. *Physician and Sportsmedicine*, **5**, 85.

Sawyer, T.H. (1985, August/September). The employee program director: Part 1. *Corporate Fitness and Recreation*, pp. 38-41.

Sawyer, T.H. (1985, October/November). The employee program director: Part 2. *Corporate Fitness and Recreation*, pp. 43-47.

Sawyer, T.H. (1986, December/January). The employee program director: Part 3. *Corporate Fitness and Recreation*, pp. 43-50.

Standard and guidelines for cardiopulmonary resuscitation (CPR) and emergency cardiac care (ECG). (1986). *Journal of the American Medical Association*, **255**, 2905.

Stoedefalke, K.G. (1973). The physical educator's role in exercise programs. In J.P. Naughton, H.K. Hellestein, & I.C. Mohler (Eds.), *Exercise testing and exercise training in coronary heart disease*. Orlando: Academic Press.

Wilson, P.K., & Hall, L.K. (1984). Personnel of adult fitness and cardiac rehabilitation programs. *Journal of Health, Physical Education, and Recreation*, pp. 40-44.

Case Studies
of Hospital Health
Promotion Programs

I nstitutional goals differ among hospitals of different sizes as well as health promotion programs, therefore the nature and scope of the programs differ.

Part V examines specific cases of hospital health promotion programs of exemplary hospitals that differ primarily in size and location. Chapter 13 provides a case study of a health promotion program for a hospital of 200 beds or fewer, chapter 14 for a hospital of 200 to 750 beds, and chapter 15 for one of our nation's very large hospitals of over 1,000 beds.

Health Promotion in Hospitals of 200 or Fewer Beds

Barbara K. Burke

C an health promotion be done in a small hospital? It is easy to think of reasons why it may be difficult. Most hospitals of this size are in rural areas. Therefore they draw from a small population base. Health promotion still shows itself to be most popular with upper-middle-class, college-educated individuals. If a hospital's population base is small to begin with, health promotion may be attractive only to this segment of an already small market. In addition, health promotion requires personnel with distinct knowledge and skills. Such personnel may not be available in rural locations. And finally, many hospitals originally get involved in health promotion to enhance their image or improve their competitive edge on other hospitals in their market. Again, this competitive motivation may not be a primary concern among rural hospitals.

This chapter examines three small hospitals that successfully provide health promotion programming to meet their own unique goals within the constraints and opportunities their settings offer. They dispel the myths of many of the above-mentioned statements.

NORTH COUNTRY HOSPITAL

North Country Hospital is an 80-bed facility in Newport, Vermont, population 5,000. The hospitals's service area extends 1,000 square miles to serve 25,000 residents. The health promotion program sees these people as their market even though it is a population that is not urban, well-educated, or affluent. It does have a higher percentage of poor, elderly, and children than do other areas of New England.

Strategic Planning

At the board level, North Country Hospital intentionally chose to remain a community hospital and emphasizes this role rather than trying for a high-tech hardware image. As a community hospital, North Country saw its primary goal as keeping the community healthy. Such a direction is certainly conducive to developing the soft technology of health promotion.

Program Development

Program development began in 1981 under Laird Covey. No formal needs assessment was done, but hospital personnel felt that they had a sense of what the community wanted and did not have much to lose in testing their theories. So they followed their instincts. From a small core of programs with a foundation in aerobics, they set as their goal to increase the number of program offerings by 300% in 5 years. As program offerings expanded, instructors reported a strong positive reaction to the socialization aspects of these community programs. Consequently, a wide variety of offerings was developed that emphasized socialization—cross-country skiing, square dancing, sign language, and others. Special programs were developed for the largest population segments in the North Country market: the elderly and children. An early decision was made to take the programs to the community, so schools, churches, and municipal buildings were used as program sites. Gradually a mailing list of 7,000 was developed to promote these program offerings.

Impact

In 1986 over 2,100 persons attended 140 health promotion programs offered by North Country Hospital. These numbers do not include those who participated in health fairs or screenings. All participants completed evaluation forms to help the hospital refine and direct its efforts.

Staffing

What is surprising is that all of these programs were generated with less than one full-time staff person. A 0.5 full-time equivalent (FTE) serves as a coordinator and a small fraction of clerical time is devoted to the project. The bulk of the services are provided by a staff of 25 to 30 contract personnel. Sue Alward, the coordinator, reports that to her amazement finding suitable contractors has never been a problem. Such people are available. Health promotion has permeated the hinterlands.

Funding

Participant fees pay for all direct costs and most of the indirect costs of North Country Hospital's health promotion program. The direct costs of instructor fees are covered by participant fees in all programs. The indirect costs of mailing, promotion, and staff coordination are covered by fees in many of the programs.

MYRTUE MEMORIAL HOSPITAL

Myrtue Memorial Hospital is a 49-bed hospital in Harlan, Iowa, population 5,000. Its health promotion program began in 1986. Even though Myrtue Memorial is the only hospital in the county, it views its competition as 50 miles away in Omaha, Nebraska.

Strategic Planning

Because of its location, Myrtue has developed many health services that entail specialists from "the city" coming to Harlan periodically to do specific procedures. Myrtue Memorial's first cataract surgery was performed in the summer of 1987. The hospital decided in its planning that it wanted its image to be one of good care close to home. Consequently, the health promotion program has become a cornerstone of this public relations theme.

Staffing

The program is staffed by a full-time coordinator (who also is responsible for staff development) and a part-time secretary. Many of the programs, however, are done by the hospital staff. The hospital wants the community to have a sense of who will be taking care of them when they need the services of the hospital. Consequently, nurses, dietitians, and physical therapists all are involved in doing health promotion.

Program Development

Health promotion had its roots in the community prenatal classes. From there a variety of programs have been developed in just one year. Cardiopulmonary resuscitation, "Women's Health Forum," "Healthy Heart Cooking" (taught at a local high school), and "I Can Cope" are just a few of the program offerings.

Since there is no local competition, the hospital easily aligns itself with the county school system. In 1987 the hospital did a smoking program in all 5th-grade classrooms in the county. The hospital has worked with the Red Cross in an AIDS education program and with the county extension and Emergency Medical Services commission on various efforts. Its senior citizen programming takes place at the senior citizen center meal site.

One of the hospital's most active components is a speakers bureau that gives two or three community talks a week. One of the more creative ways Myrtue Memorial has used its speakers bureau is to present talks on breast cancer prevention and then track the impact these talks have had on increasing usage of the mammogram procedure at the hospital.

The programs are promoted through a variety of ways:

- Mailing lists to distinct target groups (e.g., schools, diabetics, new parents)
- Ads as well as press releases in 10 to 12 local newspapers
- Press releases to all local churches and radio stations
- Promotion in the hospital direct mailer newsletter, a bimonthly publication mailed to 15,000 local households

Impact

Such promotion efforts have paid off. In the program's first fiscal year, 6,840 people attended its various public education efforts. An additional 1,621 participated in blood pressure screenings.

Funding

Nancy Boettger, education coordinator, reports that though many of its programs charge small fees to participants, its weight loss class has really made money for the health promotion program. While the health promotion personnel are feeling no pressure to recover all indirect costs, they are happy to be covering most of the direct expenditures for instructor costs. Most coordination, promotion, and facility expenses are not attributed to the program.

ST. VINCENT CARMEL HOSPITAL

St. Vincent Carmel Hospital is a 110-bed facility that opened its doors in the fall of 1985 as a satellite suburban hospital in Carmel, Indiana, 9 miles away from St. Vincent's main facility in Indianapolis.

Strategic Planning

Carmel, Indiana, is in one of the fastest-growing counties in the country and has the highest per-capita income of any county in Indiana. The St. Vincent Wellness Centers, a department of the main hospital corporation, were eager to provide health promotion services to meet the needs of this new facility. And the strategic needs of this new suburban hospital were very specific. St. Vincent Carmel Hospital wanted

- to have people from the community become familiar with the new—and only—hospital in their community and to begin to identify it as their hospital,
- to get potential clients acquainted with physicians who had taken offices in the new professional building adjacent to the hospital, and
- to have the hospital become involved in the fabric of the community.

The satellite hospital had no desire to make money from health promotion. It did, however, want it as a tool to achieve its aims with the community.

Program Implementation

The Wellness Centers were eager to meet these needs. An arrangement was made with the Carmel Hospital to coordinate local promotion and advertising of health promotion programs that would highlight the role of the hospital. Program topics were discussed with the hospital administrator to complement the newly arriving physicians. The Wellness Centers handle registration and budgeting, arrange instructors, conduct evaluations, and do program planning and implementation for the health promotion efforts run at and sponsored by Carmel Hospital. The Carmel Hospital's facility and name are used. Meeting the specific health promotion needs of the hospital was addressed in these ways:

- Transferring two existing prenatal classes into the Carmel Hospital conference center. Instantly more than 80 people per week were coming to the new facility.
- Developing a health information series, "Medically Speaking," to highlight new physicians and serve as a client recruitment tool for them. Physicians were asked to track new clients from these programs for 1 month after their program presentation. In the first 6 months of this series as many as 63 people attended these individual seminars, and physicians reported receiving up to six new clients each.
- Developing "Fit Families: A Day for Your Good Health," a spring extravaganza cosponsored by the hospital, the Wellness Centers, and the local school corporation. The Wellness Centers had a major corporate contract with the school system for several years. Carmel is a very family-oriented community. Promoting a day of family wellness activities seemed like a good fit. Through this joint effort, the hospital further developed its working relationships with the fire department, the school board, and the city and county councils. The day began with a walk from Carmel Hospital to Carmel High School in which 500 people participated. This Fit Families Day is now an

annual event. It has high recognition in the community as a Carmel Hospital project.

CONCLUSION

Health promotion is alive and well in rural and suburban America and in small hospitals. These three hospitals reveal models that work and that in some ways contradict popular stereotypes:

- Each of these hospitals had a strategic plan through which it identified how it wanted health promotion to assist it in reaching its goals.
- Small hospitals do feel competition and use health promotion in the same way as larger, more urban hospitals to keep their name and message in the minds of their market.
- Small hospitals in rural areas have some advantages over urban hospitals. They do not have to compete for local loyalty. With some ease they can align themselves with any organization in the community, whether it be churches, schools, the Red Cross, or other groups, and can be seen as the local health care experts.
- Staffing such health promotion programs does not seem to be a problem. Hospitals use their own staff, or contract with community personnel or personnel from affiliated health care institutions or other health and educational organizations. Each such arrangement can emphasize the hospital's strategic plan for health promotion.
- Small hospitals use health promotion for marketing their institutions and their services; little pressure is exerted for the programs to do more than cover their direct costs. There are few expectations that such programs make money for the hospital.
- Even though net financial goals are not primary, accountability is evidenced in programs beginning to track their success not only by numbers of participants, but by predetermined impact in such areas as physician referrals or special procedures requested later by program attendees.

CHAPTER 14

Health Promotion in a 686-Bed Hospital

Christine A. Aguiar

A not-for-profit hospital with 686 licensed beds, St. Luke's Hospital of Kansas City, is the largest of 25 hospitals in the Kansas City metropolitan area of approximately 1.5 million people. It has a medical staff of 510 with an employee base of 2,800 and services more than 25,000 patients per year.

As an excellent teaching hospital, St. Luke's supports medical and allied health education through its seven residency programs, its School of Nursing, and its educational programs in medical technology, radiologic technology, nuclear medicine technology, phlebotomy, radiation therapy technology, and clinical pastoral care.

SPECIALIZED PROGRAMS

St. Luke's offers many specialized programs and services that support the institution's philosophy of "the presence of care." Centers of excellence include the Level I trauma center and Level III intensive care nursery, the highest designations awarded by the state; comprehensive cardiac treatment in the Mid-America Heart Institute; a regional center for high-risk maternity care and neonatal service, as well as family-centered maternity care; ambulatory surgery; medical/psychiatric unit; a state-designated arthritis treatment center; a sexual assault treatment center; a pre-school speech and hearing program; and a kidney dialysis and transplantation center.

These centers of excellence are complemented by St. Luke's commitment to providing educational programs for its personnel and the public. Preventive health care and maintenance are the focus of Lifewise, Programs for Healthy Lifestyles. As the health promotion unit within the larger Department of Health Enhancement, Lifewise has become a comprehensive corporate and community health promotion program.

The History of the Lifewise Program

Initiated in 1980, Lifewise became the premier health promotion program in Kansas City. Early emphasis was almost exclusively on corporations and corporate leads through the offering of a specialized program, the Lifewise Executive Plan. These executive retreats, held in resorts across the country, enabled executives and their spouses to participate in health assessments, consultations, and fitness programs. Efforts to expand services to the community market included the offering of the lifestyle intervention programs of the National Center for Health Promotion: Smoke Stoppers, Be Trim, and Personal Stress Management. Management of a racquetball facility on a 151-acre fitness and recreation complex called Horizons was also a part of Lifewise's early function.

In 1983, Lifewise had the honor of being selected an Innovator of Community Health Promotion by the American Hospital Association (AHA). This recognition was given to 49 hospitals across the country that were identified as having high-quality, innovative health promotion programs. Lifewise participated in the Innovators Program of the AHA for several years.

Reorganizations and changes in management over the years have seen Lifewise move in and out of a for-profit subsidiary of St. Luke's, organized as a single department of the hospital, and most recently become a unit within a newly formed Department of Health Enhancement.

The mission of Lifewise has been to provide comprehensive, medically directed health promotion programs to individuals and organizations, to provide program and facility management services, to serve as a source of hospital referrals, and to maintain a financially self-sustaining position.

Lifewise supports the hospital's mission statement, "to ensure the highest level of excellence in providing health care services to all patients in a caring environment . . . to provide resources and encouragement for professional, and public, health-related education and research," through its delivery of high-quality health promotion services.

The Organization
of the Health Enhancement Department

The Department of Health Enhancement was formed in February 1987 by the merger of Lifewise with the Health Institute, the hospital's Phase II and Phase III clinical exercise and cardiac rehabilitation program. In addition, a commercial fitness center, the Lifewise Health and Fitness Center (formerly Lifewise at the Vista, which opened in April 1985) atop the Allis Plaza Hotel, became a part of the department. Two new units—Optifast, a medically supervised weight loss program, and a sports medicine program—became functional programs. In February of 1988, the department moved into a new two-story, 47,106-square-foot health and fitness facility, the Center for Health Enhancement. This multipurpose facility will strengthen St. Luke's community involvement by promoting more diversified programs to multiple target markets.

Approximately 35 FTEs (full-time equivalents) staff the entire Department of Health Enhancement. There are 7.60 FTEs dedicated to Lifewise programs, 5.25 FTEs dedicated to the management of a corporate client's health and fitness club, 8.50 dedicated to the management of the commercial fitness center, and 6.80 assigned to the Health Institute; the remaining staff are allocated to the Center for Health Enhancement. In addition to this staffing, numerous health professionals are utilized as instructors and facilitators for community and corporate programs. The Lifewise staff specifically comprises the following:

- 1.0 manager, Lifewise programs
- 1.0 exercise specialist
- 1.0 recreation specialist
- 2.6 health promotion specialists
- 1.0 nutrition specialist
- 1.0 program specialist

Several staff dedicated exclusively to the management of the health and fitness club of a major firm in Kansas City include the following:

- 1.0 fitness center manager
- 1.0 exercise specialist
- 2.0 recreation specialists
- 1.25 club attendants

The manager, Lifewise Programs; the manager, Health Institute; the manager, Lifewise Health and Fitness Center; the manager, Optifast; the manager, Sports Medicine; and a financial manager all report operationally to the department of Health Enhancement. The coordinator of Health Enhancement reports to a senior associate director, who reports to the chief operating officer, who reports to the chief executive officer.

A Health Enhancement Committee of the St. Luke's Hospital's Board of Directors provides advice and counsel regarding Health Enhancement services. This committee is made up of Kansas City business leaders and physicians from various specialties. One of the physicians serves as medical adviser to Lifewise.

COMPLEMENTING SERVICES

Services of St. Luke's that complement and support Health Enhancement but are not a part of the department structurally include the following.

St. Luke's Employee Assistance Program (EAP)

The EAP program, which is a part of the Human Resources Department, provides programs and counseling for hospital personnel and for corporations in the Kansas City metropolitan area.

Community Relations

Having no department of community education, St. Luke's provides health care information to the public through its Speakers Bureau, housed in the department of Community Relations. Advertising support for community services is also provided by this department. Health Enhancement collaborates with Community Relations in the provision of a weekly health column in the business section of the *Kansas City Times* newspaper and in the provision of special community events, such as health fairs.

Marketing and Sales

Two departments support Health Enhancement's marketing and sales efforts. Staff from the marketing department provide marketing and promotional efforts through the development of a market plan, the production of promotional literature, and overall marketing support. Specifically, marketing staff facilitate the physician's utilization of Lifewise prescription pads that allow for special program discounts, and coordinate a tracking project that documents hospital referrals from Lifewise. A representative from the sales department initiates sales calls to business and industry and enables Lifewise health promotion specialists to follow through with program proposals and health management consulting for corporate clients.

Older Adult Resource Center

As a specialized program designated to meet the needs of older adults, the Center coordinates benefits, assistance programs, and information for individuals 60 years of age and older. These "Sterling Club" members are given special discounts to Lifewise programs. In addition, special exercise programs such as t'ai chi ch'uan and aquatic fitness are offered exclusively to Sterling Club members. Joint staffing of preretirement seminars is another example of cooperative efforts.

Industrial Clinics

St. Luke's offers a full range of occupational medicine services through its Industrial Clinics, health care facilities located in the various parts of the metropolitan area. A few of the services offered that particularly complement the health promotion efforts are

- health evaluations for business clientele,
- work hardening and functional capacity assessments,
- return-to-work assessments,
- Back-In-Shape (a back-care program), and
- coordination of in-plant employee health services.

COMPREHENSIVE HEALTH PROMOTION COMPONENTS

With its reorganization in 1985, Lifewise set out to become the most comprehensive health promotion provider to the Kansas City community at large, as well as to business and industry. A market study initiated in 1986 to assess the corporate consumer's interests and demands has been continually updated and supported by marketing data. As a result, Lifewise maintains a comprehensive product line in the four areas of

- assessment services,
- educational services,
- awareness and promotional services, and
- management services.

Assessment Services

Lifewise offers a wide range of programs that screen and assess an individual's health. Comprehensive fitness assessments, executive physicals, health risk appraisals (HRAs), and nutritional analyses are examples of services that pinpoint existing and potential health problems. For company-wide programs, Lifewise offers services such as health needs assessments, health exchanges (on-site lifestyle-oriented health fairs), and cafeteria enhancements. These programs assist the company in determining the present needs of its employees and provides Lifewise with important information for program design and implementation.

Educational Services

The educational service area provides the backbone of Lifewise's programs. The short programs are popular with companies that provide ongoing health promotion services to their employees. Lunch-n-Learns, brief health programs, and four-hour Living and Working Life-Wisely lifestyle change seminars are easily implemented at the worksite. The comprehensive lifestyle intervention programs are key services for employers to provide their personnel. In 1987, Lifewise developed its own smoking cessation program, No Smoke. This program provides a comprehensive approach to smoking cessation, which includes information and practical skill mastery in the areas of stress management, healthy nutrition, and fitness. Equally comprehensive is the Diet No More program developed by Lifewise in 1986. Management of food intake without the use of scales or a diet plan is the focus of this popular and effective program. Less Stress, the stress management program, is adaptable to meet the needs of the consumer; it can be presented in a seminar series format or as a comprehensive intervention program.

Fitness classes, offered primarily for the community and for St. Luke's personnel, include

- For Mothers Only—a pregnancy and postpartum exercise class,
- Get Fit—a comprehensive program geared to introduce nonexercisers to the many options of aerobic exercise,
- Stay Fit—a self-paced exercise program for the graduates of Get Fit and for those who are already exercising,
- Heartfelt Rhythms—a fitness program choreographed to music, and
- Health Watch—an exercise program targeted to high-risk populations.

Awareness and Promotion Services

During the initiation of health promotion services at the worksite and as support to existing programs, Lifewise provides a wide array of communications activities and awareness events. From seat belt campaigns to fitness walks, Lifewise coordinates special events to motivate employees and to keep them adherent to their healthy lifestyles. Other services in this area include

- theme and logo development,
- health newsletters,
- health columns for existing company publications,
- bulletin boards, and
- health fitness displays.

Management Services

A unique aspect of Lifewise's services is the management of programs at the worksite. Being flexible to accommodate the different needs of companies, Lifewise provides facility management as well as program management.

For 5 years, Lifewise has managed a health and fitness club for a major company headquartered in Kansas City. Providing facility management at two locations is a dedicated Lifewise staff of 5.25 FTEs. Recreational leadership and program development are included in the range of management services for this particular corporate client.

Task group facilitation and coordinator training are popular with companies that have multiple sites. General planning, development, implementation, and consultation are also key services provided in the management area.

COMMUNITY AND CORPORATE MARKETS

Lifewise delivers to both the community at large and to business and industry. The community market dictates that Lifewise provide educational programs on an ongoing basis and in different geographical areas of the city. Revenues from 1986 showed that more than 50% of the earnings came from community programs. No Smoke and Diet No More are by far the most popular programs and continue to reflect the community's demand for high-quality lifestyle change programs. A specific segment of the community market that receives special attention is the older adult, through the provision of programs for Sterling Club members.

On a yearly basis, Lifewise provides services to approximately 50 different companies in the Kansas City metropolitan area, ranging from single programs to comprehensive management services. Although most companies purchase single services, like No Smoke or a series of Lunch-n-Learns, several opt for multiple services purchased under a service contract and paid for on a monthly fee basis. A third alternative for the purchase of Lifewise services is an annual management contract. The health promotion specialists and manager serve the corporate clients as account executives, providing management consulting for the company.

A response to the specific corporate market of downtown Kansas City prompted St. Luke's Hospital to lease the 22nd floor of the Vista International Hotel for the purpose of managing an executive fitness center. The hotel, now under new ownership and management and called the Allis Plaza Hotel, still houses an exclusive personal health management center for the downtown Kansas City corporate clientele. This Lifewise Health and Fitness Center is staffed by approximately 8.5 FTEs, including

- 1.0 manager, Lifewise Health and Fitness Center,
- 1.0 health promotion specialist,
- 2.0 fitness specialists, and
- 4.5 center attendants.

The Center's services include a 20-yard lap pool, state-of-the art exercise equipment, fitness classes, and towel and laundry services. More important than the amenities of the Center is the personal attention to the more than 300 members who receive professionally designed programs for cardiovascular conditioning. A highly qualified staff, supported by Lifewise faculty, provide nutrition and exercise information designed to produce positive results and to accommodate the demanding schedules of corporate clients.

THE LIFEWISE PROGRAM
FOR ST. LUKE'S HOSPITAL'S PERSONNEL

While it is an operational unit within the hospital, Lifewise is in the unique position of also being a provider to St. Luke's. Under the arrangement of a special cost center, Lifewise dedicates a 1.0 FTE, a health promotion specialist, to the coordination of a comprehensive health promotion program for hospital personnel.

A Lifewise task force, chaired by the coordinator of human resources and consisting of managers and supervisors from various departments in the hospital, meets monthly to approve programming and activities for the personnel. This committee administers a special budget dedicated to subsidization of Lifewise services for employees. Through this budget, all educational and assessment services offered to the community are offered to the hospital's personnel at substantially reduced fees. Some services are offered exclusively to the employees, and others are totally funded by this special budget. For example, employees may choose to have blood cholesterol and body fat analyses included in their annual physicals free-of-charge. This service facilitates a greater health awareness and an opportunity for education and support through the employee's participation in suggested lifestyle change programs.

Special events to promote health awareness, with incentives for participation, are popular with the hospital personnel. Efforts are made to accommodate different shifts without interrupting normal work patterns. Walk/runs in which participants estimate their finishing times have topped the charts for the most participation and are actively supported by the employee's Walk/Run Club. Recreational clubs and leagues complement the provision of more traditional health education programming.

A major special event, carried out over the course of 12 months, combined awareness, health education, and support for lifestyle change. A comprehensive seat belt campaign facilitated an increase in seat belt utilization by employees from 45% to 75%, as documented by random observational audits. This program, inspired by the Missouri Hospital Association and supported by the hospital's Community Relations department, received a Certificate of Special Achievement from the Health Promotion Council of the Civic Health Foundation of Greater Kansas City.

Special programs in the hospital cafeteria, including Lunch-n-Learns and Lifewise Lunches, enhance the visibility of the health promotion programs. Cooperative projects with other departments, such as Respiratory Services for the "Great American Smokeout," have been successful ventures. The offering of health promotion programs at the hospital worksite provides support for a corporate culture that encourages optimal health and allows for the modeling of the hospital's program by other corporate clients.

THE FUTURE GROWTH OF LIFEWISE

In February 1988, the health promotion and cardiac rehabilitation services of Health Enhancement moved into the Center for Health Enhancement, a new 47,106-square-foot fitness facility that includes

- a 17-lap-to-a-mile track,
- two racquetball courts,
- a 25-meter lap pool,
- a weight-training room,
- a gymnasium,
- two classrooms,
- four locker rooms,
- a conference room,
- a sports medicine clinic,
- an Optifast clinic, and
- the Health Enhancement offices.

This multipurpose facility allows for improved efficiency in staffing, enhanced coordination of services, and greater accessibility of wellness programs and outpatient cardiac rehabilitation services to the community and to hospital personnel. Recent expansion of related services includes the offering of Optifast, a special weight loss program, and a sports medicine program that provides prevention and rehabilitation programs for athletes.

The Lifewise program of St. Luke's Hospital of Kansas City remains committed to providing quality comprehensive, cost-efficient health promotion services that are responsive to a diverse market. As identified within the hospital's strategic plan and supported by marketing and business plans, Health Enhancement and Lifewise will continue to extend existing health enhancement services. The hospital's support of Lifewise programs since 1980 demonstrates its commitment to the "presence of care" across the health continuum and ensures that St. Luke's Hospital of Kansas City will remain a recognized leader in the health care field. Lifewise, Programs for Healthy Lifestyles and the Department of Health Enhancement should serve as examples to other tertiary care hospitals that value diversification of services and extension of traditional clinical care.

CHAPTER 15

Health Promotion in a 1,400-Bed Hospital

Carolyn I. Speros

Methodist Health Systems of Memphis, Tennessee, is a not-for-profit corporation founded by the North Arkansas, North Mississippi, and Memphis Conferences of the United Methodist Church. It was established in 1982 by the board of directors of Methodist Hospitals of Memphis to provide a framework for a regional multihospital system.

MARKET POSITION, MISSION, AND FINANCIAL GOALS

Methodist Health Systems is the 14th-largest health care system in the country. It is diversified and fully integrated, encompassing 17 organizations that include, among others, home care services, an insurance company, a durable medical equipment company, and a freestanding substance abuse center. It is the third-largest private employer in the city of Memphis, employing more than 5,000 associates.

Methodist Hospitals of Memphis is the flagship of Methodist Health Systems. It is a 1,400-bed tertiary care center that includes one urban hospital and two satellite community hospitals in Memphis. Methodist Hospitals of Memphis, together with seven regional community hospitals owned and managed by Methodist Health Systems, service a 62-county referral area covering four states in the mid-southern region of the country.

Methodist Central serves as the hub of medical and administrative activities for the system. With more than 1,000 physicians on staff, it is a center for research, professional education, acute inpatient care, and outpatient services.

Methodist Health Systems is a dynamic, progressive organization that is fully committed to being a leader in the health care industry. Its focus in the future will center on strategic growth, integrated services, and alternative delivery systems. Its commitment to person-centered care is reflected in its position statement: "Relentless dedication to the art of healing."

The WELLTH program was established in 1983 initially as a community outreach campaign. Because of the strong ties that exist to the Methodist Church, health screenings were conducted in churches within the three owning conferences to service the Methodist community. The program quickly proved to be successful in increasing loyalty for Methodist Hospitals in the primary service area, and generated incremental admissions into the regional and Memphis hospitals of the system.

Shortly after the community outreach activities began, employers in the region demonstrated interest in many of the same services, such as health education, screenings, and fitness activities. The scope of the health promotion effort expanded quickly to respond to the needs of a changing marketplace.

Early in 1984, the WELLTH program was funded and structured to service area employers, Methodist Health Systems employees, and groups and individuals within the Memphis community at large. The Methodist Health Systems WELLTH program was designed to

- enhance Methodist Health Systems's image in the corporate community and the community at large,
- create top-of-mind awareness of Methodist Hospitals as a source of health-related services and information,
- meet target market demand for health promotion and disease prevention products and services,
- increase market share of patients for Methodist Hospitals through health assessment and referral activities, and
- evaluate the risks for preventable diseases among the Methodist clergy and church community and provide services to intervene.

The program's financial goals were to

- break even by the 2nd year of operation and be profitable by the 3rd year, and
- generate incremental revenue from direct sales of health promotion products and services.

The objectives of the WELLTH program relate directly to the strategic goals of Methodist Health Systems and its mission: "To promote healthful living and wholeness in all persons."

ORGANIZATION

The organizational structure of the WELLTH program was designed to centralize the program's administration and coordination of preventive services being provided by Methodist Hospitals of Memphis and the regional hospitals. The program is administered by the Department of Health Promotion within the Division of Health and Welfare Ministries at the corporate level. Sales, budgeting, planning, and quality control are the responsibility of the Department of Health Promotion management. The Department of Patient and Community Education within the Division of Nursing collaborates in the execution of the program and coordinates the provision of the educational services associated with the effort.

The staff assigned to the WELLTH program include exercise physiologists, dietitians, nurses, physical educators, and clerical personnel. Additional contract staff are utilized to teach health education programs and provide fitness services in the community. Health professionals from all areas of the system are called upon to contribute their expertise to assure multidisciplinary involvement in the WELLTH program.

PRODUCTS AND SERVICES

The success of the WELLTH program is based on its customer-driven, comprehensive line of products and services. Figure 15.1 represents the variety of service areas that constitute WELLTH.

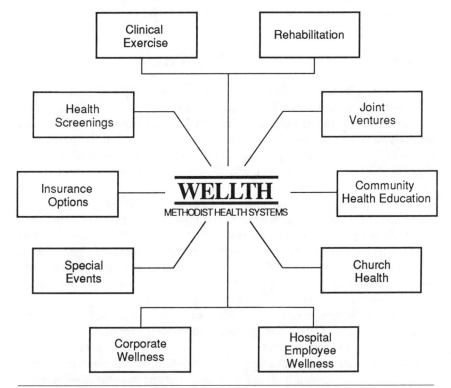

Figure 15.1.   Health promotion services provided by WELLTH.

Each service shares resources with the others, assuring cost-effective, efficient delivery. The needs of each service's target audience determine the products and activities offered.

CLINICAL EXERCISE AND REHABILITATION PROGRAMS

The cardiac rehabilitation program is a three-phase, structured clinical exercise and education program that serves as the cornerstone of the hospital's health promotion effort.

Physical therapists, dietitians, exercise physiologists, and registered nurses within the Departments of Health Promotion, Patient and Community Education, and Rehabilitation Services are assigned to the hospital's cardiac rehabilitation program. A medical advisory committee approves treatment protocols and supervises the effort to assure quality and consistency of treatment practices in all three hospitals and adherence to medical standards of practice for cardiac rehabilitation. Clinical exercise is also provided to inpatient and outpatient psychiatric patients, and to inpatients in the eating disorder unit. Because these services are reimbursed by third-party payers, revenues associated with the clinical rehabilitation programs offset expenses of other, nonrevenue-generating health promotion activities.

HEALTH SCREENING PROGRAMS

Approximately 30 health screenings are conducted annually in churches, malls, and community centers within the primary service area of Methodist Health Systems to fulfill the organization's outreach objective. These highly publicized events are designed to enhance awareness of the services of the Systems hospitals, connect participants with staff physicians and referring physicians loyal to Methodist Hospitals, and create goodwill in the Methodist church community that founded and governs the board of the system.

A team of health professionals employed and contracted by the hospital is taken on the road to conduct the screenings in Arkansas, Mississippi, and Tennessee. Standards and protocols for the screenings are established by the Department of Health Promotion and Nursing at the Memphis hospital. The staffs of the regional hospitals owned by Methodist Health Systems are trained by the Memphis personnel to conduct the screenings in their respective communities in accordance with the standards established for the activity.

Referrals to Methodist Hospitals of Memphis that are generated by the health fairs are tracked annually to justify continued funding over time. Participants' Social Security numbers are loaded into the hospital's mainframe computer and compared to inpatient and outpatient admissions data. In this manner, a record of admissions, services utilized, and revenue generated from the admission can be credited annually to the health fairs conducted by the WELLTH program. Approximately 1% to 2% of those seen in a health screening result in direct admissions to the hospital within 6 months of the event.

WORKSITE HEALTH PROMOTION

Health promotion services are sold directly to local employers primarily to generate revenue for the hospital, but also to nurture a positive relationship between the hospital and the local business community. Lifestyle and wellness programs conducted at the worksite are designed to be customer-centered and appealing to those employers committed to enhancing employee morale and productivity. The diversity of services and large number of health professionals associated with an organization the size of Methodist enhance the hospital's ability to provide an unlimited range of health promotion programs to employers at the worksite.

Risk reduction classes, assessment services such as health risk appraisals, on-site screenings, and executive physicals, fitness programs from aerobics to specialty exercise classes, and consultation services make up a comprehensive product line of health promotion services marketed to business and industry under Methodist Health System's WELLTH logo.

Services are priced to be competitive with other providers of similar products in the Memphis area. Most are priced at 40% above cost, with occasional discounts offered to employers purchasing a large volume of services. The most profitable product for Methodist is an on-site program-management arrangement in which a health promotion specialist employed by the hospital is contracted by the company to manage the worksite health promotion effort. Salaries and benefits associated with the specialist, fees for a package of services, and remuneration for consultation are calculated into the fee for the management contract. This product has proved to be highly attractive to large employers, particularly those with on-site wellness centers.

A sales force of three full-time employees of Methodist handles all sales calls and contract negotiations. Individuals from the hospital are often called upon to accompany the salesperson to offer detailed explanations of products in their area of expertise. Sales of health promotion products and services exceeded $350,000 in 1988.

HEALTH PROMOTION
FOR AFFILIATED CLERGY

Because of the close ties that the hospital maintains with the United Methodist Church, Methodist clergymen and their families have been a target for health promotion services. Special clinics for the clergymen were initiated early in the program's development to provide health assessment and intervention services to this at-risk population. Participants undergo a comprehensive medical examination at the hospital and are made aware of the roles nutrition, exercise, stress reduction, and spirituality play in health maintenance. Information about Methodist Health Systems is provided to all of the ministers participating in the clinic to enhance their awareness of the resources available to them and their parishioners at the hospital.

Experience has revealed that Methodist ministers are at extremely high risk for cardiovascular disease. Approximately 30% to 40% of the clergymen examined are found to require medical attention for asymptomatic disorders and early stages of illnesses. The gratitude of these and other program participants frequently translates into referrals to physicians and various services of Methodist Health Systems.

JOINT VENTURES
WITH FITNESS CENTERS

At a time when capital expenses are closely scrutinized in hospitals, Methodist has elected to joint-venture with others in securing access to fitness facilities. In 1984, Methodist entered into a management relationship with a large racquet club in Memphis. The club was interested in converting the space from indoor tennis courts into a comprehensive fitness center. Methodist was contracted to develop, staff, and manage the sports medicine and fitness program conducted at the club facility.

The hospital receives a management fee, reimbursement for staff salaries, and additional revenue for contracted services. The contract includes the provision of on-site fitness evaluations, monthly screenings, supervised weight training and exercise, sports medicine services, health education classes, and consultation in the design and operation of the fitness program. The medical and scientific expertise provided by Methodist Hospitals gave the racquet club the competitive edge in the health club market that its management sought. Membership at the club quadrupled in the first year of the joint venture.

A joint venture with the YMCA in Memphis provides the WELLTH program with four convenient neighborhood facilities in the Memphis community while lending a health orientation to a long-standing leader in the fitness arena, the YMCA. Access to the community at large for health promotion services is enhanced through the established network of YMCA members. Profits made on jointly sponsored programs are split between Methodist Health Systems and the YMCA to provide an incentive for each to support the other. In the highly competitive Memphis marketplace, the YMCA has become a partner with the hospital in providing health promotion and wellness services to the community.

FUTURE CONSIDERATIONS

The success of the WELLTH program at Methodist can be attributed directly to its interface with the goals of Methodist Health Systems. The program is managed in a cost-effective manner, utilizing existing resources within the organization to provide a broad scope of customer-centered health promotion services to a variety of markets in the hospital's primary service area.

Many challenges exist in administering a multidisciplinary, nontraditional hospital service within a large organization. Assuring consistency among a variety of internal providers, defining those products and services that come under the purview of health promotion, and designing systems that decrease the likelihood of duplication are the biggest challenges that are faced in managing a health promotion program for a hospital with more than 1,000 beds.

Issues being explored now as long-range plans are being developed include facility ownership, joint ventures with physicians and physician groups, and health promotion as a viable for-profit diversification option. Although the changing health care marketplace will be the primary determinant of the future for hospital-based health promotion, the WELLTH program at Methodist is committed to being a responsive, innovative leader in the health promotion arena of tomorrow.

PART VI

The Future of Hospital Health Promotion

American society is shifting toward greater self-responsibility for disease prevention and for health. Many individuals are making attempts to eliminate unhealthy lifestyle behaviors. However, society does need professional direction and leadership to speed achievement of greater health.

As the American public has become astute about health promotion issues due to media bombardment, hospital admissions have declined. Competition among hospitals is fierce. Government regulations are wreaking havoc with traditional hospital operating procedures, and hospital revenues are declining. These factors are forcing hospitals to plan and operate like businesses.

Many hospital administrators have realized they must diversify and provide nontraditional services and products related to health care. Formalizing and providing comprehensive health promotion is one form of diversification. The yield will be contributions to overall institutional goals and mission. Some hospitals dabble in health promotion, while others make a major commitment. Hospitals that invest in health promotion invest in their futures.

Chapter 16 reviews efforts by hospitals to become entrepreneurial with health promotion products and services. Responding to market demand, hospitals have profitably developed and provided new, nontraditional services that offer many benefits to the hospital.

Chapter 17 looks into the future by examining current health care trends and the ability of the health promotion industry to respond to these trends and ensure the viability of health care institutions.

CHAPTER 16

Hospital Innovation and Entrepreneurship

Jean Storlie

Debra Daly-Gawenda

Diversification of hospitals into the health promotion market is growing fast. The need for increased revenues, increased markets, and decreased costs has heightened interest in the health promotion and wellness field.

BARRIERS IN TRADITIONAL HOSPITAL SYSTEMS

Although more than half of the hospitals in the United States have some element of a health promotion program today (O'Donnell, 1985), there are major barriers in traditional hospital systems inhibiting wellness entrepreneurship. These barriers can be grouped into four categories: (a) economic, (b) legal, (c) political, and (d) philosophical.

Economic Barriers

As retrenchment, cost containment, and diagnostic related groups (DRGs) become common terms in the health care industry, economic barriers pressure new and existing hospital-based programs—health promotion included. Hospitals not yet into the area must answer queries on the amount and source of start-up capital, resource allocation (staff, space, equipment), and the lack of hard evidence regarding return on investment. The programs have low profit margins, are labor intensive, and have not demonstrated long-term payoffs. Those hospitals attempting quick entry into the market must assess venture partners such as fitness clubs or national health promotion franchises for positioning and distribution.

Health care professionals have done little to justify health promotion in business terms. The 1987 *Optimal Health*/Price Waterhouse Health Promotion Survey of 397 health promotion directors and hospital administrators found that only 15% of the hospitals in the sample had developed business plans within the previous 2 years. The measure of success for 69% of hospital-based health promotion programs was public relations, while only 39% cited profitability as an important measure. Community service, customer satisfaction, and image enhancement were also frequently cited as important.

More than half of the administrators of these organizations stated that health promotion contributed relatively little to patient accrual or revenue diversification. In fact, most programs (85%) lost money and few (15%) reported a profit.

Lengthy budget planning cycles, common in traditional hospital systems, present another economic constraint. Budget preparation may begin 6 months prior to the beginning of a fiscal year. This time frame makes it difficult to predict events and business opportunities that may occur 18 months later. Further, the budgeting process is directly tied to projected fluctuations in patient days. Loss leaders and support services (e.g., patient education, physical therapy, ambulatory care, or nutrition) are vulnerable during budget cuts.

If these trends are representative of today's hospital-based health promotion programs, economic barriers could slowly phase out their existence. It will be the commercial sector that profits from growth in the health and fitness movement. Survival of health promotion in traditional hospital systems will require shifting to profit-oriented program management based on strategic business planning.

Legal Barriers

Should nonprofit hospitals begin to operate profitable health and fitness programs, they may face another obstacle when reporting profits to the Internal Revenue Service. Income derived by tax-exempt organizations from regularly conducted unrelated trade or business is subject to federal income taxation (Lohmann, 1980). "Unrelated trade or business" is defined as activities that are not substantially related to the performance of the organization's tax-exempt mission statement (Internal Revenue Code 513[a]).

Stating profitability as a goal and measure of success for a hospital-based health promotion program places it in the category of unrelated trade or business, subject to tax liability. Furthermore, if IRS audits determine that a nonprofit organization is generating substantial unrelated business income, the organization may lose its tax-exempt status. It is difficult for hospitals to know their boundaries because the tax laws governing unrelated business income do not clearly define what is "substantial." Adding to the confusion, mission statements can be vaguely written and misinterpreted.

Fitness clubs may fall under IRS scrutiny, especially if managed as a profit center within the nonprofit structure of the organization. Therefore, it is advisable tnat institutions proceed cautiously, and with legal advice, when structuring these business opportunities, to protect their tax-exempt status.

Political Barriers

Red tape and political obstacle courses may stifle innovation and entrepreneurship in hospital-based health promotion programs. The issues of control and coordination emerge from a number of sources inside and outside the hospital itself.

Internal "turf battles" can arise over program management, organizational reporting relationships, and client referrals. Interestingly, the 1987 *Optimal Health*/Price Waterhouse survey noted that most health promotion leaders reported directly to the top hospital administrator, vice president, or a high-ranking division or department head. It is speculated that health promotion is either a top priority or that placement in the organizational structure has not yet been determined because the area is so new.

Commitment, support, and communication from hospital decision makers are important for both development and growth. Resource allocation, client referrals, start-up capital, and strategic planning decisions have a major impact on program operations. By keeping abreast of the forces shaping internal policies, business planning and development are facilitated. Top-level managers have contacts in the local communities, which can be important referrals. The administrators will have to decide where to direct a lead if a number of internal entities are providing services targeted at the same markets. For example, a corporate inquiry for employee assistance could be referred to specialists in human resources, health promotion, or chemical dependency. The larger the hospital, the greater the degree of specialization, and the more complicated this becomes. Few busy executives have the time or patience to sort the client's needs and determine the best match. Often the referrals are made to those individuals or departments that have the best pipeline to the top.

Jealousy may motivate subtle and direct forms of sabotage when a new program is placed at the top of an organization chart, provided with referrals, and infused with capital though the rest of the hospital is undergoing budget cuts. These obstacles may surface when the health promotion program or wellness center attempts to barter or buy services from other departments (e.g., physical therapy, nutrition, patient education, or cardiology) in order to assemble an interdisciplinary team.

Externally, the health promotion program may be viewed as a threat or competition to alternate delivery systems, such as health maintenance organizations (HMOs), preferred provider organizations (PPOs), and independent practice associations (IPAs). Further complications can arise if the hospital is also diversifying into these insurer-provider product lines.

Philosophical Barriers

Although hospitals have a wealth of technical expertise in diagnosing and treating diseases, they may lack the experience in marketing, business plan development, and fitness facility design and operation.

An intangible, yet often significant, barrier to hospital-based health promotion comes from differences in philosophies. Hospitals have historically focused on medical care, treatment, and diagnosis; however, the emergence of prevention through health promotion programs is still seeking complete acceptance within the health care system ("Seeking the Perfect Fit," 1986). In working with more than 20 hospitals, Chapman (1986) found the health practices of hospital employees to be poor and resistant to change. Obviously, these individuals will be threatened by programs that introduce changes into their work environment to alter their personal habits.

Since health promotion programs do not deal with life-threatening issues of immediate concern, many physicians do not consider prevention a serious medical discipline. Though a consensus is emerging (Green, 1986), rigorous scientific evidence documenting the role of disease prevention and the benefits of health promotion remains sketchy. Some practitioners, particularly those based in academic medical centers, use this as a barrier to participation.

Wellness is a vague concept that can be interpreted with many philosophical approaches and program models; in fact, defining wellness is a personal choice. Brox (1986) states that wellness is hard to define because it is a relatively new concept with a broad scope. Until hospitals fully accept this concept into their philosophies of care and develop concrete models for management, this newness can introduce controversy and skepticism. Wellness committees sometimes argue over approaches and models, dwelling on controversy and slowing the development process. Various departments may even develop their own program philosophies resulting in a fragmented approach to comprehensive programming. There are few hospitals serving as role models in health promotion management, which further inhibits the process of technical and philosophical evolution.

THE FOR-PROFIT SUBSIDIARY

To overcome these barriers, a recent trend in the health care industry has been the development of for-profit subsidiary corporations. These subsidiaries have business structures that provide freedoms not found in traditional hospital systems. A recent survey of 310 for-profit subsidiaries in 24 states characterizes this trend (Lauhoff, 1987). The data on operational structures, markets, product lines, profitability, and growth rates of these subsidiaries will be summarized.

Operational Structures

Most of the subsidiaries were developed since 1984 (63.6%), though the responses ranged from 1968 to 1986. Of the survey respondents, 39.5% were subsidiaries of an academic medical center, and 27% were from multi-institutional systems. The majority (65%) were structured as wholly owned, for-profit subsidiaries. The most frequently cited reasons for development were to

• generate alternative income in patient care areas,

- generate alternative income in nonpatient care areas, and
- enhance image and awareness of the parent institution.

Relationship to Parent Corporation

The relationship to the parent corporation was described as collaborative by 97.7% of the respondents. Only a small percentage (11.1%) characterized the degree of day-to-day autonomy as "very autonomous." They listed the following disadvantages of their association with a nonprofit parent corporation:

- Lack of autonomy
- Bureaucratic structure
- Conflicting goals
- Accounting practices of allocating institutional overhead
- For-profit entity viewed as initial capital drain
- Aggressive marketing changing the image of parent corporation

Joint-Venture Activity

Many of the subsidiaries (73%) reported joint-venture projects. They listed the following reasons for engaging in joint ventures:

- To get into new product lines or expand existing ones
- To expand into new markets
- To capitalize product development
- To associate with a well-known entity for credibility

Markets

Geographically, it appears that most subsidiaries targeted local markets, with 87% of the respondents reporting that 80% or more of their revenue was derived locally, and 71% reporting that 100% of their revenue was derived from local sources. The percentage of revenue by customer categories is shown in Table 16.1.

Product Lines

The source of product development tended to be the parent corporation, as was the source of capital, although other sources were occasionally cited. A variety of product lines were described, with the most common product lines being

- home health nursing,
- laboratory services,
- billing and collection services,
- durable medical equipment,
- retirement housing,

Table 16.1 Percentage of Revenue by Customer Categories

Customer categories	Percentage of revenue
Hospitals	30
Patients	25
Physicians	25
Other hospitals	10
Consumers at large	5
Other institutions	5

Note. Data from [For-Profit Activities: Preliminary Analysis] by K.J. Lauhoff, 1987 (unpublished data; research sponsored by Illinois Hospital Association/Rush University Fellowship Program, Chicago, IL).

- consulting services, and
- managed care (e.g., HMOs, PPOs, IPAs).

Wellness programs (e.g, smoking cessation or weight control) were provided by only 9, and fitness programs by only 6, of 45 respondents who answered this question.

Profitability and Growth Rates

Gross revenues ranged from $0 to $100 million, with an average of $2,392,000 for the few respondents who disclosed financial information. Net income ranged from $871,000 to $3 million, and the percentage of net income for the parent corporation was most often less than 1%. Growth rates varied, with the general trend being higher rates of growth in 1983 to 1985 and lower rates in 1985 to 1987. The most common reasons cited for failure were not allowing the entity enough start-up time, and poor marketing.

Recommendations

The respondents related these lessons learned from their developmental experience:

- The importance of preparing a detailed business plan
- Development of management within the for-profit entity
- The need to manage aggressively yet maintain control
- Sufficient capitalization

These insights and experiences will benefit hospitals when they are considering the development of a for-profit subsidiary, and will also facilitate branching into new product lines. Since the evolution of for-profit, hospital-owned subsidiaries is in its infancy, existing operations are still experiencing growing pains. As these forerunners become more sophisticated, their efforts will be easier to duplicate. Most importantly, the subsidiary structure provides a vehicle for hospitals to diversify into new markets through a range of business structures. Expansion into health promotion and fitness may become more common as the subsidiaries grow and stabilize.

This survey concurs with the *Optimal Health*/Price Waterhouse survey observation that health promotion tends to be organized within the nonprofit hospital structure and positioned as community service or loss-leader programs. Health promotion professionals based in hospitals may want to consider the for-profit subsidiary as an avenue for marketing their programs.

ANALYZING MARKET OPPORTUNITIES

Whether investing in an entirely new business, a new product, or simply an extension of an existing product, it is important to subject the opportunity to rigorous business analysis. This should include market research, internal analysis, product definition, and financial analysis. A detailed business plan should be written that describes the product features, local and national industry trends, customers, competitors, profitability patterns, start-up costs, operating budgets, 3- to 5-year proformas, return on investment, and marketing plan. Health promotion professionals may need to seek outside consultation in the preliminary research and preparation of a business plan. A worksheet that will assist managers in conducting an initial concept evaluation is presented in Form 16.1.

After the analysis stage, the product must pass certain screening criteria for further investment. Key considerations include (a) the "make versus buy" decision, (b) investment payoff analysis, (c) the source of capital, and (d) the business structure.

Make Versus Buy

It is often more advantageous to acquire an existing product than to invest in new-product development, because it allows quicker entry into the marketplace and reduces start-up costs. On the other hand, an internally developed program creates a specific identity in the marketplace and may have better long-term payoffs. Further, pride of authorship may make it easier for the hospital to feel a sense of ownership and support the product during start-up. Both options should be analyzed for their advantages and disadvantages. The decision to make or buy a product will have a major impact on the nature of the investment, product positioning, and business strategy. It is a decision that is unique to each situation and important to analyze thoroughly.

ArcVentures, Inc.
New Product Concept Evaluation

Date: _____

Name: _____ Phone: _____

Title/Organization: _____

Address: _____

This questionnaire is the first stage of our new product (or service) development process. The questions will enable us to evaluate your product concept. If the product appears promising, we will take the following steps:

1. Develop a business plan. (Describe the product and its market in more detail, and present a proforma budget of both start-up costs and projected revenues, expenses, and income.)
2. Evaluate the risk and potential return from the product. (How much capital are we risking? How long will it take for the product to succeed or fail?)
3. Evaluate the product against the alternative potential products Arc could invest in.

Whether a product "passes" these evaluations depends not only on the product itself, but on what else is going on at Arc (or at the medical center) at the same time. If your product does pass, the next steps will be prototype development, market testing, and product introduction.

1. Concept: Describe proposed product.

2. Unique Characteristics: What distinguishes this product from its competitors? (List features.)

3. Manufacturing Process: What manufacturing process is necessary to deliver this product?

4. Customer Demand: Describe the potential customers for this product (type, location).

Why do you think there is a customer demand for the product?

What distribution method is required?

5. Potential Life of Product: What is the expected life cycle of this product?

6. Competitors: Describe competitors (number, size, location, quality). What is our competitive advantage? Our niche?

7. Competitive Threats: What are the potential significant threats to the success of this product from actions taken by competitors, suppliers, customers, product substitutes, or potential competitors? How should we expect to respond?

8. Complementary Products: Does this product complement other products already offered by RPSL Medical Center or ArcVentures?

9. Prior Product Experience: What is your prior experience with this product?

10. Critical Success Factors: What product, market, or distribution features are critical to this product's success? What risks are inherent in this product?

Note. Used with permission from ArcVentures, Inc., 1988.

Investment and Payoff

The amount of investment capital and payback will need to be analyzed. The length of time to break even, acceptable profit margins, and rate of return on investment will vary from product to product and market to market. Health and fitness managers are taught to develop balanced operating budgets, but not to pursue further analysis of financial performance, so it may be necessary to seek financial consultation either internally or externally.

Source of Capital

Depending on the size of the hospital and its overall financial situation, capital may be obtained internally or it may be necessary to go outside the hospital and secure capital. The hospital's top-level management will be integrally involved in the decision to back a new product whether the capital is obtained internally or externally. A well-documented business plan will be necessary in either case.

Venture Partners

When considering these issues, it may be relevant to explore the possibility of entering into a partnership arrangement whereby two or more business entities share risk and equity. Venture partnerships are pursued for the following reasons:

- Quicker entry into the market through a partnership with someone already in the business
- Reduced amount of investment capital required
- Specialized expertise that is complementary to the new product and/or existing business

These partnerships are becoming more popular as hospitals diversify into new markets and consider partnerships with fitness centers, real estate developers, insurance companies, and corporations. These opportunities can be viable and profitable avenues for entering markets where hospitals have not traditionally done business.

TYPES OF VENTURE RELATIONSHIPS

The term "joint venture" has been overused and misused. Since it is not a legally defined term, it is necessary to examine the legal definitions of business entities before defining joint-venture relationships. Table 16.2 presents characteristics of the three types of legally defined businesses: corporations, partnerships, and proprietorships.

Table 16.2 Matrix of Business Entities

Characteristics	Corporation	Partnership	Proprietorship
Life of business	Determined by state law or charter Does not cease upon death of a stockholder	Exists for an agreed time Death of a partner usually terminates partnership	Death of a proprietor usually terminates business
Liability	Exempts stockholders Limits liability to capital contribution	Each partner is individually liable for all obligations Liability of "limited partners" is limited to amount of contribution	Liable for all obligations
Transfer of ownership	Stock certificates are transferable	Consent of partners necessary for transfer or change	May transfer assets easily
Capital	Easier to obtain capital Investor is limited as to liability	Can obtain capital by loan Can increase number of partners Can increase amount of partner's contribution	Can obtain capital only by loan guaranteed by proprietor

(Cont.)

Table 16.2 (Continued)

Characteristics	Corporation	Partnership	Proprietorship
Business decisions	Board of directors generally has majority control	Unanimous agreement among partners generally required	Sole decision rests with owner
Credit	Possesses separate credit from stock-holders Stock certificates can be used as collateral	Creates joint and several liabilities Interests not pledgeable or assignable on loan	Must make loan individually
Management responsibilities	Stockholders can receive dividends without sharing in management	Partners are normally involved in management	Proprietor has full management responsibility
Flexibility	Must function within state laws and its charter Not as flexible	Must operate within terms of the agreement Can define own terms	Complete flexibility
Tax status	Is a separate taxable entity	Each partner is taxed for proportionate share of income Has fewer tax problems	Proprietor taxed on full earnings

Characteristics	Corporation	Partnership	Proprietorship
Withdrawal of profits	Dividend (double-taxed) Salary Capital Loan	Once tax paid on dividend, all distributions are tax free	Once tax paid on earned income, all distributions are tax free
Contributions	Limited by federal income tax	Dividends among partners and fully deductible	Fully deductible to extent of individual limits
Assignability of interest	Stockholder can can unqualifiedly transfer stock and dividends	Normally requires consent of other partners May require a new agreement	Proprietor has full authority to transfer assets
Events upon liquidation	Creates taxable gain	Normally does not result in gain to partners	Does not result in gain to proprietor

Note. Adapted from material developed by Stephen Weiser, Ross & Hardies, Chicago, IL, 1987. Used with permission.

Each structure has its advantages and disadvantages. A proprietorship has the most flexibility, has more control over management decisions, and can easily transfer assets; however, the liability is high and it is more difficult to obtain capital. A corporation protects investors from liability and, therefore, can more easily obtain capital. On the other hand, a corporation is more complicated to establish and is subject to greater legal restrictions. Partnerships have some characteristics associated with each structure but tend to share the flexibility of a proprietorship.

Joint ventures are formed when two or more legal business entities enter into business together. A proprietorship and a corporation, two partnerships, two corporations, or any other combination of structures can form a joint venture. Even a for-profit business and a not-for-profit organization can enter a joint venture, provided the venture partnership adheres to the associated tax regulations. The venture must be structured as either a corporation or a partnership.

Joint-Venture Corporation

When a joint-venture corporation is formed, it becomes a legal entity separate from each partner. It insulates the partners from liability and can be structured with varying percentages of control and equity. A corporation is more difficult to establish and dissolve. Before entering into a joint-venture corporation, it is important to be certain about the relationship, the market potential, and all legal implications of the relationship. It takes many months and extensive planning to establish a successful joint-venture corporation.

Joint-Venture Partnership

A less complicated structure is one in which each business participates as a partner, just as two or more individuals would engage in a partnership. The members of the partnership are exposed to more liability, but the arrangement is more flexible and easier to dissolve if conditions change and it is no longer advantageous to be in business together.

Subcontract

A simple method for structuring a business opportunity with another organization is to have one entity become the general contractor who subcontracts specific services or goods from the other on a project-by-project basis. This approach allows for the greatest amount of flexibility and may be useful in the early stages of exploring the business opportunity. Should it turn out that the organizations are incompatible, or if for some other business reason it becomes necessary to restructure the relationship or dissolve the partnership, the contract can easily be modified or terminated. This provides a mechanism for exploring the viability of a business relationship before investing the time and legal fees in forming a joint-venture partnership or corporation.

LEGAL ISSUES

Legal consultation is critical, when structuring venture relationships, to develop contracts and protect the hospital's tax-exempt status and community image. A hospital's relationship to its for-profit entities is complicated by legal issues requiring an "arm's-length" relationship, on one hand, while on the other, maintaining control as various entities market programs or products on behalf of the hospital. This section will address developing contracts, maintaining an arm's-length relationship, and marketing and advertising.

Contract Development

When pursuing a business opportunity, it is important to consult with an attorney once the business terms have been established and before services are initiated. Minimally, the contract should define the following:

- the responsibilities of both parties delineated in specific terms and conditions,
- the length of contract,
- the compensation and payment schedule,
- the conditions for termination, and
- methods for arbitration and resolution.

In addition, it may be relevant to consider other clauses, such as nondisclosure of trade secrets or business interests, exclusivity in representing a defined market niche, or ownership when product development is involved.

An attorney can apply legal terminology to the agreed-upon business terms and generate a contract for review by both parties. The contract will become the basis for further negotiations and a mechanism for defining the legal aspects of the engagement. This approach can be used for developing relationships with vendors, clients, or venture partners.

Maintaining an Arm's-Length Relationship

The concept of *private inurement* is an essential factor in distinguishing the activities between nonprofit and for-profit corporations. An organization will not be considered tax-exempt if any part of its net earnings "inure" to the benefit of private shareholders or individuals. In addition, a tax-exempt organization must serve a public rather than private interest. Violation of the private inurement prohibition is punished severely, and even an insubstantial breach of prohibition is enough to endanger the organization's tax-exempt status (Treas. Reg. Sect. 501[c] [3]). Private inurement prohibition is a concern when a for-profit subsidiary benefits from the tax-exempt status of its parent corporation in conducting business activities. For example, employee benefits programs available to nonprofit organizations cannot be passed along to employees of the subsidiary. This concept may apply to other support services a hospital provides to its subsidiaries, such as legal consultation, or accounting.

When there are no clearly defined boundaries between a nonprofit parent corporation and its for-profit subsidiary, another concept, known as *piercing the corporate veil*, may precipitate legal exposure. Piercing the corporate veil refers to situations where a subsidiary is engaging in business for the parent corporation, or in simple terms, acting as a "sham" corporation. The nonprofit parent corporation can suffer severe tax consequences for nonrelated business income and can even jeopardize its tax-exempt status.

From a legal perspective, the ideal situation is to have

- the subsidiary capitalized in its own right,
- no board overlap between parent and subsidiary, and
- separate officers and employees.

The nonprofit parent corporation can receive dividends on stockholdings and can even be the sole stockholder. A parent can invest in a subsidiary and capitalize its new ventures.

Marketing and Advertising

Although it is necessary to establish clear boundaries between a hospital and its subsidiary, the public's perception of a hospital (i.e., its image) is an asset of immeasurable value. This asset can be passed along to its affiliates, which is a strategic marketing advantage. Protecting this asset, however, can be difficult when marketing programs through various venture relationships and subsidiary activities.

When the arms-length relationship does not allow the hospital to control how subsidiaries and venture partners are using its name, the hospital's reputation can be compromised. In corporate law the intrinsic value of a business is recognized as its "goodwill." The legal definition of goodwill is ". . . that advantage or benefit which is acquired by an establishment beyond the mere value of capital stock, funds, or property employed therein . . ."(38 Am Jur 2d GOOD WILL). In the broadest interpretation, goodwill includes every positive advantage associated with an established firm, its premises, or name. Any use of the hospital's name in advertising should be reviewed by the public relations department to assure unity and harmony in the image that is projected to the community. Marketing materials (e.g., advertisements, brochures, mailers) should be scrutinized for misleading or erroneous statements that may result in marketing fraud and malpractice litigation. In some cases, the legal department will need to be involved. Material should be screened to avoid any of these deceptive advertising practices:

- Fantasy advertising (e.g., miracle weight loss techniques)
- Explicit untruths
- Implicit untruths (i.e., deception by implication, innuendo, or inference)
- Deceptive truths (i.e., truthful information that is incomplete and leaves the consumer deceived)

- Deceptive silence (i.e., withholding information about risks associated with a product or service)

Implicit untruths can be avoided by accurately describing how a hospital participates in the delivery of services outside the medical setting (e.g., home health care or worksite fitness). Although a cardinal rule in advertising is to keep the message simple and the copy brief, oversimplification may result in misinterpretation of the hospital's role.

Hospitals must be particularly cautious when their affiliates are using advertisements that may be construed as endorsements by the hospital. Under regulation by the Federal Trade Commission (Fed. Trade Comm. Sect. 255), endorsements are defined as any advertising messages that reflect the opinions, beliefs, findings, or experiences of a party other than the sponsoring advertiser. Endorsements by expert organizations are viewed as representing the judgment of a group whose collective experience exceeds that of any individual member and whose technical expertise is superior to that of the general public. The endorsing organization must be able to prove its expertise and demonstrate that a process was used to establish "collective judgment."

A hospital's goodwill is not only an asset, but also a responsibility. The public's perception of a hospital encompasses a certain amount of implied safety (Ben-Sira, 1983). Circumstances that compromise this expectation can lead to disappointed consumers, lawsuits, and damage to the hospital's goodwill.

The benefits of using the hospital's reputation as a marketing advantage must be balanced with protection of this asset as well as maintaining an arm's-length relationship. These legal issues must be examined routinely as new ventures are pursued and marketing campaigns unfolded. Understanding the issues and ramifications will facilitate the management process.

IMPLEMENTATION: A CASE STUDY PRESENTATION

ProActive Health of ArcVentures, Inc., presents a case study illustrating how to organize an interdisciplinary approach to health promotion by overcoming barriers of traditional hospital systems, and how to utilize sound business practices in operating a program out of a related for-profit subsidiary.

ArcVentures, Inc., a wholly owned subsidiary of Rush-Presbyterian-St. Luke's Medical Center (RPSL), was formed in 1968 and has four divisions that market and distribute 13 different health care product lines. The product lines include collection and billing services, a mail-order pharmacy, and home health care. ProActive Health, the newest division, was added in 1986 to market health promotion and fitness programs tailored to business and industry in the Chicago metropolitan area. ProActive Health enjoys a unique position within a for-profit subsidiary of an academic medical center.

Linkage to the Medical Center

In structuring ProActive Health's relationship to the RPSL Medical Center, the management team considered all the complex factors that have been discussed previously. To establish a separate identify, yet link ProActive Health to the Medical Center, specific considerations included

- maintaining an arm's-length relationship;
- benefiting from, yet protecting, the medical center's reputation;
- mobilizing resources from the medical center; and
- managing politics through mutually beneficial arrangements with individual departments.

Figure 16.1 presents a functional model that graphically illustrates how ProActive Health mobilizes medical center resources in implementing programs and managing new product development.

This model was used as a discussion document when developing the internal support network and organizing the preliminary business strategy for ProActive Health. The functional relationship of ArcVentures and the RPSL Medical Center has become a key element in ProActive Health's success.

Medical Center's Role

In this model, the medical center functions as a technical resource base for ProActive Health, which offers several advantages. First, the academic medical center operates clinical programs that serve teaching, research, and patient care goals. This not only lends credibility and prestige to programs but also provides a fertile environment for technical innovation. Due to the diversity of departments and staff involved in research and development, numerous programs are constantly being created and refined. A comprehensive portfolio of state-of-the-art products can be compiled.

Second, medical center personnel can be contracted for service delivery and consultation. This arrangement is beneficial for both entities. ArcVentures has access to a wide range of experts while managing staff as a variable expense, which reduces fixed overhead. During budget cuts and layoffs, the medical center departments have both revenue and outside work to offset fluctuations in number of patient days.

A third advantage is the medical center's role in health care education. The academic staff can consult on staff selection and training. Rush University uses a teacher-practitioner staffing model that blends operational and academic responsibilities for all professional staff who supervise students' educational experiences in research and program delivery. ArcVentures professional staff members can hold faculty appointments and serve as preceptors, lecturers, or research advisors. For example, the Department of Clinical Nutrition is developing an alternative curriculum to train dietitians in sports, fitness, and wellness. ProActive Health provides a training site for practical experience in corporate wellness and fitness.

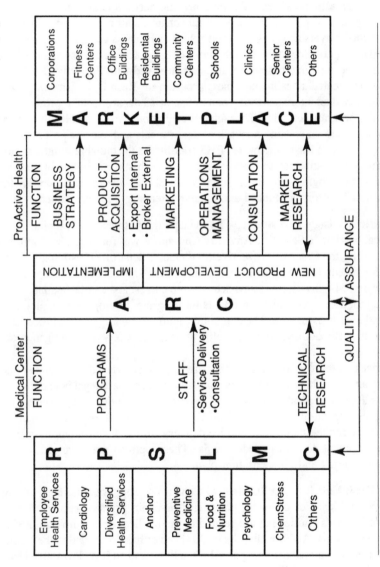

Figure 16.1. Functional model of organization. Used with permission from ArcVentures, Inc., 1988.

The fourth contribution from the medical center is in conducting technical research. Statisticians. epidemiologists, and scientists from multiple disciplines can collaborate with ArcVentures in ongoing program evaluation and original research. This maintains a feedback loop between market and technical research.

Employee Health Services.   To minimize the barriers common in traditional hospital systems (e.g., turf battles, reporting channels, or program coordination), departmental players need to know their roles in a business venture. In this model, the Department of Employee Health Service (EHS) acts as the internal clearing-house for coordinating various departments involved with ProActive Health. In 1982, EHS created a health and fitness program for Rush University employees and established an internal steering committee of 23 departmental representatives to oversee program activities. Through this affiliation, ProActive Health was able to gain access to an existing network of departments and over 30 programs that had been tested on Rush employees. EHS coordinates the initial program develop-ment and pilot testing, and assists ProActive Health staff in mobilizing internal resources for program implementation. With EHS as the internal coordinator, duplication of effort is reduced and similar interest groups are united.

Scientific Advisory Committee.   To manage the political, philosophical, and technical barriers, a Scientific Advisory Committee was formed. The committee is chaired by the Chair of Preventive Medicine, a department nationally recog-nized for research in risk factor intervention. This interdisciplinary committee is made up of 14 physicians, 2 advanced degree nurses, and a PhD dietitian. These experts function as technical consultants for program development, implementa-tion, and quality assurance. The committee approves quality control procedures, evaluation methodology, staffing qualifications, and safety and emergency care management.

Services of the committee members are legally contracted and compensated through an annual honorarium. This maintains the necessary legal boundaries and permits ProActive Health to market its programs as "reviewed by experts from Rush-Presbyterian-St. Luke's Medical Center." Members also have the oppor-tunity to extend their roles into service delivery, in-depth consultation, or prod-uct development on an as-needed basis. These options are arranged under a separate contract and compensation plan.

Other Rush Entities.   RPSL Medical Center also supports a number of other affiliated entities. For example, physicians maintain private practices that are separate business entities but are related to the medical center through medical staff appointments. Additionally, the medical center has diversified in the insurer-provider organizations, operating an HMO, a PPO, and an IPA. ProActive Health can work with these affiliates in a number of capacities. For example, it is pos-sible to contract for services and programs, participate in joint ventures, or even sell services and programs to them at discounted rates.

ArcVenture's Role

As the for-profit subsidiary, ArcVentures is the vehicle to export internally developed programs and the creator of the overall business strategy to service the marketplace. Specifically, ArcVentures manages the marketing, implementation, and product development processes. Packaging internal programs and supplementing them with commercially available programs is a major activity. ArcVentures also manages the product positioning using market research to design the marketing and advertising campaign.

Customer service and innovation are corporate philosophies important to entrepreneurial companies (Peters & Waterman, 1982). These concepts link marketing, operations, and product development. ArcVentures studies its customers' needs, develops product features that meet those needs, and creates quality operational systems to deliver the product to its customers. Within this market-driven management system, ProActive Health's business strategy has been created.

MANAGING THE MATURE STRUCTURE

As ProActive Health evolves into a mature structure, the functional units will include (a) product development, (b) operations, and (c) marketing and sales. Figure 16.2 diagrams the mature structure of ProActive Health and outlines the major activities within each area. Note how product development is linked to marketing and sales through market research, which drives innovations to meet customers' needs. Customer service is critical to maintaining the balance between

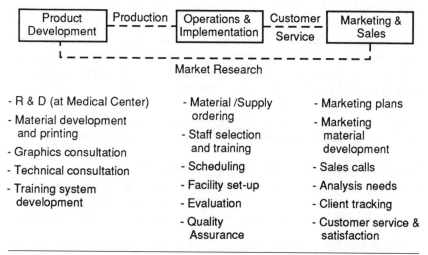

Figure 16.2. Mature structure for ProActive Health. Used with permission from ArcVentures, Inc., 1988.

short-term sales and loyal long-term customers. Production systems that supply the operations with required products and programs is another key link. In the early stage of development, an interdisciplinary team of health care professionals with complementary talents is assembled. Consultants within ArcVentures, the RPSL Medical Center, and outside vendors supplement the core team.

Product Development

Every product has a natural life cycle that undergoes introduction, growth, maturity, and decline (Porter, 1980). Continual investment in product enhancements will perpetuate a product's life cycle, but must be balanced with profitability goals in the short term. When determining the extensiveness of a product development system, it is important to remember the make versus buy decision.

Program Acquisition: The "Buy" Decision

If the decision is made to acquire external programs, this component of the business will have a different focus than had the decision been to develop programs internally. It will involve constant monitoring of innovations in the marketplace. Managers will want to secure price/volume discounts and select reliable vendors. The goal will be to obtain the highest quality for the best price in a time frame that meets operational requirements. Learning to manage suppliers will become a significant variable in achieving both profitability and customer service.

In fact, when ProActive Health was first conceptualized, the plan was to acquire commercially available programs and invest only minimally in product development. Programs were categorized into four levels of intervention (Table 16.3) for each content area (e.g., nutrition, fitness, smoking cessation, stress management, preventive health).

Evaluation criteria were developed and applied to both commercial and internal programs. The Scientific Advisory Committee reviewed each program and made recommendations to the ProActive Health management team. The decision was made to invest in packaging the in-house programs since the commercial programs were attractively packaged but lacked the training and support systems needed to assure quality delivery. Furthermore, packaging the internal programs would create a uniform image. Eventually, these packages can be sold to other providers.

In-House Development: The "Make" Decision

If the decision is made to develop in-house programs, this process will involve (a) research and development (R&D), (b) packaging and producing materials, (c) a training system, and (d) a delivery system. Figure 16.3 outlines these steps.

Research and Development (R&D). R&D should be driven by market trends and customer needs (Pfieffer, 1986). Even an excellent product will not sell if the consumer does not perceive a need for it. The biggest marketing mistake providers make is the failure to listen to clients and help them determine their

Table 16.3 ProActive Health Portfolio of Programs*

Programs	Nutrition	Exercise	Emotional well-being	Smoking control	Preventive health
Screening and assessment	Nutrient analysis	Coronary risk	Self-assessment	Lung volumes	Health risk
	Behavior profile	Pre-exercise screening	Stress profile	Passive smoke	Cholesterol
	Body composition	Strength	Self-conception		Blood pressure
		Flex	Communication skills		Diabetes
		CV			Cancer
		Spirometry			Self-exam
		Body composition			Hearing
					Vision

(Cont.)

Table 16.3 (Continued)

Programs	Nutrition	Exercise	Emotional well-being	Smoking control	Preventive health
Awareness and education	Weight control	Fitness news	Coping strategies	No smoking signs	Risk management
	Osteoporosis	Calorie charts	Identifying personal stress	Smokeout campaign	Safety management
	Cafeteria food labeling	Walking trails		Smoking trivia	CPR
	Heart healthy classes	Mileage signs			Health fairs
	Pregnancy & lactation	Exercising safely			Special events
	Eating out	Proper foot-wear and clothing			Use of OTC drugs
		Exercise in cold weather			
		Exercise in hot weather			

Lifestyle management courses	Spouse program Low cholesterol diet HTN Diet Weight reduction	Exercise prescription Group classes Walk/Jog clubs Special populations Relaxation Back care	Stress management Biofeedback Sleep disorders	Smoking control courses	Blood pressure monitoring
Culture Development	Cafeteria programs Food and beverage service	Facility design Facility operation Sponsoring sport events	Time management Managing organizational stress	Smoking policies	Special events Benefits appraisal Mail-order pharmacy

*Used with permission from ArcVentures, Inc., 1988.

Research & Development	Packaging & Producing Materials	Training System	Delivery System
- Literature review	- Copy development	- Manuals	- Promote concept
- Market research	- Legal consultation	- Workshops	- Needs assessment
- Pilot testing	- Design image consultation	- Consultation	- Program and/or facility design
- Results review	- Computer programming	- Quality assurance	- Program implementation/ management
	- Printing/Production		- Evaluation

Figure 16.3. ProActive Health product development process. Used with permission from ArcVentures, Inc., 1988.

needs ("Selling to Employers," 1987). A product must have flexibility in its features and structure in order to meet a range of customer needs.

Health professionals tend to focus program development efforts on technological advancements rather than customer needs. The combination of the two should formulate the conceptual design of new product ideas. Once a conceptual framework has been established, prototype development and pilot testing is the next step. To progress from "concept" to "operations" involves creating an "elastic structure," whereby the idea is shaped and reshaped as new information and experience is acquired.

In the case of ProActive Health, programs are developed to meet customer needs. The prominent feature is the customization that is afforded by a comprehensive portfolio and flexible service delivery cycle. Each program has options that can further accommodate specific audiences and the constraints of different corporate systems. For example, FitWeigh^{SM} is a system of weight loss programs consisting of a nutrition education program, a walking club, and a contest. The three units can be sold as a comprehensive weight loss system or debundled into component programs. Within the nutrition program, there are 20 educational modules that can be combined into a 10-, 12-, or 16-week series. All in-house programs are tested on RPSL Medical Center employees before being introduced into the marketplace. In this way, program kinks (e.g., content, materials or supply problems, participant flow, etc.) can be modified for maximum efficiency and effectiveness. The pilot testing also enhances program image because a proven track record at home is available. These at-home results also assist with developing program evaluation and quality assurance criteria.

Packaging and Producing Materials.   Once the prototype is tested and refined, the tangible products are specified. For example, lifestyle courses have participant manuals, leader manuals, audiovisual aids, incentive prizes, and record-keeping forms. The content is copyrighted and the program names searched and service-marked with assistance from the Office of Legal Affairs. A graphic designer is contracted for logo design and layout of printed materials. All associated costs are analyzed against the return on investment. The labor, design, legal, and printing fees can be very expensive, so priorities are established before extensive investment at this stage. Storage and assembly of materials require space and labor. An efficient production system is important to ProActive Health for supporting the operational needs and controlling costs.

Training System. No program is any better than the staff who deliver it. Adherence studies in exercise programs have identified leadership as the most important factor in participation rates (Patton, Corry, Gettman, & Graff, 1986). A training system is essential to assure uniformity in program delivery when using a variety of contract professional staff. The training system for ProActive Health involves leader manuals, workshops, support materials (e.g., record-keeping forms, question and answer sheets), staff selection criteria, performance and evaluation criteria, and quality assurance procedures.

These guidelines are developed and formalized through the Scientific Advisory Committee, using standards established by certifying organizations such as the American College of Sports Medicine and the American Dietetic Association.

According to Port (1987), training systems should have a systemized approach for measuring quality, effectiveness, and efficiency. At ProActive Health, trained personnel observe delivery staff during implementation. Evaluation includes program outcomes and participant feedback. Program developers and presenters work together to refine, update, and enhance the program on a regular basis.

Delivery System. The last stage of product development is to establish the mechanism for delivery. Forms, procedure manuals, and equipment and supply checklists need to be developed. The delivery system or program implementation step becomes the "operations" unit of the business.

Operations

Wellness and fitness promotion can be delivered through a wide range of operational systems. Three major factors—the facilities, programs, and staff—can be combined to deliver narrow- or broad-based services. Patton et al. (1986) pointed out that different management models or processes are needed for different organizational structures due to variations in their purposes. ProActive Health operates a program-driven or staff-based delivery system, rather than a facility-based operation. This requires a lower capital investment for start-up, and the programs can be taken on-site to corporations with relative ease. A cyclical delivery model (Figure 16.4) is used to customize program packages and provide flexible entry and exit points in servicing customers' needs.

Each stage of the cycle consists of services that can be expanded or deleted to meet client needs. This offers ProActive Health the flexibility to tailor program packages to meet individual customers' needs. For example, Table 16.4 (corporate model) shows how services can be customized for a corporate client. Table 16.5 (real estate model) illustrates how they can be modified for fitness centers in office buildings.

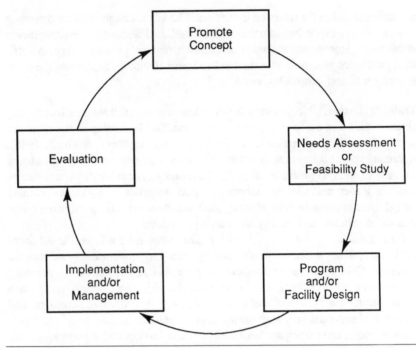

Figure 16.4. ProActive Health service delivery model. Used with permission from ArcVentures, Inc., 1988.

Table 16.4   ProActive Health Description of Services: Corporate Model*

Needs assessment

Interview top/middle management
Survey employees
Determine health risks of employee group
• Study demographics
• Conduct a health risk appraisal
Resource appraisal
• Financial support
• Facility
• Cost-benefit records

Program design

Internal steering committee
Conceptual design
 • Philosophy and scope
 • Goals and objectives
 • Desired outcomes
 • Time line
 • Content definition (general vs. focused)
Program recommendations and selection (from menu)
Facility recommendations and selection
Implementation plan

Program implementation

Promotion
Scheduling
Staffing
Facility set-up
Results/Feedback

Evaluation

Program effectiveness
Employee satisfaction
Absenteeism
Morale/Job satisfaction
Cost-benefit analysis

*Used with permission from ArcVentures, Inc., 1988.

Table 16.5   ProActive Health Description of Services: Real Estate Developer Model*

Feasibility study

Competitive analysis
Corporate tenant interest
 • Interview top management
 • Site/Facility review

(Cont.)

Table 16.5   Continued

Program design

Program recommendations by tenants
Financial support by tenants
Time scheduling
Staff requirements
Facility requirements
Overall program priorities

Facility design

Site selection
Square footage requirements
Space plan
Equipment needs and costs
Staff requirements
Financial projections

Management contract

Preopening
  • Promotion/Advertisement
  • Staff recruiting/Selection
  • Equipment selection
  • Service/Amenity selection
  • Operating procedures
  • Support material (e.g., sales and program literature)
Operations
  • Programming/Special Events
  • Staff supervision
  • Equipment/Facility Maintenance
  • Reports/Record keeping
  • Inventory control
  • Financial control
  • Quality control

---

*Used with permission from ArcVentures, Inc., 1988.

Promote Concept. If the corporation is not already convinced that it needs an employee wellness program, the relationship begins with sales and promotion. Educating a skeptical customer can take several months to a few years; in fact, some skeptics will never be convinced. These factors are recognized early in the sales cycle.

Needs Assessment. Once the client has decided it wants a program, a common scenario is the "ready-go" mistake—going ahead with implementation before getting "ready-set." Enthusiasm and naïveté about critical success factors may drive the client to duplicate another program or implement an idea without considering how it will fit into the existing corporate culture. To plan strategically for long-term success, the first step in service delivery is a needs assessment (Patton et al., 1986). The top-level managers are interviewed to determine their level of support and commitment. Employees are surveyed to incorporate their priorities and interests. Demographics on the employee population or health risk appraisals are used to predict health risks. The facility, level of financial commitment, and other resources are appraised.

Program and Facility Design. Once the specific needs and expected outcomes are determined, a customized package can be designed. It is important to involve the corporation in defining the scope, objectives, and program choices. The depth of this consultation varies with the client's interest level, organization size, financial risk, and project goals. If a facility plan is involved, a management contract may be suggested for its operation. If a client already has an existing program, their staff are integrated into the approach. An internal steering committee is often formed to organize the corporation's input. The results of the needs assessment and steering committee recommendations are then combined to formulate a unique plan for each corporation.

Implementation. The implementation or management step follows. ProActive Health will provide turnkey services, including staff, equipment and supplies, scheduling, and internal promotions. In some cases, it is possible to use lay leaders as program coordinators. If the corporation has a medical department, occupational nurses may be available. ProActive Health has found that it is important to have flexible approaches for implementation, as each corporation has a unique culture and set of resources. Minimal involvement in staffing is appropriate for short-term, education-oriented programs (e.g., weight loss or smoking cessation courses); in-depth management contracts are required for facility-based operations. For example, ProActive Health manages a fitness center in an office complex for the real estate developer who owns it. The fitness center exclusively serves corporate tenants and employees in the complex who buy memberships in the club.

Evaluation. Sound evaluation methods are necessary for quality assurance. A documented track record also helps to sell additional services. ProActive Health has developed standardized evaluation procedures to measure a program's results each time it is implemented. The results are compared to preestablished performance criteria to maintain uniform delivery and superior quality. Overall client satisfaction and specific parameters important to individual customer needs should also be monitored through accurate record keeping. For example, a corporate client will be interested to see evidence of how a health promotion program has impacted absenteeism, productivity, and health care costs. A real estate developer will be more interested in the impact of the fitness center amenity on vacancy rates and tenant satisfaction. These records will be important for future sales, product enhancements, personnel management, and quality assurance.

Specific, measurable outcomes must be defined at the onset if proper evaluation is to be conducted. The procedures and record-keeping systems should be in place before program implementation. ProActive Health contracts with RPSL Medical Center experts to evaluate program results; this maintains objectivity and accuracy in the analysis. Upon completion, results are compiled and a final report is presented to the client.

Marketing and Sales

A recent article in *Optimal Health* ("Selling to Employers," 1987) discussed common mistakes health promotion providers make in marketing their programs and presented these guidelines:

- Listen to customer's needs—don't go into a sale with a preconceived idea of what you want to sell.
- Plan for the sales cycle—it may take 6 months before a company is ready to implement a program.
- Use needs-analysis tools—these approaches allow you to get a foot in the door.
- Involve the employees in program planning—this builds trust between the vendor and the corporation.
- Start with simple, inexpensive programs—these programs should be priced reasonably to demonstrate good faith and commitment to a long-term relationship.

ProActive Health has incorporated these concepts into its philosophy and program structure. Extensive market research was conducted to determine the level of interest among corporations in Chicago and profile the competition. This research was used to develop a detailed marketing and advertising campaign.

The development of a successful marketing campaign involves much more than placing a few advertisements and printing a brochure ("Slick Ads Don't Guarantee Success," 1987). A marketing plan is a clearly defined strategy with a detailed time line designed for maximum market visibility and penetration (Kotler, 1984). Four variables are combined to create the strategy:

- Product
- Price

- Place
- Promotion

The product features of ProActive Health reflect the careful attention to market demands that is essential to marketing. Pricing structures were established according to competitive trends in the marketplace, using small services and products as loss leaders to open doors. Convenience was identified in the market research as an important factor to employers when considering a purchasing decision, so ProActive Health has used a "mobile program" concept to take programs into the worksite. The product has been launched through a variety of promotional vehicles:

- Personal sales calls
- A three-tiered mailing with follow-up phone calls
- Display and classified advertising
- Cross-marketing with existing product lines in ArcVentures and RPSL Medical Center
- A sales-call brochure with insert panels to help the salesperson tailor the discussion to the potential customer's needs

SUMMARY

Innovation and entrepreneurship have become essential to hospital survival in the changing health care industry. Growing interest from both employers and consumers presents an opportunity for hospitals to diversify into new markets through health promotion and fitness businesses. Unfortunately, the nonprofit, traditional hospital system has barriers to innovation and entrepreneurship ranging from political hurdles to serious legal issues. During the last 5 to 10 years there has been an increasing trend in the development of for-profit subsidiaries as vehicles for diversification into new business ventures. Hospital health promotion programs have typically been developed within the nonprofit parent corporation; however, it may be advantageous or even necessary because of tax liability to market these activities through a for-profit subsidiary.

When considering a health and fitness or any other business venture, it is important to scrutinize the opportunity with rigorous business analysis. A detailed business plan, supported with market research and valid financial assumptions, should be prepared. Partnership arrangements may be pursued using joint-venture business structures. The advantages and disadvantages of alternative business structures must be considered during new business or product development. Legal consultation is critical during this process.

ProActive Health is a product line of health promotion and fitness programs tailored to business and industry. It is a division of ArcVentures, Inc., which is a subsidiary of Rush-Presbyterian-St. Luke's Medical Center in Chicago,

Illinois. ProActive Health has been used as a case study to illustrate the operation of health promotion within a for-profit, hospital-owned subsidiary.

REFERENCES

Ben-Sira, Z. (1983). The structure of a hospital's image. *Medical Care*, **21**(10), 943-953.

Brox, A. (1986, April). Wellness: A closer look. *Club Industry*, pp. 27-31.

Chapman, L. (1986). Hospitals provide special challenge to health promotion program directors. *Employee Health & Fitness*, **8**(9), 104-105.

Fed. Trade Comm. Sect. 255. 16 C.F.R. § 255.

Green, L.W. (1986). Research agenda: Building a consensus on research questions. *American Journal of Health Promotion*, **1**(2), 70-72.

Health promotion young, but growing: *Optimal Health*/Price Waterhouse health promotion survey. (1987, July/August). *Optimal Health*, pp. 22-24.

Internal Revenue Code 513(a). 26 U.S.C. § 513 (a).

Kotler, P. (1984). *Marketing management: Planning, analysis, and control.* Englewood, NJ: Prentice-Hall.

Lauhoff, K.J. (1987). [For-profit activities: Preliminary analysis]. Unpublished data. (Research sponsored by Illinois Hospital Association/Rush University Fellowship Program, Chicago, IL.)

Lohmann, R.A. (1980). *Breaking even: Financial management in human service organizations.* Philadelphia: Temple University Press.

O'Donnell, M. (1985, September/October). Finding your niche in the marketplace. *Optimal Health*, pp. 20-24.

Patton, R.W., Corry, J.M., Gettman, L.R., & Graf, J.S. (1986). *Implementing health/fitness programs.* Champaign, IL: Human Kinetics.

Peters, T.J., & Waterman, R.H. (1982). *In search of excellence.* New York: Harper & Row.

Pfieffer, G.H. (1986). Management aspects of fitness program development. *American Journal of Health Promotion*, **1**(2), 10-18.

Port, O. (1987, June 8). The push for quality. *Business Week*, pp. 131-154.

Porter, M.E. (1980). *Competitive strategy: Techniques for analyzing industries and competitors.* New York: The Free Press.

Ross, C.T. (1985, June). Managing risk. *Athletic Business*, pp. 22, 24, 26-27, 29.

Seeking the perfect fit: Hospitals and health promotion. (1986, July/August). *Optimal Health*, pp. 14-16.

Selling to employers: First you have to listen. (1987, July/August). *Optimal Health*, pp. 22-26.

Slick ads don't guarantee success. (1987, May/June). *Optimal Health*, pp. 28-30.

38 Am Jur 2d GOOD WILL.

Treas. Reg. Sect. 501 (c)(3). 26 U.S.C. § 501 (c)(3); 26 C.F.R. § 1.501 (c) (3) - 1 (d)(l)(ii).

CHAPTER 17

The Future of Hospital-Sponsored Health Promotion
Neil Sol

Today's health care environment is clearly in a state of transformation, rapidly changing in response to industry challenges and societal demands. Between increasing government involvement and scrutiny from corporate clients as well as shifting community health care requirements in general, many hospitals are now finding their viability and longevity at risk. In this unstable environment, hospital administrators are being forced to examine alternative strategies for survival.

Today's dynamic industry makes even last year's strategies nearly archaic, requiring administrators to adjust to changes on short notice. As Stewart Westbury (1986), past president of the American College of Hospital Administrators, commented, hospital administrators who graduated as recently as 5 years ago and who still implement the management techniques they learned in school are doomed to failure.

HEALTH PROMOTION'S ROLE IN MODERN HEALTH CARE

In the face of these challenges, health promotion is becoming an integral component of modern health care. The inclusion of health promotion within the health care system represents a response to a changing market demand. American society is in the midst of a health care paradigm shift, evolving from the past medical era's focus on medical repair to that of the current health era where holistic prevention is the priority (McClary, Zahrt, Montgomery, Walker, & Petry, 1985).

John Naisbitt (1982) has suggested that American society has lost faith in the medical establishment, giving a strong symbolic push to the shift from institutional help to self-help. Future generations will reveal an increasing affinity for health and fitness. According to estimates (Naisbitt, 1982), at least 100 million Americans, or 50% of the population, exercise in some form today as compared to 25% of the population in 1960.

This growing societal awareness of health and fitness will lead to greater demands for the provision of these services by qualified and experienced professionals. The hospital will become the primary provider or resource of support to the prevention movement. However, the diversification process necessary to provide these nontraditional services mandates a change in hospital strategy and management philosophy.

As competition in the health care environment intensifies, the hospital will face unprecedented challenges to survive. It will be forced to operate under business tenets that previously were not applicable. In fact, Bezold, Carlson, and Peck (1986) have suggested that health care will change more in the next 5 years than it has in the last 50 years.

CURRENT HEALTH CARE TRENDS

Naisbitt (1982) has commented that the most reliable way to anticipate the future is by understanding the present. The current flux within the health care industry and American society at large will establish the foundation upon which to build future strategies. And, as suggested, health promotion will be a viable strategic response to the trend indicated by the present movement.

In order to understand the future implications of the evolving health care industry and societal emphasis on preventive rather than restorative health care, it is important first to examine fully the recent changes that have led to this trend.

Decline in Patient Admissions

Across the country, hospitals are experiencing a decreasing inpatient census. Though the average hospital census in 1970 was 80.3%, average census had dropped to 67.7% by 1980, with a 1990 projection of 50% (French, 1987). In 1980, there were approximately 1,200 patient days per 1,000 population. In 1985, patient days had decreased to 956 days per 1,000 population (French, 1987), a decrease of 20%.

It is anticipated that this decline will continue into the foreseeable future. This alarming trend reflects a widespread decrease in demand for inpatient services as a result of several factors, including overbedded communities, the growing availability of outpatient services, and declining lengths of stay (LOS) due to prospective payment limitations.

Hospitals Becoming Businesses

Historically, as long as insurance paid for most services performed, hospitals flourished with little responsibility to standard business guidelines. However, the advent of third-party payer limitations and the overabundance of facilities and beds have established a fiercely competitive environment, initiating the need for hospitals to operate under sound business tenets.

To offset revenue losses from inpatient declines, health care institutions are being forced to diversify and generate new revenue streams. The peak in acute-care service has passed, and to operate at similar levels, hospitals must now present new products to the marketplace. Diversification options may range from wellness centers to medical software companies to real estate ventures.

Though new revenue is the primary motivation, hospitals also must compete to maintain market share of both patients and clients of other diversified services. Hospitals are realizing that they must evolve from a production philosophy to a market-driven one. The current buyers' market demands that hospitals be willing to customize programs and services to meet the patient's or client's needs.

Hospitals are also realizing that patient relationships should be long-term and that a well-treated patient or client will be most probably a repeat customer. The initiation of guest relation programs is an example of the incorporation of new programs to motivate multiple hospital users and the recruitment of physicians to capture incremental patients.

Physician Glut

A recent report (French, 1987) revealed that there were 218 physicians per 100,000 population compared to 197 in 1980 and 156 in 1970. Obviously, physicians too are facing growing competition, a trend that is projected to continue in the coming years.

The current physician surplus is causing physicians to reevaluate the way they do business. They too are becoming more business-oriented, marketing their practices and aligning with services and activities of interest to the communities they serve. The successful physician of the future will select a specialty based on market need. The formation of physician groups (bringing together a variety of specialists into multispecialty groups) and PPO formation also reflect physicians' efforts to maintain their market share.

ALTERNATE DELIVERY

Market demand for accessible, inexpensive medicine has manifested a trend toward alternate delivery. In response to this demand, nontraditional health care providers have emerged, such as minor-emergency clinics and freestanding diagnostic facilities, luring away prospective hospital customers with consumer incentives such as convenient accessibility and lower patient costs.

As a result, hospitals have experienced a declining market share and a decreased demand for inpatient beds, fostering a need for the development of alternate means of delivering their services. Hospitals' increased participation in outpatient services is a direct response to this market demand, exhibited through activity in minor-emergency rooms, ambulatory surgery services, freestanding birthing centers, diagnostic and therapeutic facilities, home health services, and wellness and fitness facilities.

Increasing Importance of Aggregate Purchasers

Business and industry have traditionally been the major purchasers of health care, bearing the burden of health care costs for their employees. The Commerce Department estimated that in 1978, U.S. businesses spent $42 billion on insurance premiums, paid $12.6 billion in compensation, and lost 496,000,000 work days to illness and injury (Galginaitis, 1980).

In recent years, hospitals' corporate clients have become particularly attentive to health care delivery, scrutinizing potential providers and looking for ways to cut costs. Business and industry have been thrust into a powerful role in a consumer market. Large employers and coalitions of employers, with the purchasing power of thousands of employees behind them, are battling health care costs together and seeking "deals" for inexpensive and quality health care.

Businesses' demands for price concessions have led to the development of preferred provider and health maintenance organizations. The idea of businesses providing employee incentives to utilize a preferred provider can be threatening to the institution that is not awarded the contract. Accordingly, the aggregate purchaser is becoming the primary target of health care business.

Government Regulation of Prospective Payment

In response to rising health care costs, the federal government stepped into the arena with a redesign of the Medicare claim reimbursement system. The new reimbursement formula, which specifies predetermined fixed payments based on diagnosis, limits reimbursement for services and has contributed significantly to decreased hospital LOS (length of stay) and, consequently, hospital profit margins. In addition to fixed payments, government regulation has also led to increased preadmission certification, bill audits, and retrospective chart reviews, all efforts to manage costs while assuring quality control.

Managed Care Programs

The creation of business alliances has been a corporate reaction, similar to government's, to increasing health care expenses. In an attempt to satisfy corporate demands for cost containment, many health care organizations and institutions have entered joint-venture projects with insurance agencies, resulting in preferred provider organizations (PPOs) and health maintenance organizations (HMOs). Through participation in these types of "shared risk" programs, employers and employer groups are assured increased control of pricing, quality, and accessibility of services.

In 1 year, between 1983 and 1984, PPO contracts increased almost tenfold, from approximately 107 to 1,000 (Bezold et al., 1986). Similarly, in 1985, HMOs accounted for 6% market penetration, according to the Health Insurance Association of America. These same industry sources predict that by 1995, HMOs will have achieved a full 30% market penetration (Bezold et al., 1986).

It is apparent that the present health care environment is changing rapidly and drastically. Hospitals are being forced to rethink strategies and reprioritize goals. Clearly, maintaining and increasing market share and profitability are becoming key strategic objectives, more so now than ever before. However, in developing game plans for the future, hospitals must also look beyond their own arena and into the societal changes that are influencing the health care industry.

CURRENT TRENDS IN AMERICAN SOCIETY

In addition to widespread flux within the health care industry itself, American society at large is also changing, particularly in its attitudes toward and awareness of health and fitness.

Increasing Popularity of Exercise

A 1985 Gallup poll reported in its findings that 54% to 58% of Americans surveyed were involved in a regular exercise program. Of those, 33% exercised 5 or more hours a week ("The New Individualism," 1987). Consumers' most common motivations for exercising were

- increased general health,
- to be and feel more attractive,
- increased energy,
- inward confidence,
- improved love life, and
- increased creativity at work.

Table 17.1 lists the most popular forms of exercise and the number of people claiming participation.

Annually, Americans spend approximately $50 million on health and diet books. It is also estimated that total annual consumer expenditures on products related to health and fitness is at $30 billion, with $5 billion going to health clubs and corporate fitness centers ("Health Clubs," 1982).

Table 17.1 America's Most Popular Forms of Exercise

Forms of exercise	Participant response
Exercising with aerobic equipment	44 million
Basketball	42 million
Fitness walking	40 million
Fitness swimming	39 million
Exercising to music	39 million
Weight training	36 million
Volleyball	36 million
Running/jogging	33 million
Football	32 million
Fitness cycling	30 million
Softball	28 million
Tennis	27 million
Baseball	26 million
Backpacking	25 million
Golf	21 million
Gymnastics	17 million

Note. Data from *U.S. News & World Report,* August 11, 1986.

Consumers' Development
of Self-Responsibility

The media has quickly responded to this mounting public interest, accommodating the increased demands for information with a proliferation of popular health-related magazines, newspaper articles, and radio and television programs. In turn, this abundance of educational material has resulted in highly informed, discriminating consumers who are more intelligent and sophisticated about their health care options.

The desire to maintain an attractive and youthful appearance, an increased awareness of the high costs of illness, and the fear of succumbing to disease are motivating individuals to practice prevention. As the general public continues to recognize that the major causes of mortality and morbidity are now directly related to unhealthy lifestyle practices, more people are assuming greater degrees of responsibility over their lifestyle habits and choices. They are also becoming more assertive in provider selection, expecting and demanding services provided by quality, dependable suppliers. Not surprisingly, according to some industry analysts, investments in health care are now considered by consumers as a form of long-term capital investment rather than a consumed expenditure ("The New Individualism," 1987).

Consumers' Loss of Respect for Medical Technology

Even in today's environment of scientific advancement, solutions to some medical problems are still difficult to pinpoint. Justifiably or not, however, the general public has grown impatient with physicians' and hospitals' inability to offer cures for such "common" afflictions as heart disease and cancer. The lack of answers to such life-or-death situations has diminished consumer confidence in many health care professionals and institutions. In return, the public's loss of confidence in medical technology has further cultivated consumers' development of self-responsibility in the form of practicing health improvement and maintenance.

An Aging Population

As America's baby-boom generation matures, population statistics are skewing toward an older public. Analysis has revealed that older people, age 65 and over, represent the fastest-growing age bracket. Already, there are more adults age 65 and over (estimated at 25 million) than there are people under age 25. It has been projected that by the year 2035, older adults will number 55 million and constitute 20% of the total population (Dychtwald, 1984). Additionally, advances in health care and improvement in the quality of life have resulted in an extension of longevity to an average age of 75 (Machin, 1985).

Unfortunately, older people of today are still being served primarily with sick care and chronic care. As America's population continues to age, however, senior adults are also being affected by health education and awareness, and. in increasing numbers, they too are beginning to practice health promotion and preventive care.

Concern for Health of Children

USA Today ("Help Kids Get Fit," 1986) reported an alarming survey regarding the physical fitness of American youths. In a survey of 18,000 students, ages 6 to 17, findings revealed that 70% of the boys could do only one pull-up, while 55% could not do even one. The survey also indicated that 50% of girls 6 to 17 and 30% of boys 6 to 12 could not run a mile in less than 10 minutes. The same article reported that, among elementary school children tested in Michigan, 41% had high cholesterol, 28% had high blood pressure, and 98% showed at least one major risk factor.

From a logical viewpoint, unhealthy youngsters mature into unhealthy adults. Somewhere in the communication link, the current adult interest in and awareness of health and fitness are not being passed along to our nation's children. Clearly, fitness among adolescents is an area of critical concern.

Increasing Corporate Interest in Health Promotion

Motivated by a desire to reduce health care costs, more and more businesses are investigating the development of health promotion programs for their employees. In their efforts to reduce employees' health risks as well as costs for acute care, many corporations are promoting health improvement and maintenance by offering occupational health programs, educational programs, executive physicals, and employee assistance programs (EAPs). In fact, the Association for Fitness in Business has estimated that as many as 50,000 corporations in America now offer employees some sort of health promotion program ("American Business," 1985).

THE IMPORTANCE OF HEALTH PROMOTION IN THE FUTURE

As previously discussed, changes in the health care industry and the marketplace are forcing hospitals to reexamine their focus on acute inpatient care and to diversify into new lines of products and services. The concept of an integrated health care system, one that meets a wide range of consumer needs from acute care to prevention to mental health to insurance, is now and will continue to be a major focus in the health care industry.

Hospitals Integrating into Comprehensive Health Care Systems

Integration in health care is both a horizontal and a vertical process—horizontal in its diversification of services to penetrate more of the marketplace, and vertical in its birth-to-death approach that includes prevention, treatment, and rehabilitation. A comprehensive integrated system gives users a single entity that can meet all of their health care needs.

In today's highly competitive health care arena, the implementation of a health promotion program is one of the most viable and logical diversification options available to a hospital. Figure 17.1 shows a practical model of the integrated health care system, with health promotion as an integral part, including its role as a casefinder. The health promotion unit offers nonthreatening access to both corporate and community markets for services. Once in place, wellness and EAP services can offer health assessments and make appropriate referrals to those com-

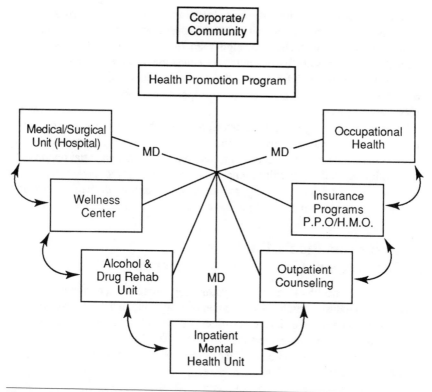

Figure 17.1. Practical integrated health care system model, including assessment and referral possibilities.

ponents of the health care system best equipped to deal with the identified problems.

Even in future integrated systems, the traditional hospital medical/surgical unit will remain the hub of the system, but health promotion will increasingly become a crucial component, contributing to new institutional goals and strategies.

Health Promotion's Contribution to Institutional Goals—Profitability

Hospitals have begun to realize that health promotion services and products are no longer value-added services that complement traditional health care; they are now valuable commodities, to be marketed as such and sold at a profit. These commodities must be developed in response to a discriminating public, which will continue, as awareness heightens, to expect quality services from a respected provider. The hospital, with its wide array of professional expertise and advanced resources, is in the perfect position to offer these services.

A comprehensive health promotion program will carry numerous specific products, including health screenings, stress management courses, executive physicals, smoking cessation classes, weight reduction programs, prenatal education, mental health services, EAPs, nutrition education, sports medicine, exercise classes, and alcohol and drug counseling. Programs may also include a hospital-owned or joint-venture wellness center, incorporating a wide variety of marketable services and products.

If developed, managed, and marketed correctly, the sales of such services will generate new revenue streams to augment revenue losses from current and anticipated inpatient declines, with each product representing a potential opportunity for profit contribution. It will be important for health promotion administrators to remember that pricing of each product must be carefully determined not only to cover expenses, but also to include a margin of profit.

Health Promotion's Contribution to Institutional Goals—Patient Referral

Hospital-based health promotion programs reach three primary audiences: local business and industry employees, community groups and individuals, and existing patients. As a uniquely efficient case-finding source, health promotion identifies individuals with asymptomatic illnesses and refers them for follow-up care. It also offers access to the majority of the community, directing essentially healthy individuals into a full continuum of care.

The benefits of health promotion as a referral arm are many, both for the provider and for the client (whether corporate or individual). Clients benefit from early detection and rehabilitation of problems, decreased cost, and increased convenience. The provider, on the other hand, is rewarded with greater market penetration, and subsequently greater market share, through the recruitment of incremental patients.

Clearly, hospital-sponsored health promotion programming represents the potential capture of incremental patients, reducing the role of the physician as the sole referral source. In an environment where increased competition is anticipated, the patient referral potential of health promotion is and will be a key benefit to the hospital.

Health Promotion's Contribution to Institutional Goals—Enhancement of Physician Relations

In the past, hospitals have been forced to acknowledge, if somewhat begrudgingly, the primary care practitioner's critical role as the gatekeeper to hospital admissions. However, as already noted, physicians have recently found themselves in a fiercely competitive situation and realize they must somehow position themselves as being unique in the marketplace. Consequently, many have discovered the benefits of aligning with a hospital in presenting new, nontraditional products to consumers.

More and more often, physicians are looking at affiliations with hospital-sponsored health promotion as a means of gaining the attention of prospective patients. The initiation of a competitive health promotion program by a lone physician is next to impossible, from both a financial and an expertise standpoint. However, by joint-venturing with a hospital in health promotion products (such as sports medicine, prenatal education classes, or drug and alcohol counseling), physicians can present their services as being unique in the community and can create an image of themselves as progressive professionals. In this respect, affiliation with a hospital-sponsored program can be very beneficial for physicians, particularly in marketing their practices as well as generating new revenue streams.

In return, the hospital gains the loyalty and vested interest of a "partner" who will be much more likely to maintain, if not increase, admissions. It is this type of mutually beneficial hospital/physician relationship, gained through health promotion programs, that will become a primary goal for both partners.

Health Promotion's Contribution to Institutional Goals—Enhancement of Corporate Relations

The need of the aggregate purchaser (business and industry) to reduce health care costs has stimulated an intense interest in health promotion services. In an attempt to attack the causes of health risks among employees, businesses have recognized the value of disease prevention and health maintenance through wellness programs. Consistently, studies of businesses' efforts to encourage employee health improvement and maintenance indicate that health promotion programs not only cut health care costs but also help reduce absenteeism while bolstering employee morale and productivity.

As perfect complements to PPOs and HMOs, health promotion programs will lead, for many corporate participants, to discounted health care services. As managed care programs proliferate, the role of health promotion will become more significant in reducing expenses by treating the cause (sick employees) rather than the symptoms (rising health care costs).

Through the provision of inexpensive, quality services, hospital-sponsored health promotion will open wide the corporate door, serving as a conduit to other hospital services, including traditional acute care when needed. Health promotion will also provide more opportunities for the hospital to offer tailored service packages and will support a visible hospital effort to contribute to cost containment efforts.

Health Promotion's Contribution to Institutional Goals—Service Emerging Markets

As they develop particular health promotion programs, many hospitals are segmenting their markets into specific target groups. Typically, health promotion's target audiences, in addition to corporations, are seniors, women, and youths.

Each market will require careful attention and sensitivity to its needs and expectations.

A particularly important example is seniors. As today's health-conscious baby-boom generation ages, the demand for health promotion products and services for older adults will increase dramatically, leading to the development of more adult day-care centers, home health care, life-care centers, congregate housing, and so on.

In terms of direct health care services, it has been estimated that 80% of Americans age 65 and older suffer from at least one chronic condition and are therefore more likely to suffer from functional impairments. "On the average, older persons . . . account for 33 percent of all hospital beds occupied and 30 percent of all health bills paid . . . . If current prevalence trends continue, it is estimated that 50 percent of healthcare expenditures will be related to the care and treatment of the older population by the year 2000" (Machin, 1985).

Clearly, the older adult will become a major focus of health care marketing efforts in the future, and the senior boom offers an excellent opportunity for the hospital-sponsored health promotion program. While health promotion remains a tough sell for many older adults today, the older adult population 10 years from now will already be sold on the concept of wellness. Tomorrow's adults will be the same individuals who today are assuming responsibility for their health. As today's generation grows to be tomorrow's older Americans, they will become even more intelligent health promotion consumers and will continue to seek the highest quality provider for their needs.

Health Promotion's Contribution to Institutional Goals—Image Enhancement

Health promotion's potential contribution as an image enhancer is an indirect yet invaluable benefit. Health promotion programs, even if sold at a fee, are still basically considered community services and promote public goodwill by presenting the hospital as a good citizen. The incorporation of wellness services, in addition to sick-care services, contributes to the hospital's overall image of quality care and establishes the hospital in the community's top-of-mind awareness as a full-service provider.

As consumer interest in health promotion grows, the media will devote increasing attention to health-related topics. In this respect, hospital-sponsored health promotion will present excellent public relations opportunities, often resulting in drawing the hospital's name to the forefront. Such free media exposure may also lead to consumer utilization of other hospital services. Health promotion may even serve as the hub of a general hospital marketing campaign where, in today's budget-conscious environment, free publicity can significantly augment paid advertising.

Health Promotion's Contribution
to Institutional Goals—Support of Other Departments

Health promotion is a multidisciplinary effort, relying on and supporting resources from a variety of in-hospital areas. Products such as health screenings and EAPs draw on the expertise and cooperation of professionals from numerous specialties, eliciting a team effort that strengthens interdepartmental relationships.

On the other hand, many clinical programs, such as occupational rehabilitation, mental health, drug and alcohol treatment, and cardiac and pulmonary rehabilitation, benefit greatly from the inclusion of an exercise therapy component. In many markets, the addition of a health promotion component to such services represents a unique combination that can ultimately give the provider an edge on competitors' programs.

By supporting the hospital's traditional services and departments, health promotion products and services will deepen the health promotion niche within the hospital and in the integrated health care system.

SUMMARY

Hospital-sponsored health promotion represents a logical and natural response to current health care industry challenges. In many cases, hospitals' long-term viability will depend on their adaptability to market needs. As consumers' awareness of the benefits of health maintenance grows, it appears certain that public interest in health promotion will be relatively permanent.

Not only will a philosophy of health, fitness, and disease prevention soon permeate almost every service provided by the hospital, it also will express itself in a new, diversified, hospital-business line that will supplement revenues lost in the current downward spiral of inpatient care. Additionally, health promotion will continue to gain recognition for its potential contributions in accruing new patients, improving the health care system's image, increasing its attractiveness in the marketplace, and establishing new markets.

While health promotion is certainly not a final solution to all problems, it does offer undeniable comprehensive advantages as a profit-generating patient accrual service. When implemented properly, health promotion will also strengthen the hospital's relationships with physicians, corporate clients, and the community at large.

To be successful, however, a health promotion program must be carefully developed and managed. Unfortunately, today's unexpectedly intense interest in health promotion will, in the short term, create a critical shortage of competent program administrators. Hospitals must resist the impulse to designate existing employees who, though willing and perhaps clinically skilled, are not business-oriented enough to handle the program in an entrepreneurial fashion. Undoubtedly, however, many health care professionals (particularly physicians who are being crowded out of their fields) will seize the opportunity for training in health promotion and will soon alleviate the shortage.

Above all else, hospitals in their fight for survival must manage all aspects of their business efficiently, maximizing resources and integrating into true, full-service institutions. In essence, proper hospital management will mean constant attention to the bottom line. And, in this respect, health promotion deserves immediate serious consideration.

REFERENCES

American business gets fit. (1985, October 7). *Business Week* [Special issue].

Bezold, C., Carlson, R.J., & Peck, J.C. (1986). *The future of work and health*. Dover, MA: Auburn House.

Dychtwald, K. (1984). The aging of America and the implication for health promotion. *Promoting Health, 5*(5), 1-3.

French, E.O. (1987). Survival of the fittest: An integrated approach to healthcare. *The Journal of Fitness in Business, 2*(1), 126-130.

Galginaitis, C. (1980, September 8). Tickets to health: Promotions relay the message. *Advertising Age*.

Health clubs. (1982, February 8). *Advertising Age*.

Help kids get fit; thin health matters. (1986, May 16). *USA Today*, p. 14a.

Levine, A., Wells, S., & Kopf, C. (1986, August 11). New rules of exercise. *U.S. News and World Report*, pp. 52-56.

Machin, J. (Producer/Director). (1985). *Health promotion for older adults: Planning for action* [Proceedings of video teleconference]. Chicago: American Hospital Association.

McClary, C.L., Zahrt, L., Montgomery, J.H., Walker, H., & Petry, J.R. (1985). Wellness: The mode in the new paradigm. *Health Values, 9*(6), 8-12.

Naisbitt, J. (1982). *Megatrends: Ten new directions transforming our lives*. New York: Warner.

The new individualism: What fitness means to today's consumer. (1987). *Club Business, 8*(2), 87-88.

Westbury, S. (1986, June). *The role of the educator on top management team*. Presentation to the 16th Annual American Society of Health Care Education and Training National Conference, San Antonio, TX.

Contributing Authors

Christine A. Aguiar, PhD
Manager, Lifewise Programs
Center for Health Enhancement
St. Luke's Hospital of Kansas City
4200 Wornall Road
Kansas City, MO 64111

Jeffrey M. Bensky, PhD
Senior Manager
Price Waterhouse
National Healthcare Strategic
  Consulting Group
One Boatmen's Plaza
St. Louis, MO 63101

Daniel J. Bonk
Vice President
Fort Sanders Alliance
Knoxville, TN 37916

Barbara K. Burke, EdD
Manager, Sports Medicine/Wellness
St. Vincent Hospital Health Care Center
2001 W. 86th St.
Indianapolis, IN 46240

Kevin M. Clair, MA
Bethesda Healthcare Corporation
2815 S. Seacrest Blvd.
Boynton Beach, FL 33435

Debra Daly-Gawenda, MS, RN
Associate Director
Employee Health Service
Rush-Presbyterian-St. Luke's
  Medical Center
1753 W. Congress Pkwy.
Chicago, IL 60612

Laurie A. Kelley, MEd
Director, Baptist Center for Health
  Promotion
2000 Church St.
Nashville, TN 37236

Stephen M. Schmitz, MD
Meriden-Wallingford Hospital
181 Cook Ave.
Meriden, CN 06450

Neil Sol, PhD
The Houstonian
111 North Post Oak Lane
Houston, TX 77024

Carolyn I. Speros, MEd, RN
Patient and Community Education
Methodist Hospitals of Memphis
1265 Union
Memphis, TN 38104

Jean Storlie, MS, RD
Director, ProActive Health
ArcVentures, Inc.
910 W. Van Buren
Chicago, IL 60607

Philip K. Wilson, EdD
Professor, Physical Education
 Department
College of Health, Physical Education
 and Recreation
132 Mitchell Hall
University of Wisconsin–La Crosse
La Crosse, WI 54601